THE RELUCTANT SURGEON

THE RELUCTANT SURGEON

A BIOGRAPHY OF JOHN HUNTER

JOHN KOBLER

1960

DOUBLEDAY & COMPANY, INC.

GARDEN CITY, NEW YORK

Library of Congress Catalog Card Number 60–6887
Copyright © 1960 by John Kobler
All Rights Reserved
Printed in the United States of America

FOR MY WIFE, RUTH

ACKNOWLEDGMENTS

I am deeply indebted to Dr. John F. Fulton, Sterling Professor, History of Medicine, and Keeper of Medical History Collections at the Yale Medical Library, where most of my research was done; to Miss Madeline E. Stanton, Librarian of those collections; Mrs. Henrietta T. Perkins, Assistant Librarian; and Miss Ursula Price, Reference Librarian and Research Assistant.

I wish to thank the staff of the Yale Sterling Library, in particular, Mr. Herman W. Liebert, Curator of the Rare Book Room and Research Associate, for permission to draw upon unpublished material, including the Boswell papers.

For the privilege of examining a wealth of Hunterian manuscripts, letters, diaries, and notebooks, and for clarifying innumerable obscure points, I am indebted to Mr. William R. Le Fanu, Librarian of the Royal College of Surgeons of England, and Miss Jessie Dobson, Recorder of the Royal College of Surgeons Museum; Dr. Arthur Underwood, Director of the Wellcome Historical Museum, London; Mr. R. O. McKenna, Librarian of the University of Glasgow, and Miss Anne Robertson, Underkeeper of the Hunterian Museum in Glasgow.

I wish also to thank the librarians of the American Philosophical Society, the College of Physicians of Philadelphia, the New York Academy of Medicine, and the New York Public Library; Mr. Guy Klett, Research Historian of the Presbyterian Historical Society; Dr. Jane Oppenheimer, Professor of Biology, Bryn Mawr; Dr. Loren C. Eiseley, Provost of the University of Pennsylvania and formerly Chairman of the Department of Anthropology; and Dr. Fenwick Beekman of New York, who granted me access to his collection of Hunteriana, the most extensive in private hands.

I am additionally indebted to Dr. Beekman and to Dr. George W. Corner, Historian, the Rockefeller Institute, for correcting technical errors in the manuscript.

I owe a particular debt to Dr. Reuben I. H. Solway of Westport, Connecticut, who first aroused my interest in John Hunter.

PREFACE

Since his death at the end of the eighteenth century John Hunter has been variously described by his fellow scientists as "the Shakespeare of medicine," "with the exception of Hippocrates, the grandest figure in his profession," "a philosopher whose mental grasp embraced the whole range of nature's works," "one of the greatest men the English nation has produced."

To commemorate the bicentenary of Hunter's birth, the Harvard Medical Society held a symposium at which six speakers, each eminent in a different field, acknowledged his achievements in that field. "What is known as 'the Hunterian method,'" said the brain surgeon, Harvey Cushing, "revolutionized surgery. . . . Hunter was the first to teach the science of surgery as Paré two hundred years before had advanced the art."

Dr. William Pearce Coues, a member of the New England Dermatological Society, referring to Hunter's treatise on venereal diseases, said: "Much of it could appear in the journals of the last twenty years as the thoughts of the leading urologists of today. . . . John Hunter was a urologist a hundred and fifty years ahead of his time."

"Dentistry today," said Dr. Leroy M. S. Miner, Dean of the Harvard Dental School, "is being developed along biological lines with mechanics the servant rather than the master of biological principles. It is clear that Hunter had this idea strongly developed and it seems a pity that it has taken us more than a century to appreciate the truth of what he had to say."

Professor William M. Wheeler of the Harvard Law School, and an entomologist, declared Hunter to have been "the most important naturalist between Aristotle and Darwin."

The remaining eulogists were Dr. Arlie V. Bock, Professor of Internal Medicine, and Dr. Frederick T. Lewis, Professor of Anatomy and an embryologist. The roster could have been extended almost indefinitely to cover pathology, physiology, biology, hematology, military surgery, orthopedics, obstetrics, genetics, artificial insemination, psychology, psychosomatics, sexology, veterinary science, zoology, botany,

9

geology, and paleontology, for in all of these fields Hunter, though barely literate by the academic standards of his contemporaries, made lasting contributions. "To attempt to set forth," says the *Encyclopaedia Britannica,* "what in Hunter's teaching was new to pathology and systematic surgery, or was rendered so by his mode of treatment, would be well-nigh to present an epitome of all that he wrote on those subjects."

Hunterian literature crowds the shelves of medical libraries the world over. The *Britannica* devotes more space to Hunter than to Linnaeus, Paré, Harvey, Jenner, Lister, Simpson, Pasteur, Freud, or Fleming. Yet outside the scientific community the name today strikes only a dim spark of recognition, if any at all. The reason is not hard to find. Although his practical contributions were legion, none had the kind of dramatic impact, the easily grasped significance, that excites the lay imagination. He did not, like Jenner, discover a vaccine that conquered a universal scourge, nor, like Simpson, an anesthesia. What Hunter accomplished, however, transcended specific discovery and technical invention, and, in its totality, was no less spectacular. He introduced a new spirit of inquiry, a philosophy, which not only transformed the medical theory and practice of his epoch, but profoundly influenced scientific thinking everywhere down to our own times.

Hunter has not fared well at the hands of his biographers. The early portraits were flawed by either idolatry or hatred; the more recent have been sketchy, specialized, or overformal.

This book is an effort to reclaim the scientist from the archives and the man from the shadows.

Wilton, Connecticut
October, 1959

CONTENTS

V. JERMYN STREET, 1771–1783

VI. THE GOLDEN CALF OF LEICESTER SQUARE, 1781–1783

VII. PROTEUS, 1783–1793

VIII. AFTERWARD

I. THE HUNTERS
OF LONG CALDERWOOD
1717-1748

1. THE QUEST BEGINS

In Calder Glen, high above the Clyde Valley, a small, homely boy crouches by a rock pool, raptly watching the busy life beneath the surface. The pool lies still and shallow on a pebbly bed, penetrated by shafts of summer sunlight, affording him a view of brilliant clarity. In awe and delight his gaze follows the ingenious, larval caddis worms, mottled brown and shaped like furled leaves, as they build around their own bodies tubular shelters of pebbles, cementing the chinks with a silky secretion. Some, seeking more building materials, are lugging their uncompleted masonry after them. Others, their houses roofed, are sealing themselves in to await the moment of freedom as pupae, secure against small hungry fish—though an occasional trout glides through the pool, sweeping into its gullet houses, inmates and all. Those already at the pupal stage have gnawed open the seal, have struggled, their hairy legs flailing, to the surface, have cast their molts, and with antennae and wings full-formed are taking flight. Below them float the corpses of adult caddis flies, the males dead soon after their aerial mating, the females after spawning.

For a long time the avid watcher puzzles over the microcosm at his feet. What purpose do they serve, these ephemeral tittles of living matter, in their winking span between birth and death? What aspect is here reflected of that Divine Intelligence the minister invokes in the kirk every Sabbath? Do they build and breed only for larger creatures to feed upon? (Many years later, when he would strive passionately to trace a pattern of creation through a multitude of organisms, animal and human, healthy and diseased, quick and dead, through plants, minerals, and fossils, he would hold it as an article of faith that, "In nature nothing is irregular, nothing is perturbed, nothing is disobedient, but everything is really regular, uniform, and obedient to recognized principles.")

He scoops up a handful of larvae for his collection, and reluctantly starts back through the glen toward school. Hours have passed since the school janitor finished his morning rounds, pounding on each door and blowing his horn to rouse sluggards. Every day in the year, save high holidays and the fortnight summer recess, as soon as the dawn grows light enough to read by, the classroom drudgery begins, not to let up until dusk. For his truancy the boy can expect a birching to make his head ring, and at home the despairing reproaches of his mother, the harder to bear because she loves and indulges him more than her other children. He has less to fear from his father, who is too old and sick to wield a firm hand. In any event the delinquent knows how to weather parental storms. He will fling himself to the ground, force the tears, and howl until they leave him to his own devices.

Now the sun hangs at the zenith. But still he lingers, for at every turn the glen offers some new enticement. In the fork of a tall yew he spies a bullfinch's nest, and he must climb it to compare the construction, the number, size and color of the eggs with those of other species he has gathered. So, spellbound, he ambles to and fro, stopping here to pluck a tuft of purple-flowered chickweed, there, by a freshet, to catch a polyp, that oddest of aquatic freaks, a greenish, filmy blob, sprouting many tentacles, which, if cut to pieces, from each piece generates another polyp. A hare streaks across his path, and he darts after it, observing as he runs the powerful mechanism, like snapping bowstrings, of its haunches. He moves clumsily on legs too short for his heavy torso. He is undersized, almost dwarfish, but strongly knit in the thighs and chest. His large head sits on a short, thick neck. His jaw is long, his mouth full and firm, his nose blunt, his eyes blue-gray and deep under a broad brow. His hair is a wiry tangle the color of rust.

The chase leads him out of the glen by the crumbling ramparts of Calder Castle, past scraggy pasturage and farmhouses of rough-hewn stone scattered along the rim of a plateau. The broom-yellow valley below, broken by fierce crags, slopes steeply for some eight miles down to the River Clyde and the suburbs of Glasgow. On cloudless days like this he can glimpse the distant summits that loom in a vast arc between the Lowland coasts—to the west, Arran's bleak Ben Ghoil, "Mountain of the Wind"; to the north, twin-humped An Gobaileach, "the Cobbler," grassy Ben Lomond, and gnarled Ben Ledi; to the east, Arthur's Seat like a couchant lion.

At length he sets his steps toward school. But then he comes to Farmer Crawford's byre, and what he sees puts his good intentions to rout. Knife in hand, the farmer is bending over an Ayrshire heifer. From her straddling stance and the jointless look of her forelegs the boy recognizes the sickness called tail-flip. The damp and the cold, which beglooms that land from summer's end to summer's beginning, brings it on, as they do a host of evils to animals and to people. The cattle blight starts as a softening at the tip of the tail, spreads swiftly upward, and, if not arrested before it reaches the spine, proves fatal.

Seeing the solemn boy approach, old Crawford bends closer to his task, as if to fend off the spate of questions he knows will besiege him. Jockie Hunter's obsessive curiosity is a parish joke. Almost the first words the neighbors can remember him uttering were "what?" and "how?" and "why?" Now, at the age of twelve, he is forever pursuing the shepherds, the drovers, the farriers and foresters, anybody who works with growing things. ("I pestered people," he recalled in later years, "with questions about what nobody knew or cared about.") Why did cows retain their milk when deprived of their calves? Why did the quality of the milk, so rich after calving, diminish as the udders emptied? Why did gelding transform a mettlesome horse into a docile one, and a lean bull into a fat steer? Why did oxen treat new members of the herd as outcasts, yet accept them as soon as all were driven together into a strange pasture? Why did the hue and texture of animal droppings vary with the fodder?

Death and disease prompt his keenest questioning. They lurk everywhere around him. They have been frequent invaders of his home. The first two Hunter children died in infancy. Now two of his older sisters, "Tibbie" and "Nannie," are wasting with a spitting of blood. Hunter, senior, endures the daily torment of bladder stones. And not even Willie Cullen, who is probably the best doctor thereabouts, can ease the father or save the daughters.

Such afflictions spare few houses. Of all the children born between Land's End and John o' Groats, not two thirds survive their first year, not three fourths live to be six. Smallpox is the great killer of the young. Consumption decimates the adults. The bereaved speak of their losses submissively, almost casually, accepting them as the normal lot of humanity.

But this resignation the boy cannot share, and from his tireless observations of nature and animals he learns lessons that will one day help him to heal men: how birds he has found frozen in the snow, carried indoors, gently chafed and slowly warmed by the peat fire, revived, whereas those he treated too hastily or vigorously died. He notes, too, the body's properties of recuperation and regrowth, the broken bones that mend of themselves, the wounds, exposed to air, that close without ointment or sutures.

Now bursting with questions, he watches Crawford prod the heifer's forelegs above the fetlocks, then with his knife make two long, deep slashes. The animal heaves and sways as her blood stains the straw, but she keeps to her feet. The farmer nods confidently; a copious flow is thought to ensure recovery. When the bleeding slows a bit, he rubs in black soap mixed with crushed garlic. To the boy's wonderment, the heifer rallies, her joints seem to stiffen.

Jockie Hunter does not get to school at all that day, and it is twilight before he goes home, to the farmstead known as Long Calderwood.

The Hunters stemmed from a modest but ancient line of Norman cultivators, who proliferated throughout the shires of Peebles and Ayr. Skilled at the sports of field and forest, they emblazoned their escutcheons with coursers, stringed hunting horns, and the motto, "Hunter, blow thy horn." The Peebleshire Hunters, the oldest branch, were said to have received their earliest landholdings in the eleventh century, for yeoman service in the chase, from Malcolm, "the Big-Headed," who vanquished Macbeth. The terms of the royal grant, according to a doggerel version of what purported to be the original charter, were comprehensive: "I, Malcolm Kenmure, King, the first of my reign, gives to thee, Normand Hunter of Powmood, the Hope [an enclosed piece of ground] up and down, above the earth to heaven and below the earth to hell, as free to thee and thine as ever God gave it to me and mine, and that for a bow and broad arrow when I come to hunt in Yarrow; for the mair suith I byte the white wax with my tooth. Before thir witnesses three—May, Mauld, and Marjorie."

The Ayrshire Hunters acquired successive grants from Alexander II,

James II, and James V. Towards the end of the seventeenth century one of the younger heritors, John Hunter, following a family quarrel, struck out on his own, and without any patrimony moved to the town of East Kilbride in adjacent Lanarkshire.

The town derived its name from *kill*, "graveyard" in Gaelic, and Bridget, an early Celtic saint, whose miraculous attributes included the power to restore by her touch a withered tree to leaf. For centuries it had been a market town, and its inhabitants chiefly farmers, an astonishing record of perseverance, since no soil in the region was less fertile. Hard and clayey at the surface, cold and wet beneath, it rotted more seeds than it nourished. Not a single cart did the townsfolk possess when Hunter came to live among them. But then they needed none, for there were no roads, only sludgy, rutted paths. All produce and materials moved on the backs of horses or men. The tradition-ridden farmers mistrusted such newfangled English husbandry as manuring, liming, drainage, selective seeding, and crop rotation, clinging blindly to methods dating from Celtic antiquity. It was the same all over Scotland, and by this obtuseness they brought upon themselves atrocious suffering.

Every few years famine and plague ravaged the North. Hunger-maddened men fought like beasts over weeds, slugs, carrion. Mothers sold their children into colonial slavery. In city streets as well as country lanes the dead lay too numerous for the living to bury, many of them with shreds of raw animal flesh clenched between their teeth, the women with babies still sucking at their dry breasts. Not far from Glasgow, a boy, carrying his father's body to the cemetery, fell at a farmer's door, whimpering, "I can carry it no further. For God's sake bury the corpse, or put it, if you like, on the dyke of your kailyard to keep out the sheep."

East Kilbride, which had a population of about a thousand, consisted of dark, squat, stone buildings, with gabled windows above their eaves—some hundred and fifty dwellings, an inn, a smithy—clustered around a cobbled square. Market day was Tuesday, and four times a year there was a fair to which the farmers brought their thin-shanked cattle for sale or barter, their beef and mutton, tough as bark beneath preservative layers of salt, their stunted groats and "tatties" and kale, their shoddy flax.

Close behind the square, on a hillock, rose the dank, gray walls of the parish kirk, custodian of dour doctrines, the legacy of Calvin and

Knox, which bounded the parishioners' every step from cradle to grave. The bell under its Gothic tower crown was the proudest relic of a community whose monotonous existence few stirring historic events had ever enlivened. Cast in 1590 by a famous Flemish foundry, it bore a crack from shoulder to mouth, an injury inflicted a century later when the townsfolk, celebrating the death in the Battle of Killicrankie of a cruel oppressor, the Jacobite Viscount Dundee, pulled the bell rope too hard. It would become necessary, with the rise of the Glasgow medical schools, to install a curious structure in the kirkyard—a "watcher's house" to shelter the sexton at night while he kept vigil against anatomy students on the prowl with pick and spade for newly buried cadavers.

Hunter set himself up as a grain merchant. But though he fared well enough, he was not naturally suited to the hurly-burly of provincial trade. Somewhat frail in health, in disposition mild and diffident, he tended more to introspection than action. "A man of good understanding," so a family letter described him, "of great integrity, and of an anxious temper."

Among his customers for barley was a prosperous maltster named John Paul, a Bailie of the City of Glasgow and its honorary treasurer. This Bailie Paul had a daughter, Agnes, whose beauty and domestic talents attracted as many suitors as the *tocher* her father could furnish. In 1707, the year of the Union between Scotland and England, when Hunter was forty-four and Agnes half his age, they were betrothed. It is pleasant to imagine that on the eve of marriage, he sent to her home, according to a widespread custom, a jar of henna, that the bridesmaids washed her feet, stained them with the henna, and whitened her eyebrows with antimony. Next day, from the wedding in a Glasgow kirk, bridegroom, bride and attendants went by horseback eight miles uphill to Hunter's house in East Kilbride. Probably a townsman hailed them on the threshold, holding out a two-handled wooden stoup brimful of robust ale, toasted the couple, and passed the stoup around; the maid of honor broke an oatcake over Agnes's head, and everybody scrambled to retrieve the crumbs, which were supposed to bring the finders good luck; then all day and night, long after the couple had retired, the company gorged and guzzled and capered to skirling pipes.

The Hunters stayed ten years in East Kilbride. There they lived through the famine of 1709, when wheat fields reverted to heather, when thousands perished and thousands fell into beggary. There six children were born to them, and there they buried two of them. The

Scottish funeral rites could be both barbaric and costly: the bellman, as soon as the death was known, hurrying into the square, shaking his dead bell, proclaiming, "All brothers and sisters, I let you wot there is a brother departed out of this present world according to the will of Almighty God." A summons to strangers as well as friends to gather for the long lyke-wake at the house of mourning where shortbread and bannocks without stint awaited them, ale, sack and usquebaugh in quantities that had exhausted the tavern's stock—joyous occasion for the poor, the starving, the gluttonous. The door painted black, with tear-shaped white splotches, symbolizing the family's grief. Inside, the clocks and mirrors masked, white sheets draped over the furniture. The corpse, embalmed by the chirurgeon, laid out upon a board in cerecloth and stockings. The hired watchers already besotted. The motley guests thronging the hot room, leaving off their swilling only long enough to view the corpse, or to mumble "Amen" after the minister's frequent words of grace. Drink is a national vice, never more freely indulged in than at funerals, and forced looks of dolor soon give way to sodden mirth. The climactic "kisting"—the watchers unsteadily lifting the corpse from board to coffin and nailing the lid fast, as the minister rattles the rafters with thunderous prayer. (But his funerary duties are not wholly ecclesiastical; by an Act of Parliament, designed to encourage domestic trade, the shroud must be woven of Scottish wool, and it behooves him to make sure that this is done.) The procession to the kirkyard, the tipsy mourners stumbling behind the coffin borne on spokes, the bearers in danger at every pothole of pitching their burden into the mire. The cracked kirk bell tolling. And, with the last earth fallen from the sexton's spade, the bleary crowd winding back to the house for the "dredgy," a second bout of feasting and toping. . . The expense of such obsequies left many a burgher financially crippled.

At the age of fifty-four Hunter decided he had had enough of the grain business. He looked forward to a contemplative life in retirement on a farm no larger than need be to sustain his growing family. Long Calderwood, a tract of some seventy-five acres lying a mile north of the town, was for sale at £147. What he had saved, together with his wife's dowry, enabled him to buy it and to build on its northern boundary a house of fieldstone. By the modest standards of the parish it was a fine house, having two stories, five rooms, a thatched roof, and gables mounting in steps to the chimneys, called corbie gables. A long wing, abutting on the western gable, enclosed a scullery, a "bothy," or hut for servants, and stabling for five horses. Past the front door, separating it from a path leading into town, ran a stone wall, and behind the wall a narrow strip of lawn, flowers, and vegetables. Hunter later added a coach house at the rear and a byre where the cows were milked and the grain winnowed. [a]

He thus became, like his forebears, a "little laird." But that honorific connoted more respectability than material substance. The sour soil, the killing climate, the depressed produce market, the rental payments in kind, rarely in cash, kept even the noblest clansmen, owning vast lands, in a thralldom of debt. Hunter found that he had exchanged an uncongenial mode of life for a precarious one, and to finance the higher education of his sons, whom he wanted to enter professions, he had to sell off portions of his estate. "This," wrote a grandson, "increased the constitutional anxiety of his mind, and he was often kept awake in the night from thinking upon the difficulties of his situation."

As his health deteriorated, Mrs. Hunter took upon her sturdy shoulders more and more of the management of the farm. She also bore, between her thirty-third and forty-fourth years, four more children—William, Dorothea ("Dolly"), Isabella ("Tibbie"), and John, variously called "Johnny," "Jock," and "Jockie." Of their ten children both husband and wife outlived all but three.

John, their runty, red-haired youngest offspring, was born in the upstairs bedroom over the kitchen. There was a lot of sickness in the house at the time, and in the general confusion nobody noted the hour. Someone wrote in the parish register: "John a lawfull son procreate betwixt John Hunter and Paul, born Feby. 13th and baptized March 30th 1728." But John himself always observed the fourteenth as his birthday. He was probably born a few minutes before or a few minutes after midnight of the thirteenth.*

Scottish children trod a thorny path. Though their parents loved them no less than parents normally love their children, the all-pervasive spirit of Calvinism inhibited outward shows of affection. The English were always petting and praising their young. Here austerity ruled the nursery. Man, in the view of the Established Church of Scot-

---

* The flyleaf of a family Bible, a notebook belonging to a latter-day descendant, and a memoir written by John's brother-in-law, Everard Home, all give different dates—February 7, February 9, and July 14 (the last almost certainly a typographical error).

land, entered the world foul with Original Sin, "a guilty lump of hell." Only through continual suffering on earth could he be purged of his total depravity and achieve eternal salvation. Pleasure was Satan's bait; God was pitiless. For the spiritual ordeal ahead, and for the harsh conditions of daily existence, Scottish parents began preparing their children early: physically by frequent beatings and exposure to rough weather, sometimes turning them out of doors in winter thinly clad; mentally by exacting absolute subjection, humility, and self-denial. In the presence of the patriarch, who sat through the evenings hat on head in the fireside armchair exclusively reserved for him, a figure of remote, Jovian majesty, children spoke to each other under their breath, and to him not at all unless spoken to. The mother was scarcely less awe-inspiring. "My children," said Lady Strange, the wife of a noted Edinburgh engraver, "from the youngest to the eldest loves and fears me as sinners dread death. My look is law." Lady Balcarres chastised her eleven children so severely that her husband, the martial fifth Earl of Balcarres, protested, "Odsfish, Madam, you will break the spirits of my young troops! I will not have it so!" Such Draconian training, which sometimes denied to babes in arms the warmth of a swaddling blanket, doubtless added to the high infant mortality. But those who survived it few hardships could ever daunt.

Necessitous frugality, the incessant toil, in addition to doctrinal strictures, allowed little scope, especially in the country, for social graces or cultural pursuits. The household retired soon after dusk, there being few diversions to keep them up. Dancing and games the Presbyteries frowned upon (though they never managed to suppress dancing at marriages and funerals), books were scarce, and the light from the homemade tallow candles too feeble for reading. The Hunters, like most country people, slept in box-beds behind sliding panels on tick bags stuffed with straw or chaff. If they closed the panels, they stifled; if they left them open, they froze.

The day's work got under way at dawn. Before riding out to inspect his policy (the improvements to lands and buildings), his cattle and his fields, the laird quaffed his "morning," a jolting eye-opener of gin, rum, whiskey, or brandy. The Scots ate badly, but they ate a lot. Breakfast at eight, accompanied by more spirits, consisted of skink (water gruel) eaten cold, collops (fried slices of meat), oatmeal cakes, and barley bannocks. Some preferred a variant of gruel known as "sowans," which had been left standing several days to sour. The "meridian," at eleven o'clock, called for a third round of spirits. The women drank as heartily as the men. Lunch followed at midday, then the "fours," an interval of tippling, and dinner between six and seven. The two main repasts were indistinguishable. Both usually included a broth of "knockit bear" —so designated because the bear, or barley, was beaten on a knocking stone to remove the husks—fortified by "neeps," a mash of parsnips and kale. Other green vegetables rarely appeared on the table. There were no sweets, and fresh meat only in summer and autumn, the cattle, fed mainly straw all winter, being too scrawny for slaughtering. At Martinmas enough mutton and beef were salted to last the winter. This "matt" was occasionally supplemented by "kain" (in kind) hens, which tenant farmers contributed as part of their rent, too tough for anything but boiling, and so thin that, as one laird complained, they could be carved with their own breastbones.

Except on ceremonial occasions, or when entertaining guests, the country Scots ate out of wooden bowls. The servants deposited all the courses together before the laird's chair. He plied the only knife and fork, and divided the meat for the others, who tore it into manageable bits with their fingers. Everybody drank in turn from the same tankard. In a manual designed to elevate Scottish deportment Adam Petrie, a schoolmaster, wrote:

"You must drink out your glass that others may not have your blown drink, and do it with as little noise as possible."

"Do not gnaw your bones too clean."

"It is indecent to fill the mouth too full; such cramming is more suitable for beasts than a rational creature."

"Be sure to throw nothing on the floor; it is uncivil and disobliging."

"It is rude to suck your meat out of a spoon with an ungrateful noise."

"To wipe the nose or sweat off the face with a table napkin is most rude."

But what the Scots lacked in prandial amenities they made up for in piety. A lengthy grace preceded each dram and snack, with constant praying during full meals. "If you crack a nut with them," a stupefied English visitor to Glasgow reported, "there is a grace for that; if you drink a cup of coffee, ale, or wine, and what else, he presently furnishes a grace for the nonce."

Practically every decision and every undertaking moved the Scots to prayer, so fervently did they believe in the direct intervention of

Providence. They sought Divine guidance before whipping their children, planting an orchard, trading a horse. In most homes a room or closet was set aside as an oratory. The wealthier families employed Mess Johns, young student clergymen, who supervised their devotions. At frequent intervals the parish minister would descend upon the household in all his awesome authority to catechize the "examinable" members, meaning all those older than twelve, assay the general moral tone, and dispense grim homilies. Evidence of transgression he referred to the Kirk-Session, which exercised civil as well as ecclesiastical powers, fining offenders, sentencing them to the pillory or to sackcloth, and in extreme cases banishing them forever from the "Lord's Table."

The Sabbath was fraught with pitfalls. To draw well-water even for an invalid, to fodder cattle, cook before nightfall, speak or look frivolously, appear anywhere without a jacket—all carried dire penalties, and patrols of elders roamed the parish, spying through windows in search of violators. The six o'clock kirk bell signaled the start of the day's solemnities. After family prayers the parishioners trooped to their pews with empty bellies. The morning service lasted two and a half hours. Two model schoolboys were appointed to stand before the pulpit, the one to ask, the other to answer the catechism "in a loud voice for the edification of common and ignorant persons and servants on the grounds of their salvation, that they may learn the same, perquair, and be brought to the knowledge thereof."

The sermon took up the rest of the morning, and it was a hardened sinner who failed to cringe as the minister, his face pouring sweat, his voice raised in drant, the piercing singsong affected by Scottish evangelists, depicted inferno. "What must it be to be banished from the Almighty God?" ran a typical sermon by the mighty Dumferline "wrestler," the Reverend Ralph Erskine. "But whither must they go? Into everlasting fire? O what a bed is there! no feathers, but fire; no friends, but furies; no ease, but fetters; no daylight, but darkness; no clock to pass away the time, but endless eternity; fire eternal is always burning and never dying away. O who can endure everlasting flame? It shall not be quenched night or day. The smoke thereof shall go up for ever and ever. The wicked shall be crowded like bricks in a fiery furnace. Good Lord, what a world of miseries hath seized on miserable sinners! Their executioners are devils; the dungeon fills; the earth stands open; the furnace is burning to receive you. O, how will these poor souls quake and tremble! Every part of their bodies will bear a part in their woeful ditty: eyes weeping, hands wringing, breasts beating, heads aching with voices crying. . . . The Judge is risen from His glorious seat. The saints guard Him along, and the sentenced prisoners are delivered to the jailers. Shrieks of horror shall be heard. What woes and lamentations shall be uttered when devils and reprobate and all the damned crew shall be driven into hell never to return. Down they go! howling, shrieking, yelling, filling both heaven and earth. O miserable wretches!"

While the panting pastor was catching his second wind, his emotionally spent flock hurried home where they could, without peril to their souls, nibble a cold egg or a collop. Even if so sinfully inclined, they had no time for hot refreshment because the services resumed at two o'clock to continue without further respite until six. Only then was a substantial meal permissible. It did not, however, mark the end of the Sabbath devotions. As soon as the dinner table was cleared, the entire household gathered around the paterfamilias for two or three hours of Bible reading, hymn singing, and prayer. Finally, each drowsy child was required to recite the catechism and recapitulate the day's sermons.

If fear of the Devil breeds virtue, early eighteenth-century Scotland would have been a nation of paragons chaste and sober, which, to the perennial indignation of the Kirk-Sessions, was not precisely the case. Satan, according to the prevailing literalist interpretation of Scripture, existed as a material reality, incarnate in a thousand shapes, standing athwart every man's path. Thus, when a horned and hissing apparition, its visage red as hell flames, popped up one night near Long Calderwood, few who saw it doubted whence it came. The shock robbed an aged farmer of his wits and killed another. Jockie Hunter, who was then eleven, had dropped in on some tenant farmers. He was sitting by the hearth, listening to their talk and interposing questions, when the door crashed open and the demonic specter stalked through the room roaring with hideous glee. At first the boy, like his elders, could neither speak nor move for terror. But presently a suspicion crossed his mind. It led him to seize a poker—"I was by no means certain," he said afterwards, "that it wasn't the Devil"—and fetch the intruder a crack on the skull that sent him howling back into the night. As he fled, the horns and a red mask fell off, disclosing the imbecile face of the town practical joker.

2. ". . . A LITTLE READING AND WRITING"

Because they considered literacy essential to the propagation of the faith, the Presbyteries had drafted, and Parliament had adopted, an ambitious educational program. Under an enactment of 1696 each parish was to provide "a commodious house" for a grammar school, appoint a schoolmaster, and compel the attendance of all boys from the age of six. But between the wish and the deed stood mountainous obstacles, most of them economic. With a treasury too meager to subsidize the project, Parliament ordered the parishes to assess themselves, the assessment to be divided equally between landowners and tenants. This sacrifice few parishes could or would make, and until the middle of the century vast areas of Scotland had no educational facilities.

Where there was a public school the "commodious house" usually consisted of a rat-infested granary, stable or decrepit hovel, which also served as the schoolmaster's lodging, with no glass in the windows, and holes gaping in the rotted roof. In the Midlothian village of Cramond, "the school roof so bad the scholars could not stay because of the rain, the Kirk-Session order every scholar to bring some straw to thack the school; but the straw was so scarce the parents could not supply it to their children; therefore only half the school could be covered." Many schools lacked benches and desks. "The boys cannot sit for learning to wreatt," a St. Andrews schoolmaster reported to the town council, "so that they are necessitat to wreatt upon the floor lying upon their bellies."

The schoolmasters, especially those with families to support, abided in abject misery. The salary authorized by the Act of 1696 came to 200 merks (equivalent to about £11) a year, and they counted themselves lucky if they collected even that pittance, for they had to wheedle it penny by penny out of the reluctant burghers. Not to starve to death, they accepted the humiliating perquisites that custom assigned to them under a category called, with unconscious irony, "casualties." One of these arose from the popular sports of cockfighting and cockthrowing. On "Fasten-een" (Shrove Tuesday) the pupils were allowed, after paying the schoolmaster twelve pennies, to bring their barnyard challengers into the classroom for a series of championship mains, an event for which the whole neighborhood turned out. What was left of the de-

25

feated combatants ended up in the schoolmaster's pot. Cocks who showed no fight, the "fugies," further augmented his diet—after they had been tied to stakes as targets for stone-throwers. The fee was a bodle, or halfpenny, a throw.

There was a usage at Candlemas wounding not only to the schoolmaster's sense of dignity, if he still had any, but to the pride of impoverished pupils. All the pupils, rich and poor, were expected to give him whatever coins their families could spare, called "oblations," or "free will offerings." Upon the size of the total amount might depend whether the schoolmaster fared or fasted, burned peat in his grate or froze during the rest of the winter. As they filed past his desk, he would sit, stiff and expressionless, struggling to hide his anxiety. Sixpence was the smallest sum that could decently be offered, and it entitled the donor to no more than a curt acknowledgment. To half a crown, however, the wretched pedagogue would respond with a ritual *"Vivat!"*; to a crown, a *"Floreat bis!"*; to more than that, a ringing *"Floreat ter!"* The biggest contributor of the day he hailed with a *"Gloreat!"* and crowned him "King," while the poorer pupils, shamefaced and resentful, stared at their boots.

Not surprisingly, some families of means preferred to entrust their children's education to a Mess John, or to a private school, or sent them abroad. This they did in defiance of both the Presbyteries, which brooked no outside influences upon formative minds, and their fellow parishioners, who, since they had to pay a public school assessment, opposed any support of competitive systems. To discourage surreptitious teaching, the burgh magistrates would order "the educt pass by tuck of drum, forbidding it under a fine of £5 to £40 Scots and imprisonment, a yearly *toties quoties*." Even private music masters risked a "fulzie of 100 merks for each quarter's contravention."

East Kilbride had maintained a grammar school since the turn of the century, and all the Hunter boys went there. John detested it from the first. "It was a little reading and writing," he said in retrospect, "a great deal of spelling and figures; geography which never got beyond the dullest statistics, and a little philosophy, and chemistry dry as sawdust, and as valuable for deadening purposes." He neglected to mention the massive dosage of Latin, his particular aversion. From the age of nine the pupils were permitted to speak no other tongue either during classes or in conversation among themselves, and to ensure compliance the schoolmasters would select two or three scholars to act as "private clandestine captors," or in plain parlance, eavesdroppers. First offenders were warned *sub paena ferulae,* repeaters got a public whipping. (Whippings, in any case, were administered impartially to good and bad students alike—to the bad for forgetting their lessons, to the good so they would remember them.) It was the further duty of the school spies to inform upon classmates who skimped their daily stint of Scripture reading and prayer, went around with hands unwashed or hair unkempt, blasphemed or played dice.

Natural history, which would have captured John's interest, and perhaps convinced him of the need to contend with the conventional subjects, held no place on the curriculum. The Church, controlling every stage of education, opposed the teaching of most sciences in elementary as well as advanced schools. University studies consisted almost entirely of theology and the humanities. Independent thinking, moreover, any signs of individualism, were suppressed as firmly as religious unorthodoxies. "Say you so!" declared a Lowland headmaster when an assistant pronounced a new boy to be a genius. "Then begin to flog him tomorrow morning!"

John skipped his classes as often as he dared, and when he did attend, it was in body only, not in spirit. His exasperated teachers finally wrote him off as an idle, surly dullard, irredeemable by punishment or reward. They never suspected, nor could have understood, that he had found a classroom to his measure in nature, and teachers in his own eyes and ears and hands. When his mother took him out of school at the age of thirteen, terminating the only formal education he would ever get, he could barely write coherent English, and had acquired a permanent distaste for the halls of academe.

John's waywardness pained his parents the more by contrast to the admirable behavior of their other sons, James and William, who had stood at the top of their class and now gave promise of bright careers. John resembled these exemplars physically to the degree that a crude caricature resembles the original. The lines of the short body, of the strong jaw and broad brow, which in them was finely drawn, in him were coarsened and blunted. In temperament he might have belonged altogether to an alien breed. No reproof, no chastisement at home or at school could curb the brash, brusque way he spoke his mind, his primitive sense of the comic, his obstreperous laughter, whereas James and William had acquired early in life a measure of self-control, of tact and decorum.

James, thirteen years older than John, was a handsome, affectionate, clever youth of varied gifts. He painted charmingly, with a penetrating eye for character. A portrait of his father, completed shortly before the sitter died, suggests in the somber, faraway gaze and sensitive mouth the inner conflicts of that troubled dreamer.* Upon graduating from the parish school James began studying law, a profession that Scottish landowners, being incurably litigious, urged at least one son to take up. He became, when only fourteen, a Writer to the Signet, an office under the Secretary of State empowered to prepare writs for the King's seal. His enthusiasm soon flagged, however. If James had a serious flaw of intellect, it was a certain indecision. For a time he thought of joining the army, but his invalid sister, "Nannie" (Agnes), whom he adored, dissuaded him, and he concentrated anew on his law books. James, too, suffered from weak lungs.

3. WILLIAM

Of William, born May 23, 1718, ten years before John, Dr. Cullen, who always kept a fond eye on him, once said, "His whole conduct was more strictly and steadily correct than that of any other young person I have ever known." A less partial observer might have found William a trifle "unco' guid." Cold, devious, ambitious, snobbish, yet endearing when he wished to be, he himself observed in a letter to James, "I have no time for endeavouring to be humorous, tho' I know you have a great Gusto that way."

With his first son training for the bar, the senior Hunter wanted the second to take the cloth, and William, having won a bursary of £10 a year, matriculated in the University of Glasgow in the Bajan class of 1731—Bajan, a corruption of the French university term, *bec jaune* (yellow-beak, or, as the Scottish students vulgarized it, "yellow-neb"), meaning freshman. William was then thirteen. The courses, lasting five years, included, besides theology, ethics, philosophy, logic, mathematics, and physics, with special attention to pneumatics, a branch of physics dealing with the mechanics of air and gases.

How torpid the pace of Scottish university life may be gathered from an incident that occurred during one of the interminable faculty ban-

* Now in the Royal College of Surgeons of England, London.

quets. A professor, alarmed by the pallor of his neighbor, whispered to a colleague on the side, "What ails Drumsheugh? He's lookin' gey gash."

"Hush, mon," was the reply, "he's been wi' his Maker thae twa hours."

At the time William entered the university, that monolithic institution, 280 years old, was undergoing a transformation intolerable to the Established Church. Despite all its efforts to seal the chinks, the winds of liberalism, blowing from England and Europe, were beginning to penetrate the classrooms. As early as 1723, the Glasgow Presbytery had had to call to account a professor of divinity named John Simson because he was expounding the heresies of Arius, a fourth-century Alexandrian priest, who denied the consubstantiality of Christ with God. The outraged authorities conceded that Simson had not actually condoned Arianism; they nevertheless expelled him for exposing his pupils to it.

Now the Reverend Francis Hutcheson, who occupied the chair of moral philosophy—"the never to be forgotten Hutcheson," his most illustrious disciple, Adam Smith, called him—was promulgating a secular system of morality based not on religious dogma, but metaphysical principles, not on faith, but reason. A forerunner of David Hume, and of Jeremy Bentham, whose utilitarian philosophy of "the greatest happiness for the greatest number" he anticipated, Hutcheson applied the experimental method to ethics. Each individual, he insisted, must remain free to draw his own conclusions about the universe from rational evidence; man could arrive at a knowledge of good and evil without knowledge of God. Beauty and virtue he considered interdependent, and thus an appreciation of art, music, and poetry essential to moral health. Here were heresies hideous in the eyes of the Church doctrinaires for whom truth, immutable and sempiternal, had already been divinely revealed. Vile man, with his feeble comprehension, they held to be neither capable nor sanctioned to seek further, and sensuous beauty an instrument of satanic pollution. But so noble was Hutcheson's character, so invulnerable his prestige that, try as it might, the Presbytery failed to dislodge or to silence him.

The professor was only one of several iconoclasts on the faculty, and in Willie Hunter they produced painful mental turmoil. Imbued with their spirit of analytical inquiry, he first questioned, then doubted, and finally rejected the religious and moral absolutes of his upbringing.

Among his fellow students, too, he encountered unsettling influences, such as an impious, razor-tongued scoffer, attracted to both medicine and letters, by name, Tobias Smollett. Two postgraduates, the brothers Robert and Andrew Foulis, printers, publishers and art collectors, while continuing to reside at the University rallied around them a band of Glasgow esthetes, regularly exhibited in Faculty Hall the paintings that they bought all over Europe, and founded Scotland's first fine arts academy. From them William learned to love books and paintings. The result of these liberalizing associations was that, towards the end of his last term, he judged himself unfit, as he put it, "to wag my pow in a pu'pit." He completed the curriculum, but received no degree.

Soon after he returned home, however, and, to his father's chagrin, renounced the ministry, the benevolent Cullen opened up to William a congenial alternative, one providing unlimited scope for analytical thinking. He offered him a medical apprenticeship. William was delighted, and his father raised no objections. A doctor in the family, after all, would be as valuable an asset as a clergyman.

Born in the village of Hamilton, five miles from East Kilbride, to the Duke of Hamilton's factor, Cullen was only eight years older than his protégé. Largely self-taught, he had not yet obtained a medical degree (in those days, no legal impediment to practicing medicine). He had had considerable clinical experience, however, as an apprentice to a Glasgow surgeon, as a ship's surgeon, and as assistant to a surgeon-apothecary in London. He started his own practice near Hamilton in 1731, but two years later, having come into a small legacy, he retired temporarily to fill the gaps in his cultural education, and for three years he administered to himself heavy doses of literature and philosophy. A civic-spirited man of strange but commanding mien, with a great hatchet blade of a nose and a pendulous lower lip, he was eventually elected Bailie of Hamilton, in which office he distinguished himself by quelling a riot among famine-stricken farmers. Before resuming his practice he studied anatomy at the University of Edinburgh under Alexander Monro, progenitor of a dynasty of great teachers and founder, at Edinburgh in 1726, of the first medical school in the British Isles.

Cullen had been practicing again for about a year under the patronage of the Duke of Hamilton when William came to live with him. The apprentice stayed three years, and acquired an affection for his master as warm as he was capable of feeling for anybody. "They were," he said long after, "the happiest years of my life," and he spoke of Cullen as the "man to whom I owe most and love most of all men in the world."

It was a mutually rewarding relationship, with the roles of teacher and pupil often reversed. While learning from Cullen the rudiments of physic and surgery, William imparted to him the radical new philosophical ideas he had absorbed at Glasgow. Cullen later brought the younger man into stimulating contact with some remarkable medical men, of whom the most progressive had begun his career not far away in Lanark. His name, like his idiosyncrasies, a frequent butt of ridicule, was Smellie—William Smellie. (Sterne alluded to him in *Tristram Shandy* as "Adrianus Smelvgot.") With his wife, Eupham, Dr. Smellie had once kept the village drapery shop. He cultivated the arts, collected books, painted, carved, played the organ, the violoncello, the recorder. And he practiced both surgery and obstetrics.

In Scotland, as in England, the male accoucheur traveled a rocky road, for prudery supported what the self-interest of the midwives demanded, that no man should attend a woman in labor, an attitude reflected in the derisive term "man-midwife." The profession was a refuge for women too old, infirm or ignorant to earn their livelihood by other means. To qualify, they needed only to obtain an endorsement from some established midwife, pay a licensing charge of eighteen shillings, and forswear such prevalent offenses as abortion, witchcraft, and fee-gouging. The consequent childbed mishaps were horrendous. Sarah Stone, an English midwife more conscientious than most, though a leader in the attack against the men-midwives, publicly deplored her sister practitioners' lack of training. "I saw," she wrote, recounting the havoc wrought by a blundering country midwife who sent for her too late to help, "the child with one eye out, and the whole face injured, having no skin left on it, and the upper lip tore quite hollow from the jawbone." She went on to plead, ". . . it is not improper for all of the profession to see dissections and read anatomy as I have done. . . . In my humble opinion it is necessary that midwives employ three years at least with some ingenious woman in practising this art. For, if seven years must be served to learn a trade, I think three years as little as possible to be instructed in an art where life depends."

It was the rapid development, since the late seventeenth century, of obstetrical forceps that had weakened the monopoly so long enjoyed by the sisterhood, because forceps required a degree of skill few mid-wives could muster. They execrated all instruments and their users. In preternatural cases, however, they frequently had no choice, if they were not to lose mother, child or both, but to call in one of their hated male competitors. Such emergencies comprised the bulk of Smellie's early practice, and it infuriated him that he was seldom allowed to assist in a normal labor.

"A midwife," he recorded in his case book, "who never had any education, and who had formerly vaunted that she always did her own work and would never call in man to her assistance, was called to a case, in which the child presented wrong. After she had with great difficulty brought down the body, she could not deliver the head, from the woman's being of a small size and the child large. During the time of her making these trials, the husband sent in great haste for me. In the meantime when the midwife found that her endeavours were in vain, she rested to recover from her fatigue, and told those who were present that she would not wait for the assistance of the woman's pains. One of the servants seeing me at a distance, went in a hurry and told her I was come. She, not knowing that I was called, fell to work immediately and pulled at the child with great force and violence. Finding, as she imagined, the child coming along, she called out that 'now she had got the better of him'! The neck at that instant separating, the body was pulled from the head, and she fell down on the floor. As she attempted to rise, one of the assistants told her that it wanted a head, a circumstance that shocked her so much (being a woman of violent disposition) that she was immediately seized with faintings and convulsions, and obliged to be put to bed in another room. . . . This accident was lucky for me, and rendered the midwife more tractable for the future."

No respectable woman would expose her body to a doctor's gaze, so that Smellie had to operate under the sheets. He was once thus blindly groping when he inadvertently cut the umbilical cord above instead of below the ligature he had tied, and before he managed to seize and retie it the baby nearly bled to death. Knowing what capital the attendant midwife would make of the accident, he told her she had been privileged to witness his unique method of preventing postnatal convulsions, an absurdity that she accepted and spread abroad to the enhancement of his reputation among midwives.

Smellie's person and manners were not calculated to win favor with parturient women of delicate sensibilities, and from the upper classes he attracted no following. He was a huge, burly man. "Such monstrous Hands," according to one of his numerous detractors, "are, like Wooden Forceps, fit only to hold Horses by the nose, whilst they are shod by the Farrier, or stretch boots in Cranburne Alley." Another enemy pronounced him "in every respect a brute" and his masterly three-volume treatise on midwifery, "the most bawdy, indecent and shameful Book which the press ever brought into the World." Smellie himself ingenuously admitted that during one troublesome delivery "I sweated so much that I was obliged to throw off my waistcoat and wig, and put on my nightgown, with a thin napkin over my head." He became, nevertheless, an obstetrician as superbly skilled as he was humane, the foremost of his day, many of whose technical procedures and theories have survived with little modification. On the career of William Hunter he was to exert a decisive influence.

In 1739, when he was forty-two, Smellie left Lanark for London, hoping there to enlarge his opportunities. William's apprenticeship ended that same year, and at Cullen's urging he spent the following winter in Edinburgh attending Monro's courses. Upon his return Cullen put before him a proposal he jumped at. They would form a partnership, with Cullen confining himself chiefly to general medicine, and William to the obstetrical and surgical patients. But first they both would need a great deal more training. Cullen proposed to work toward a doctorate at Glasgow. William, he felt, should spend at least a year in London, where the choice of instructors was far greater. Such a move, however, would depend upon the willingness of William's already hard-pressed father to make further retrenchments, and the two friends approached him with some trepidation.

Listening to Cullen as, with love and absolute faith in William, he spoke of his capacities, his intense seriousness, his exceptional scholastic record (how different, alas, from Jock!), as he predicted a brilliant future for him, the sick old man had an exalting vision: he could see, if it pleased God to spare him yet a while, William back at Long Calderwood, honored and prosperous, the first of his line to raise the Hunter name above the common run of men. Thus fortified, assured that William would come home as soon as he was qualified to practice, the father agreed to make the necessary sacrifices.

In 1740, in his twenty-second year, William booked passage in a packet sailing for London on October 26, a Sunday. He had a struggle getting aboard because the docks swarmed with famished mobs trying to loot the harbor grain stores.

4. THE ENEMY CAMP

It was a harrowing voyage. On Friday, November 1, after six days of squalls and fierce cold, the ship put in at a tiny port of call, already packed with vessels, some twenty miles from the mouth of the Thames, and rode precariously at anchor between sand banks barely eight cable-lengths apart. Saturday afternoon, the wind beginning to bluster again, the captain decided to seek roomier anchorage lest his ship drag her anchor and be dashed into a sand bank or one of her crowding neighbors. Six miles farther south, as night was closing in, he sighted a likely spot. But before the sails could be lowered or the anchor had hit bottom, a tempest burst with a fury that hurled the packet toward the shallows. The anchor caught fast in time to save her from running aground. By then the swift, icy seas were raking her from bow to stern. Only her quarter-deck showed above water.

All night the ship tossed and shuddered, the pull on her ground-tackling threatening at any instant to sunder it. "Our danger," William recalled later, "was so evident that the sailors neglected the complaisance of soothing the passengers with the least hope." Terror drove a woman passenger insane.

The dawn broke gray and frosty upon a maelstrom strewn with wreckage. Other craft had moored near the packet ship, and of these two sloops had been ripped loose and swept out to sea with all hands, never to be recovered. A third sloop lay shattered against a rocky spit. From the masthead to which he had lashed himself, a sailor, frozen dead, hung like a criminal exposed in chains. Some of his mates still clung to the sides of the sloop, but in those churning seas no boat could heave to to fling them a line, a sight that moved William with "the most sincere and melting compassion." Along the shore—and, he later saw, inland as far as London—the storm, "as violent as ever in the memory of man," bowled over chimneys, steeples, and turrets, which in their fall killed many people below.

To William's amazement, the shipwrecked sailors still had a flicker of life left in them Monday afternoon when the sea at last subsided, and as the packet weighed anchor he was relieved to see a rescue party pulling toward the spit. It was Tuesday night, November 4, when the battered packet limped up to the London docks and William disembarked, shaken to his boots but satisfied that "I have got sufficient trial of myself in danger and confusion and in such a way as to give me pleasure on reflection."

". . . there is little doubt," the English medical historian, George C. Peachey, wrote, "that, amid the trials and disappointments of his London career, William Hunter was assisted by the conviction, call it superstition if you will, that the same Providence which had preserved him from the dangers of the sea was still watching over him."

Of those trials none was so galling to William's self-esteem than the anti-Scotticism of the English. Although Scotland and England had been united under one crown for three decades, the two peoples remained hostile. Historical traditions, laws, religion, ways of thinking and speaking, Scotland's poverty and Scotland's isolation—all combined to perpetuate the antagonism. An English trade commissioner compared the Union to the marriage of "a beggar with a louse for her portion," while the Scots railed against it as a blow to their freedom and pride.

The rare Englishman whom curiosity or business impelled to journey north of the Tweed would set forth in the intrepid spirit of an explorer about to venture among unpredictable savages. When safely home again, he could dine out for weeks on his horrifying memories of the strident northern speech, the mud-choked roads, the cheerless fare and drafty lodgings, the sullen, ragged peasantry and the down-at-heels lairds with their rough manners, the grim piety, the moral strictures, the cultural aridity. "I passed to English ground," one traveler related, "and hope I may never go to such a country again. I thank God I never saw such another country, and must conclude with poet Cleveland—

> Had Cain been Scot, God had ne'er
> changed his doom,
>
> Not made him wander, but confined
> him home.

Even the scenic grandeurs of the Highlands failed to wrench an admiring word from "the factitious barbarians," as that arch-Anglophobe, David Hume, called them. To the English spectator the serene hills presented "a most hideous aspect," the crag-rent heaths had "the disagreeable appearance of a scabbed head," the mountains were "black and frightful," and the whole landscape "of a dismal brown drawing upon a dirty purple, and most of all disagreeable when the heath is in bloom."

But if the English shunned Scotland, talented Scots flocked to England by the hundreds, never to return, for few of them remained content with the meager rewards their own impoverished people could bestow. The exodus gave some substance to the common taunt that though a Scot might die for his country he would not live there. It was a phenomenon as astonishing to the English as it was exasperating how many able men that backward land produced. They tended, moreover, these transplanted thistles, to band together in self-defense, forming within every area of the arts, sciences and commerce little enclaves that challenged and often triumphed over the native English, and they thereby aggravated the prejudice against them.

At the time William Hunter emigrated—in fact, almost to the close of the century—the Scot, as depicted on the London stage, in lampoons and caricatures, was a mean, furtive, avaricious lickspittle, battening upon the high-souled English. When a printer from Edinburgh founded, and Smollett, who had finally abandoned medicine for literature, edited the *Critical Review,* the entrenched *Monthly Review* characterized their contributors as "Scots scrubs and rascals, barbers, tailors, apothecaries, and surgeons' mates, who understood neither Greek, Latin, French, or any other Language." Lest he alienate his English readers, Smollett issued the first edition of his first novel, *Roderick Random,* anonymously, and in the preface craved their indulgence for having made his hero Scottish.

The northerners encountered the stiffest discrimination (as did Jews, Roman Catholics, Dissenters, and all those born or educated abroad) in the field of medicine, which they nevertheless permeated. The Royal College of Physicians would enroll them as licentiates only, not full members, whatever their abilities, and the Company of Barber-Surgeons (from which a dissident minority seceded in 1745 to organize the Corporation of Surgeons), while erecting no official barriers, discouraged Scottish applicants.

The night William reached London he found lodgings with a Mrs. Gray in the Strand. The next day, ignoring the city's blatant allurements, which might have distracted a less sober-minded youth upon exposure to them for the first time, he hurried straight to Pall Mall, carrying a letter of commendation from Cullen. In St. Alban's Street, hard by the Mall, he came to a dingy apothecary's shop, the former premises of the Key and Garter Tavern. Above the door a paper lantern rustled in the autumn breeze.

Inside the shop, amid a multicolored forest of flagons, gallipots, and alembics, he found William Smellie, exhibiting to a few students a curious apparatus. It consisted of a skeletal female pelvis and lower abdomen, re-covered with layers of imitation ligaments, muscle, and skin, and so constructed that the uterus could be contracted and dilated as in childbirth. "All the parts [according to a student's notebook] seem very Natural both to Look and Touch; the Contents of the *Abdomen* are beautifully contriv'd, the Intestines look very natural, as likewise the Kidneys and large Vessels."

Beside the pelvis lay six toy fetuses of varying sizes, the limbs maneuverable and the craniums fashioned from an elastic material that regained its shape following compression. One after the other, in the order of size, Smellie passed the manikins through the pelvic cavity and thus demonstrated the progressive fetal positions and the various presentations at delivery.

William left Mrs. Gray's within the week and moved into quarters above the apothecary's shop, where he lived for almost a year. From Smellie he learned what no teacher before in the history of obstetrics had understood—the mechanics of parturition. Every physician since Hippocrates had assumed that during normal pregnancy the fetus lay with its head towards the top and its feet toward the outlet of the uterus, reversing the position some time after the seventh month, or, as one of Smellie's contemporaries put it, "tumbling over its Head, so that the Feet are uppermost and the Face towards the Mother's Great Gut." Then, at birth, it was thought to emerge from a crawling posture on its hands and knees.

That universally held belief Smellie exploded. No such change of position, he proved, occurred; the fetus usually continued head down throughout gestation, though during labor "the widest part of the head is turned to the widest part of the pelvis, and the narrow part of the head, from ear to ear, applied to the narrow part between the pubes and the sacrum." His reasoning, based upon precise pelvic measurements in dissected cadavers, the first ever made, was impeccable:

37

Here is a body to be propelled. Here is a propulsive force behind it. Here is a channel it must travel. The pelvis measures wider at the top than at the outlet. Nature chooses the path of least resistance. Logically, therefore, the longest diameter of the head will keep accommodating itself to the widest diameters of the pelvis at the successive levels of descent.

For this discovery alone, whereby countless mothers and infants have been spared mutilation, Smellie merited the title posterity conferred on him, "Master of British Midwifery." But he was also the first to teach the safe management of forceps. While the celebrated French accoucheur, Grégoire, was blithely advising his students to insert forceps "at random and pull with great force," the Scotsman, in one of several treatises that Smollett helped him write, explained, "I began to consider the whole in a mechanical view and reduce the extraction of the child to the rules of moving bodies in different directions. In consequence of this plan I more accurately surveyed the dimensions and form of the pelvis, together with the figure of the child's head and the manner in which it passed along in natural labours. . . . From this knowledge, too . . . I have been led to alter the form and dimensions of the forceps that attend the use of the former kind."

The pair he ultimately adopted, after designing a series of improved models, was short and light, the blades shaped to the pelvic curve the better to grasp the child's head without injury to the mother's tissues, and they have continued in use, essentially unchanged, ever since. Smellie's proficiency at forceps delivery led his enemies to accuse him of abusing the operation. In reality, he taught that the greater the skill the less the need for forceps. "I have laid it down as a maxim to myself," he said, "and to the Gentlemen who attend my Course, never to use any instrument, or Violence, but where it is absolutely necessary for the safety of Mother and Child . . . only ten out of 1,000 labours requird instrumental delivery."

When William had learned as much about the reproductive process as Smellie's "machine" could illustrate, he was allowed to accompany him to the bedsides of women in labor. Smellie treated the poor in their homes without fee in return for their permission to bring his pupils, which, there being as yet no maternity hospital in London, offered the only means of clinical instruction. His paying patients, too, belonged to the lower classes. He never sought a fashionable practice, probably because he realized that he lacked, and did not care to acquire, the requisite social graces.

It was Smellie's odd though kindly notion that the professional attire of a man-midwife should be feminized, partly to dulcify the asperities of the male physique, partly to furnish concealment for any frightening-looking instruments he might have to use. "The more genteel and commodious dress," he insisted, "is a loose washing night-gown . . . his waistcoat ought to be without sleeves, that his arms may have more freedom to slide up and down under cover of the wrapper; and the sleeves of his shirt may be rolled up and pinned to the breast of his waistcoat." To this he joined a bonnet big enough to slip over his wig.

The getup provided his baiters with endless sport, and no doubt caused starchy William to blush for him. "Paint to yourself," wrote Elizabeth Nihell, the queen of the London midwives, and the shrillest of the anti-Smellie pack, "one of these sage, deep-learned *Cotts* [men who do women's work], dressed for proceeding to officiate and presenting himself with his pocket night-gown . . . add to this, fingers, of which not the nicest paring the nails will ever cure the stiffness and clumsiness; you will hardly deny its being somewhat puzzling, the giving of a name to such a heteroclite figure? Or rather can too ludicrous one be assigned to it?" Among Mrs. Nihell's own choices of a name for Smellie was "great-horse-godmother of a he-midwife." Again, in the same polemic, bearing the profuse title of *A Treatise on the Art of Midwifery, setting forth Various Abuses therein, Especially as to the Practice with Instruments; The Whole serving to put all Rational Inquirers in a fair way of safely forming their own Judgment upon the Question: Which it is best to employ In cases of Pregnancy and Lying-In, a Man-Midwife; or a Midwife* and dedicated "To All Fathers, Mothers and likely soon to be Either," she denounced Smellie as a murderous bungler, "however softened his figure might be by his pocket night-gown being of flowered calico, or his cap of office tied with pink and silver ribbon."

During his nineteen years in London, before asthma forced him to retire, Smellie trained nine hundred pupils, a number of them women. He considered women not only capable of practicing obstetrics, provided they kept abreast of advances in the field, but indispensable to a profession too shorthanded to care properly for all its patients. He never troubled to refute his slanderers, not even when they charged

him with deliberately misguiding his women pupils so that they would
have to send for him to retrieve their blunders. He took comfort in
his artistic hobbies, though he felt constrained to apologize for his
extracurricular gifts. "When not engadged in business," he wrote in a
self-appraisal archly disguised as a biographical sketch by some anonymous Scottish bumpkin, "his great pleasure was home, improving his
mind by reading the best authors, both in his own profession and
other gentile an[d] usefull branches of learning; his other amusements
by way of relaxation, was designes in drauing and musick; but no
more than what was fitt for a gentleman to know, and he used to jock
those who spent too much time in these recreations, by axing if they
were not ashamed to perform too well."

Through his imaginary biographer Smellie further portrayed himself as "a man of learning and experience in practice, his acknouleded
care and simpathy to all his patients, of every denomination, sheued
his virteous inclinations. His excellent disposition and other quelifica-
tions was so hid by an unafected modesty and selfdenyal, that they
were not fully knoun but to his intimate acquaintances . . . mild in
conversation, spoke little, but when he did it was always to the purpose;
his modesty was so great that he would frequently hear others and sit
as a larner in disputes on his own profession, and not interup, even
although he was more master of the subject, rather than shew any
superiority . . . temperate, free from show and ostentation, kind
and beneficent; he had many friends; but was only intimate with a
few select ones, with whom he sometimes though rarely would take a
chereful glass. . . . He was a sociable Husband a kind Master . . ."
He had no children.

With William Hunter, his brightest pupil, Smellie took extra pains.
He saw to it that he broadened his technical equipment under Lon-
don's best teacher of natural science, the Rev. Dr. John Theophilus
Desaguliers, and its best anatomy teacher, Dr. Frank Nicholls. Both
of these men were Oxford graduates, and both belonged to the Royal
Society of London for Improving Natural Knowledge. As the inventor
of a planetarium for measuring celestial distances according to the
Copernican and Newtonian systems, of a ventilator he installed in the
House of Commons, and of a device for applying steam to manufactur-
ing processes, Desaguliers had won the Copley Gold Medal, the Royal
Society's highest award. He had been greatly esteemed by the late
President of the society, Sir Isaac Newton. A squat, thick-bodied,

middle-aged man, hopelessly myopic, he lectured on hydrostatics, optics and mechanics at his lodgings in the Bedford Coffee-house above the Great Piazza of Covent Garden. His fee per pupil was three guineas.

Nicholls, who also taught at his home, on the corner of Lincoln's Inn Fields, charged forty guineas for a series of thirty-nine lectures covering "Anatomy and Physiology, in which the Animal Oeconomy will be explained, and the principles of Physick illustrated by proper lectures on the solids and fluids of the Animal, the action of medicines, calculous concretions, and the Art of Midwifery." His fame rested primarily on his studies of the minute structure of blood vessels. He had discerned the vasomotor nerves, recognizing their function as the regulators of blood pressure. Before the Royal Society he had shown that the internal coats of an artery could be ruptured, yet the outer coat remain intact, and he thus clarified the formation of chronic aneurysms. It was Nicholls who developed the corroded method of preparing anatomical specimens, whereby the minutest vessels could be made to stand out prominently. Into the vascular network he would inject bright-colored liquid wax, let it harden, and dissolve the enveloping flesh with corrosive chemicals, leaving a mold of the vessels.

"The professor," William, however, objected, "used only two dead bodies in his course. The consequence was, that . . . all was harangue; very little was distinctly seen." But under the law that restricted dissections to the corpses of executed criminals, and the scene of operation to Barber-Surgeons' Hall, the private anatomy teachers had no human material unless they cared to traffic with the growing gangs of body snatchers, a source both expensive and dangerous. An anatomist who had studied under Monro and then his Dutch counterpart, Bernhard Siegfried Albinus, at the University of Leyden, complained, "In Dr. Monro's class, unless there be a fortunate succession of bloody murders, not three subjects are dissected in a year. Albinus used only one cadaver a year for the whole school."

Rather than risk prosecution, many teachers confined their demonstrations to animal organs corresponding to those in man. The resultant mental image of the human system, as pictured by the doctors so trained, was apt to be part sheep, part dog, part monkey. When the Margrave of Baden Durlach appeared to be suffering from a cardiac disturbance, his court physicians all agreed that a poultice should be applied over his heart. The question was, where exactly did the heart lodge in the thorax? Some said towards the center, others on the left side. To settle the issue to the Margrave's satisfaction, they dissected a pig before his eyes in the belief—which happens to be true—that the situation of a pig's heart is the same as that of a prince's. The Margrave finding this logic admirable, they applied the poultice accordingly a little to the left of his median pectoral line. One of the physicians, who refused to accept the analogy, was banished from the court.

William's major interest continued to be obstetrics, despite the contumely its male practitioners incurred. For a man of his instinctive conformities, craving an elevated social status, the choice must have caused him a good deal of conflict. Dr. Nicholls himself, even though he taught the art, later circulated a threepenny tract entitled *A Petition of the Unborn Babes*, wherein the babes appealed to the Royal College of Physicians to censure members practicing midwifery. Only through fear and ignorance, the babes pleaded, did mothers employ men-midwives "to distress, bruise, kill, and destroy." The tract so delighted Queen Caroline's midwife, Mrs. Kennon, that she bequeathed to the author five hundred pounds.

William might more comfortably have pursued surgery, as he did for a time, or general medicine. But with his shrewdness, his finesse, and his power to charm, he was no doubt confident that he could attain an unassailable position as an accoucheur at the pinnacle of society, a position Smellie, in his sweat-streaked nightgown, could never occupy. "The delicacy of his manners, and a very quick perception of the caprices of the world," were among the assets later noted by a nephew of William's, and a member of the *Académie Royale des Sciences* was to observe, "*Il fut très-heureux pour les Dames Anglaises que M. Hunter unit à une habileté pour la moins égale, la douceur et les agrémens dont l'austere et savant Smellie avait été privé.*"

Having digested all the knowledge Smellie could transmit to him, William let the relationship cool, and eventually it deteriorated into open hostility. Through a letter of introduction from Robert Foulis, he had meanwhile come to know a celebrity splendidly situated to advance his aspirations, both social and professional. This potential benefactor was Dr. James Douglas, a Scot, to be sure, but an assimilated Scot long resident in London, with an opulent house on Red Lion Square, a collection nonpareil of early editions of Horace, an English wife, a marriageable daughter, and a rakehell of a son. Douglas, too, had practiced and taught midwifery, but with no grave damage to his footing among the city's elite. Alexander Pope paid him tribute in the *Dunciad*:

> *To prove me, Goddess! clear of all design,*
> *Bid me with Pollio sup, as well as dine;*
> *There all the learn'd shall at the labour stand*
> *And Douglas lend his soft obstetric hand.*

To the general public Douglas's name had been familiar for fifteen years, ever since his involvement in the case of Mary Toft, a clothier's wife, aged twenty-five, the mother of three normal children, who gave birth to rabbits. The first delivery, as Mary retold her experience, followed months of preoccupation with rabbits. She continually dreamt about them, she longed to eat some, a state of mind she attributed to pregnancy. On April 23, 1726, she testified, while weeding a field near her home in Godalming, Surrey, she spied two rabbits. She dashed after them, but both escaped. Frustration increased her leporine cravings, which persisted through the summer and fall.

On November 2, Mary complained of labor pains to her husband, Joshua, who fetched a man-midwife named John Howard from the nearby town of Guildford. Howard had been practicing for more than thirty years and was respected as much for his character as for his skill. The patient appeared to him to be in the final stages of childbirth, with violent uterine contractions. He delivered her of what he afterwards described as a "cat-pawed rabbit," stillborn. Between the third and the sixth of November he delivered three more, none surviving. The last, Howard stated, "had leaped in her Belly for the space of eighteen hours before it had died, and the moment it was taken away another was perceived to struggle for birth." He transferred his remarkable patient to Guildford, where she produced five rabbits. "If she had been with child, she has but ten more days to go, for I do not know how many rabbits there may be behind." There were quite a few.

Howard's breathless communiqués, disseminated by the press and by word of mouth to the remotest corners of the nation, eclipsed in the public imagination such recent marvels as the Moodiwarp, an octopus-like infant believed to have resulted from "indecent conjugal relations"; Mrs. French, the horned lady; the albino with rotating eyeballs; Joanna Stephens' pills for dissolving stones in the bladder ("snails calcined, wild carrot seeds, burdick seeds, ashen keys, hips and hawes—all burnt to blackness—Alicant soap and honey"); the Polish mother who bore a pair of fish. "I want to know," Pope wrote to a learned friend, "what faith you have in the miracle at Guildford. All London is divided into factions about it."

The King and Queen, no less excited than their subjects, ordered Nathaniel St. André, a surgeon on the staff of the Westminster Hospital Dispensary and anatomist to the royal household, to investigate the anomaly. A Swiss by birth, St. André had succeeded to his two offices without any medical degrees, after teaching languages, fencing, and dancing. He arrived at Guildford in the company of Samuel Molyneux, the Prince of Wales's secretary, just as Mrs. Toft was going into her fifteenth labor. What the surgeon-anatomist reported confirmed Howard's observations: "We found her dressed in her stays sitting on the bedside with several women near her. I waited for the coming of fresh pains, which happened in three or four minutes, at which I deliver'd her of the entire trunk, strip'd of its skin, of a Rabbet of about four months growth, in which the Heart and Lungs were contained in the Diagram entire."

Examining the first fourteen rabbits, which had been pickled, St. André was fleetingly troubled by the lack of viscera in some of them. But the bones, he concluded, dismissing his last, lingering suspicion, were the bones of true fetal rabbits. "This proves in the strongest Terms possible that these Animals were not bred in a natural Way; nor will there be any doubt remaining when those facts which are subservient to the Circulation of the Blood and Nourishment between an Adult creature and its Foetus are brought away; which I am fully satisfied must shortly happen, or, if retained, be the cause of this Woman's Death."

Their Majesties' Surgeon, the German, Cyriacus Ahlers, visited Guildford, at the King's bidding, delivered a sixteenth rabbit, and attested to the genuineness of the phenomenon. Nor was there any dearth of corroborating lay witnesses. The townsfolk said they saw the bedclothes heave, so lively was the activity of rabbits yet unborn, in some instances lasting thirty hours. They said they heard rabbit bones "snap and break by the violent Convulsive Motions of the Uterus." They said their hearts were wrung with pity by Mrs. Toft's sufferings when she "voided a Piece of Placenta rolled up like a Parchment."

But the King, still not wholly convinced, requested the redoubtable man-midwife, Sir Richard Manningham, "an ugly old gentleman in a great black wig," to delve further. Sir Richard arrived on November

28, preceding the delivery of rabbit number seventeen. He detected a hard substance on the right side of Mary's abdomen, but nothing stirring. Howard, miffed by Sir Richard's skepticism, applied hot towels, which he said would make the fetus move. "It was indeed a motion like a sudden leaping," Sir Richard noted. Out popped the rabbit, and presently Howard showed him what he claimed to be the placenta. To Sir Richard, it looked like a hog's bladder. He had Mary removed to London and kept under hourly observation. She was confined to a room in an establishment known as Lacey's Bagnio.

At this juncture Sir Richard called in Dr. James Douglas, like himself an Honorary Member of the Royal College of Physicians, Fellow of the Royal Society, and contributor of scientific papers to the society's *Philosophical Transactions*. Together they examined Mary, the dubious seventeenth placenta—a hog's bladder without question, Douglas concurred—and questioned her previous attendants and the inhabitants of Godalming. The only mystery that ever puzzled either of them was the precise mechanics of the deception.

Mary, meanwhile, though closely guarded, again "fell into violent convulsions with contraction of her fingers, rolling of her Eyes, and great risings in her Stomach and Belly." It was her farewell performance. The porter at Lacey's Bagnio relieved his uneasy conscience by informing Sir Richard and Dr. Douglas that Mary had bribed him to smuggle her a rabbit.

When the two doctors confronted Mary with the porter's story, she tried to brazen it out, swearing she had merely intended to eat the rabbit. "Confess!" roared Sir Richard. "You are an impostor, differently formed from other women, having some peculiar way of conveying pieces of rabbit into your uterus." Mary denied it. "Then," said Sir Richard, "I am resolved to try a very painful experiment upon you."

The threat succeeded, and from the confession, which Douglas transcribed, it was clear that Mary had not had to feign suffering. Nobody ever endured worse torment for the sake of perpetrating a hoax.

"She own'd [Douglas wrote] that upon her miscarrying she was seized with violent Floodings, and the womb was then as she thought open, as if she had just been deliver'd of a full-grown child, and she did verily believe one of her wicked Accomplices did then convey into her womb part of the Monster (as she calls it) being the Claws and Body of a Cat and the head of a Rabbet; this put her to much pain. After that time she believed nothing was ever put into her womb, but into the passage only by the advice of a woman Accomplice whom she has not yet nam'd, and who told her she had now no Occasion to work for her living as formerly, for she would put her in the way of getting a very good Livelihood, and promised to supply her continually with Rabbets, and should therefore expect part of the Gain or to that effect. Mary Toft asked her what the way was. The Woman told her she must put up her body so many pieces of Rabbet as would make up the number of Rabbets which a Doe Rabbet normally kindles at one time, otherwise she would be suspected. From that time Mary Toft did often by the assistance of the Woman convey parts of Rabbets into her Body till at last she could do so by herself as she had an opportunity. Now by the constant Irritation of these Extraneous Bodies the whole Uterus suffered much and became larger than it ought to be, and the Bones and other Parts of these Rabbets so conveyed into the Vagina did often offend the neck of the Uterus, which together with artful management of herself, did occasion these violent bearing-down pains which very exactly counterfeited true Labour Pains. The Motions of her Belly were partly artificial and partly real convulsions. . . ."

Three Godalming villagers then came forward to depose that they had sold rabbits to Joshua Toft. After serving a brief term in Bridewell Gaol, Mary returned to her birthplace where she died at sixty-two, celebrated in song and story as one of the supreme hoaxers of the age.

Under the avalanche of ribald broadsheets that greeted the exposure reputations collapsed like houses of cards. Howard spent the rest of his life protesting that, though a dupe, he had been an honest dupe. St. André, whom Hogarth pilloried in a famous engraving, *Credulity, Superstition and Fanaticism,* was seen no more at court. Cyriacus Ahlers never lived down the allegation by "Lemuel Gulliver, Surgeon and Anatomist to the King of Lilliput" that the rabbit he delivered was actually a cat whose stomach contained "the bones of a herring which the Creature had devoured a few hours before it was thrust into the Vagina of Mary Toft." Rabbit stew and jugged hare disappeared for months from the English dinner table. Copies of a satire called *The Wonder of Wonders,* bound in rabbit skin, sold for as high as fifteen guineas. The most widely circulated lampoon was *The Doctors in Labour, or a New Whim Wham from Guildford.* Under an accompanying caricature of St. André, with the caption, "Milk was present in one Mamma," ran the doggerel:

When I (says Moll) five weeks was gone with child
And hard at Work was weeding in the field
Up Starts a rabbet—To my grief I viewed it
And vainly tho with eagerness pursued it.
The Effect was Strange—Blest is the womb that's barren
For that can ne'er be made a Coney warren.

The Rabbet all day long ran in my Head
At Night I dreamt I had him in my Bed
Methought he there a Burrough try'd to make
His Head I patted and I stroaked his Back
My Husband wak'd me and Cry'd Moll for Shame
Lett go—What t'was he meant I need not name.

The cause of man-midwifery suffered its worst setback in years, and of all the people connected with the case only Manningham and Douglas emerged unscathed.

Douglas's subsequent renown in the scientific world, however, arose from somewhat more substantial achievements. He presented the first systematic lectures on comparative anatomy, with illustrative specimens prepared by himself. Among the uncharted regions of the human anatomy he explored was the peritoneal fold within the pelvis, since known as Douglas' Pouch. He was sixty-seven when William met him, nearing retirement, and eager to complete a laborious project—an anatomical atlas of the bones. Enormously impressed by the young man's acuity and self-possession, he offered him dual employment under his roof as an assistant dissector and tutor to his wastrel son.

No fairer prospect had ever beckoned to William. Mrs. Douglas seemed full of motherly solicitude for him. The daughter, Martha Jane, pleased him, and he, it soon appeared, pleased her. The time was approaching, however, when he would be expected to return to Scotland, there to remain as the staff of his father's old age and the partner of his preceptor, Cullen. But neither filial bonds nor those of friendship could draw William away now from the yeasty, the rich and challenging city of opportunity he called "my darling London."

5. DEATHS IN TWO FAMILIES

On the old Hunter gelding, Budge, with his sister Nannie mounted behind him, Jamie set out for Hamilton early in the morning of March 13, 1741, a Friday, to trade the animal for a mare. Nannie was then enjoying a respite from her illness and, wanting always to be with her brother, had pestered him to take her along until, against his better judgment, he had given in. They no sooner reached Hamilton than she complained of chills and faintness. Putting her to bed in a farmer's house, he rode on to find Cullen.

She seemed comfortable enough when Cullen arrived, but so dreaded to pass the night in strange surroundings that he thought she should be driven home. Jamie helped him move her, bed and all, onto a horse-drawn cart. "It put me in mind," he remembered later, "of the poets bringing Eleanora into the Sun to take her last sight and farewell of the world." She immediately felt faint again, and they had to carry her back to the farmstead. Towards evening she nodded to Jamie with a look of adoring approval. She was dead in the same instant.

"I gave myself up to the most violent grief," Jamie wrote to William after the funeral, enclosing an elegy he had composed, "which I had all along stiffled upon her account, and the Doctor, instead of comforting me, bade me indulge it to the utmost, he has shown uncommon tenderness and generous sympathy. . . . I would not advise you to stiffle your grief, no, my dear Will, indulge it heartily, give it the loosest reins, the more impetuous it is, the better 'twill soon satiate itself, while sorrow chastised turns sullen sinks down upon the heart and there securely preys upon you the less visible. When I cast my eye upon that Blanck made betixt you and me, which but a little while agoe our dear sister filled, methinks it looks a gloomy dismall vacuum. . . . I could have got one Mr. Walter a Drawyer in Crayons to have taken her face when she was in Glasgow, but I found it would have discouraged her, it was taking it at a disadvantage. If you happen to see any print or picture in London resembling her, I beg you'll purchase it, and we'll endeavour to gather her face by times. . . . Take care of your health my dear Dr. Willie, forget not to pray to Nannie, imagine

48

you have a sister in Heaven who is as able, I hope, as willing to hear and do for her friends here. . . ."

There was scant comfort for William's father, and for Cullen bitter disappointment, in a letter received from William the following July, saying he wanted to remain in London. His father sent a wistful reply:

"Nothing has proved a greater comfort than the hopes of seeing you here soon; but your letter has cast a very great damp upon us all. I think you have been in a very extraordinary manner obliged to Dr. Douglas, and whatever opinion I may have of his present offer, or however unwilling I may be to consent to it, still I must thankfully own it as a particular instance of his kindness to you. I surely must soon expect to be beyond this side of time, considering my age and present indisposition, being for some days past confined to my bed with sickness, and a severe fit of the gravel, and would be glad to have you near me for a little while I shall be in this world; though at the same time I should be sorry to hinder you from making your way in the world, the best you can. I wish you to consider well what you do. With Dr. Cullen you may be very comfortably settled, and make money, and if you miss this opportunity now, you cannot be sure of it another time. Dr. Douglas' kind offer is only for a time. He may die before you come home or are settled, and leave you without friends at a great enough uncertainty. I suppose now you know very well the difference between the expense of living at home and abroad, and that perhaps cloaths and pocket money may cost you more than the whole expense at home would. You know my willingness to assist you, but you know too that already I have gone fully as far as my numerous family will allow of. You must now do something for yourself. Consider all these things, and if you can persuade me it is for your good, I will not be against it."

The appeal did not touch nor the warning daunt his cold and confident son. The laird of Long Calderwood died three months later, at the age of seventy-eight, without seeing him again.

Fortune, however, continued to favor William. Dr. Douglas could hardly do enough for him. He got him into St. George's Hospital as a surgical student, a privilege not granted to every Scottish aspirant. He admitted him to the full bounty of his luxurious home and to the company of his well-connected friends, and he bestowed his blessing when William asked for Martha Jane's hand. The only shadow to darken that sunny household was the profligacy of the doctor's son, William George, and William had frequent occasion to purse his thin, finely graven lips in shocked reproof and the sense of his own rectitude.

As the oldest Hunter son, Jamie inherited the little left of Long Calderwood. Still vacillating between the army and the law, and piqued by William's enthusiastic reports, he decided to visit him and see whether he, too, might not find a career more to his taste in medicine. Shortly after his arrival, Dr. Douglas fell mortally ill. He died with William's hand in his and the wish that his widow would make it possible for William to study on the Continent.

During the summer of 1742, while William was availing himself of Dr. Douglas's dissecting room, library and private museum to instruct Jamie, there came an anguished letter from Mrs. Hunter. Tibbie was sick with the same spitting of blood that had afflicted so many of her children. William prescribed mare's milk. "Tell her . . . that Jamie and I will pay her a visit as soon as we have got our pockets full of gold to buy her a country seat, and give her what horses and other things she wants." But Tibbie lasted no longer than it took to receive his letter.

Jamie did discover in himself a bent for medicine, and in later years William used to say that had he been able to persist he would have risen to the top of the profession. What stopped him was what killed Nannie and Tibbie. Emaciated and fevered, he dragged himself home to Scotland where he lived only four years more, to the age of thirty.

War with France prevented the fulfillment of Dr. Douglas's plans for William. A year passed before there was a truce and the journey abroad could be undertaken. William, meanwhile, was not idle. He stayed on at the Douglases', striving to instill into his prospective brother-in-law virtue as well as knowledge. He treated his first patient, a Mr. Barnet, the victim of a venereal infection, who continued under his care for six weeks. "There only remains of the 2 ulcers one small bit to be skinned over," he wrote to Jamie. "He was a little pinched for money and I refer the whole to himself though he promises faithfully, and he is quite honest to pay me generously at our next meeting because he says I deserve it." William also communicated an original piece of research to the Royal Society's *Philosophical Transactions*, an indispensable step in the ascent to the upper strata of British savants. His paper was entitled *Of the Structure and Diseases of the Articulat-*

ing Cartilages, and in it he explained for the first time how the blood circulates to the joints.

In September 1743, he finally embarked for France. With him went William George, probably not the companion he would have chosen, but one imposed upon him, Dr. Douglas having fancied that the boy's mind might improve if subjected to continental academic discipline. No sooner did they get to Paris than William George, deaf to his mentor's remonstrances, immersed himself in Gallic frolics and piled up a sizable debt. William abandoned him. He did, on a few subsequent occasions, lend him small sums, but when, twelve years later, William George lay ruined and dying of his dissipations, he turned his back.

While his betrothed's brother thus courted disaster, William attended the anatomical lectures, all seventy-nine of them, delivered at the *Académie Royale des Sciences* by Emile Ferrein, a highly touted professor of surgery and medicine. "They contained nothing new," he said afterwards, and on certain topics, particularly the articular cartilages, he considered the professor's knowledge inferior to his own. What did strike him favorably was that Ferrein obtained enough cadavers to allow each student to make an extensive dissection, a practice unknown in England, and one William resolved to introduce if ever he could establish a lecture course of his own.

From Paris he went to the University of Leyden to inspect the magnificent anatomical drawings and preparations of Albinus and his former pupil, Albrecht von Haller. To Haller, who now held the chair of anatomy at the University of Göttingen, were consigned all the bodies of criminals executed in that city and all the stillborn illegitimate babies, a copious supply.

A shock awaited William when he got back to London in the summer of 1744. Martha Jane was dead.

What his feelings for this girl may have been, aside from the gratification of winning a fashionable heiress, no word he is known to have written or uttered ever revealed. During their betrothal his only allusion to her in letters home was elliptical: "I need not mention any particulars but everything will be to my wish." Yet her death affected him strangely. More like a lover jilted and permanently embittered than a bereaved one, unwilling or unable to surrender again to emotions that once had been thwarted, he never married, nor, as far as we know, had any amorous relations with women. Later in life he grew prone to make snide gibes at the sex, and even little professional betrayals, though none so overt that they could endanger his standing as an obstetrician. Marriage for a man of science, he sometimes contended, was folly, and when he discharged a brilliant young assistant after a quarrel over the ownership of a trifling anatomical specimen, the real reason was thought to be that the assistant had taken a wife.

For four years after his European expedition William continued to reside with Mrs. Douglas, who had meanwhile moved from Red Lion Square to Hatton Garden. He acquired a number of surgical patients, and now and then he was called to a childbed. But mainly he prepared himself to teach by developing his skill at dissecting and staining specimens, accumulating anatomical exhibits, composing polished disquisitions, and negotiating with grave-robbers for a regular provision of fresh "subjects."

His self-assurance never faltered. "Well," he wrote to Cullen, who bore him no rancor for his desertion, "how does the animal economy appear to you, now that you have examined it, as one may say, with precision? I have good reason to put the question to you, because in my little attempts that way, since I began to think for myself, Nature, where I am best disposed to mark her, beams so strong upon me, that I am lost in wonder, and count it sacrilege to measure her meanest feature by my largest conception. Ay, ay, the time will come when our pert philosophers will blush to find that they have talked with as little real knowledge, and as peremptorily of the animal powers, as the country miller who balances the powers of Europe. But, if I follow this train of thought, I shall become as pert as those I blame; therefore I'll drop the point."

In the London *Evening Post* of September 16, 1746, appeared the following advertisement:

On Monday, the 13th of October, at 5 in the evening will begin a course of anatomical lectures to which will be added the operations of surgery with the applications of bandages, by William Hunter, Surgeon. Gentlemen may have the opportunity of learning the Art of Dissecting during the whole winter season in the same manner as at Paris [i.e. one cadaver to each pupil]. Proposals to be seen at Mr. Millar's Bookseller opposite to the end of Katharine St. in the Strand.

The response was heartening. William pocketed fees totaling about seventy guineas. Strolling home with one of his pupils after his introductory lecture, the money in a bag under his cloak, he remarked happily, "It's a larger sum than I have ever been master of." Shortly afterward he leased a house in the Great Piazza of Covent Garden large enough to accommodate his classes, a dissecting room, and a consulting office.

With her husband and oldest son dead and William, the new inheritor, engrossed in remote pursuits, Mrs. Hunter faced the burden of managing Long Calderwood alone. But none of her problems weighed more heavily than John. What was to become of him? She had long ago admitted the futility of trying to keep him in school, and now, at the age of twenty, he seemed as cloddish and callow as her lowliest field hand (though no field hand studied more intently nor handled more skillfully the farm animals and plantings). Janet, her youngest daughter, had recently married a Glasgow cabinetmaker named Buchanan, and it occurred to Mrs. Hunter that John might not only learn a profitable craft from his brother-in-law, but in an urban atmosphere might take on a little refinement. Buchanan amiably fell in with the proposal, and that summer, in 1748, John went to Glasgow.

It was not an ideal solution. Buchanan, though kindness itself, preferred the jollities of the taproom to the loneliness of his lathe. As a result, his business was foundering. His neighbors had nicknamed him "Amen," not for his piety, but for the rum-inspired exuberance with which he sang hymns on Sunday. "Joined to his other companionable talents," commented one stern parishioner, "was the unfortunate endowment of a good voice and a musical ear." John spent as much time guiding Amen's faltering steps homeward from the pothouse as Amen spent showing him how to mortise a joint. John nevertheless acquired through carpentry a manual precision that would serve him in a way his mother never dreamed of.

A double tragedy befell the Buchanans after John had been living with them three months, making it impossible for them to keep him any longer. Janet developed tuberculosis. Amen went bankrupt (he ended his days quite contentedly, however, as music instructor to the Episcopalian Society of Christians).

William had once written to Jamie, in a letter justifying his plans, "I thought it the only way to settle in my darling London, and be useful to you and Jockie." That usefulness was now put to the test. Could

William find some work in London for John's empty hands? If not, John proposed to join the army.

With his autumn course well subscribed and his private practice steadily growing, William could indeed do with a helper. And so presently Mrs. Hunter and her last surviving daughter, Dorothea, were the only ones left at Long Calderwood.

John traveled on horseback probably by the same route Roderick Random took, through the Cheviot Hills, across the Tyne River, and following the Great North Road southwestward to London, a two-week journey that brought him to the city early in September.

II. WILLIAM AND JOHN
1748-1762

꧁꧂

6. COVENT GARDEN

. . . where I shone forth in the balconies at the
playhouses, visited whores, made love to orange-
wenches, and damned plays.

—FIELDING: *Joseph Andrews*

It must have been with some embarrassment that the brothers met
after a separation of eight years—John by the change in William,
William by the little change in John. Although William did not yet
command the substance, he displayed the manner of a rich and fashionable Londoner. He wore the pigtail peruke. He had succeeded in
modulating his native accent, so distressing to English ears, to a degree
that moved a colleague to comment, "His dialect had all the polish of
the southern metropolis, with enough of the northern recitative to preserve the close of his sentences from too abrupt a cadence." His
professional air had the aloofness and solemnity deemed appropriate to
the sickroom and the mortuary. He had grown strikingly handsome,
with a profile of almost feminine delicacy, long, slender hands and a
light, graceful frame.

John was raw. No wig covered his coarse, carroty hair, no conver-
sational niceties softened the harshness of his Lowland gutturals.
Unlettered, naïve, and boisterous, he reeked of the stable and the field,
and his natural pugnacity was intensified by the anti-Scotticism around
him.

All in all, he was as prickly a Scot as ever crossed the Tweed, and his fine-feathered brother would find it easier to make an anatomist out of him than a gentleman.

But however much William may have been dismayed by John's uncouthness, he welcomed him as an assistant, for his autumn course, in which some twenty students had enrolled, was to begin within a fortnight. When John had stowed his meager belongings in Mrs. Douglas's home, William took him to the Great Piazza.

He wasted no breath in generalities. He produced the arm of a cadaver, explained how to dissect the muscles, and, handing John a scalpel, bade him try it. The novice did not flinch. With a dexterity developed in "Amen" Buchanan's workshop, he neatly laid back the layers of skin, the fibrous tissue, the superficial nerves and veins and arteries, until the muscles stood exposed. William was so pleased that he shortly set him the more intricate task of exposing the arteries, after injecting them with colored liquid wax after the method of Frank Nicholls. "You will," he predicted upon inspecting the result, "be a good anatomist."

Learning by direct observation was as congenial to John as reading books was irksome. What he could see and touch excited his mind more than any abstraction, and under William's tutelage he proceeded to explore all the chambers and alcoves of the human mansion. The adventure fanned his curiosity about the nature of animate things into a passion never to be quenched.

During those first months, however, before the quest took full possession of him, John was equally fascinated by the sights and sounds of the town around him. Covent (a corruption of Convent) Garden had changed character violently in the two centuries since nuns grew flowers there. The only sign of piety was St. Paul's Church, which reared its Tuscan columns on the west side of the enormous quadrangle. "Grand Seraglio to the nation," an enthusiastic frequenter called Covent Garden. Through the Piazza's tall windows John could glimpse the accessible little actresses of the Covent Garden and Drury Lane theaters, as they tripped to and from work. Both theaters were flanked by brothels, to which large numbers of the audience repaired after the performance.

Covent Garden had six coffee-houses and eight taverns, and the range of tone and clientele was broad. Intellectuals patronized the Bedford Coffee-house, under the arcade, a step from the Hunter school.

They included Henry Fielding, whose heroes were constantly being led astray in Covent Garden; William Hogarth, who often depicted the neighborhood as a background in his caricatures; David Garrick, who had taken over the management of the Drury Lane Theatre and was successfully reviving Shakespeare; Thomas Arne, the operatic composer and Garrick's musical director. Tosspots most of them, they nevertheless maintained a high level of conversation. "This Coffee-house," reported the periodical, *The Connoisseur*, "is every night crowded with men of parts. Almost every one you meet is a polite scholar and a wit. Jokes and bon-mots are echoed from box to box: every branch of literature is critically examined, and the merit of every production of the press or performance of the theatres, weighed and determined." It was the kind of company William sought and John avoided. John felt more at ease among the habitués of dives like Tom King's Coffee-house, one of the rowdiest in London, "well-known," as the *Connoisseur* noted, "to all gentlemen to whom beds are unknown." In Fielding's *Covent Garden Tragedy* a character named Lovegirlo asks, "What rake is ignorant of King's Coffee-house?" Scarcely more than a shanty, it squatted untidily beneath the portico of St. Paul's. The incongruity appealed to Hogarth. His engraving entitled *Morning* shows a prim-lipped spinster approaching the church, followed by a lackey who carries her prayer book. In front of King's two amorous blades paw their doxies. The church clock marks the hour of seven.

For those who liked gambling—in London, almost the entire adult population—the area provided inexhaustible variety. Cockfights were regularly held next to the Drury Lane Theatre. The taverns offered wheel games like roulet and roly-poly; dice games like hazard and passage; card games like faro, brag, basset, crimp, and wisk. A single round of wisk, which Horace Walpole called a "universal opium," might involve hundreds of pounds; hazard, the most popular dice game of the hour, a thousand. The play was hottest in Mother Needham's and Mother Cole's, brothels on the south side of Covent Garden, and in a tavern forbiddingly known as the "Finish," which stayed open all night. The Finish's potboy, one Shuter, delivered so much gin behind the scenes at the Drury Lane that he learned acting through sheer propinquity and joined the company.

A Covent Garden attraction that defied precise classification was the Hummums, an Anglicization of the Turkish *hammam*, bath. A bathhouse it ostensibly was, but it also served less prosaic purposes, as suggested by its handbills, advertising accommodations for one at five shillings, eight shillings for two.

Such amusements could not be pursued in Covent Garden after dark without risk. Ruffianism, common throughout London, was here rampant. "In the Piazzas," complained William Shenstone, a poet and theater-lover, "they [pickpockets] come in large bodies, armed with couteaus, and attack whole parties, so that the danger of coming out of the playhouse is of some weight in the opposite scale when I am disposed to go to them oftener than I ought." Even the tavern-keepers were worried, and they protested to the parish authorities that their business was suffering because people hesitated to enter Covent Garden at night. The taverns, however, bred perils as redoubtable as any lurking in the street. At the Rose Tavern scarcely a month passed without somebody being slashed to death in a brawl.

Night or day, Covent Garden was never silent. Quacks hawked their nostrums for cancer and the "French pox." Strolling performers made "salt-box music" by beating a salt-box with a rolling pin, sang bawdy ballads, mounted puppet and Punch and Judy shows, juggled, tumbled and capered on tall ladders, swallowed live mice and snakes, exhibited tightrope-walking monkeys, dancing dogs, crows that fired cannons with their beaks, pigs that arranged lettered blocks with their snouts to spell out words. The street peddlers who carried their wares on their heads or in barrows, the merchants with stalls or tents under the great market shed in the middle of the quadrangle, all had distinctive cries and they uttered them incessantly:

"Fine Seville or-an-ges, fine lemons, fine; round, sound and tender, in-side and rine!"

"Please want any matches, ma'am?"

"Live mack'rel, three a shilling O, lo'ping alive O!"

"I have ripe peascods, ripe, sixpence a peck!"

"Mats, mats, a bedmat, a doormat!"

"O' clo', suits or coats!"

"Hot spiced gingerbread, smoking hot!"

"Chairs to mend, old chairs to mend; if I had the money that I could spend, I never would cry, 'Old Chairs to Mend.'"

The sow-gelder tootled a trumpet, the dustman and the chimney sweep, the bellows-mender and the knife grinder rang bells. "Rally up, ladies, rally up!" bellowed the butcher, thumping his chopping-block, "Buy! buy! buy!"

Of this rich stew, steaming away at his doorstep, John partook zestfully. With various roisterers he visited the gin dens, drinking his companions bottle for bottle, the bordellos, the shilling galleries of the theaters. He delighted in the popular game of shouting down bad plays and players.

In one respect John's intimacy with the rougher elements of the community proved valuable to William. It ensured a supply of that commodity without which no anatomical school could flourish—corpses.

7. THE SACK-'EM-UP MEN

Although private dissection by anatomical schools had been legal since the dissolution of the Barber-Surgeons' Company in 1745, there was still no legal way of obtaining enough bodies. Public sentiment dictated this illogicality; the majority regarded mutilation of the dead as sacrilege. The law did make an exception of criminals under capital sentence, but this benefited the schools hardly at all, being intended primarily as a deterrent to crime rather than an aid to science. The Barber-Surgeons' charter had specified that "the sayd maysters . . . shal and maie have and take without cotradiction foure persons condempned and adjudged and put to death for feloni by the due order of the Kynges lawe of thys realme for anatomies." So that every man might ponder the wages of sin, the Barber-Surgeons had to advertise the dissections. Under the Act of 1752 the body of any criminal executed in London and Middlesex counties could, if the sentencing judge so decreed, be conveyed for dissection to Surgeons' Hall. The Corporation of Surgeons was thus forced into a collaboration with the hangman.

Crime did not decline, though the anguish of the condemned was greatly increased. The thought of the anatomist's knife reduced callous desperadoes, otherwise capable of mounting the scaffold with a jest, to abject cowardice. In addition to superstitious dread, they were tormented by the fear that the hangman would bungle, leaving them to revive on the dissecting table. This happened in 1740 to William Duell, a sixteen-year-old murderer and rapist. The dissection had not progressed far before the anatomists detected faint breathing. They administered warm wine and drew an ounce of blood, and presently the hanged man sat up. The court commuted his sentence to transportation for life.

Until 1760, when mobile gallows were adopted, the place of execution in London was a crossroads north of Hyde Park known as Tyburn; the customary hour, 8 A.M. of a Monday. By Sunday midnight crowds would already be congregating around "Tyburn Tree." A multiple hanging might attract 100,000, a tenth of the entire London population. Most shops closed so that both employers and employees could attend. Along the approaches to the gallows, taverns and coffeehouses opened early to sell drink and to rent windowseats. "Beautiful prospect!" touts bawled. "Splendid view!"

Long before hanging time people would be roaring drunk, and as the execution cortege passed, they would comfort or curse the victims, pelt them with flowers or garbage, each according to his humor. At some point the doomed man would be offered "St. Giles' Bowl," a huge stoup of ale, so called after a former Golgotha. When Earl Ferrers, the last nobleman to be executed in Great Britain and the first felon to be hanged by the trap system, was sent to Tyburn for killing a servant in a maniacal rage, the procession took three hours to move through the mob. It was, Ferrers told the sheriff accompanying him, an ordeal far worse than the contemplation of death.

The taste for Tyburn was not confined to the hoi polloi. George Augustus Selwyn, a clubman and wit, was only one of countless prominent Londoners who hated to miss a hanging. Circuit judges, after pronouncing sentence of death, would reserve a seat near the gallows for Selwyn. Walpole described him as a man who loved "nothing upon earth so well as a criminal except the execution of him."

To shorten the victim's suffering, friends and relatives would pull his legs. In the belief that a hanged man's sweat cured scrofula, people so afflicted would crawl under the scaffold to anoint themselves with a drop. If no anatomization had been ordered, the body could be removed for burial. Otherwise there was a great deal more ritual to be observed. The hangman and his assistants transferred the body to a tumbrel, the sides of which they demounted the better to afford the citizenry a final view of justice triumphant, and slowly drove off. Hard behind, full-panoplied on a gleaming charger, rode the City Marshal, whose duty it was to see the letter of the law fulfilled. Any attempt to interfere constituted a felony. Many were made all the same by the dead man's friends, often resulting in bloody riots. But the hangman's party usually prevailed, being reinforced by beadles from the Corporation of Surgeons, determined to let nobody cheat their masters.

Surgeons' Hall was a long, low building faced with Ionic pilasters. The body was carried through the basement door up into an octagonal amphitheater. Here waited the president and member surgeons, lugubrious in their mortarboards and full-bottomed wigs. The hangman, his chores completed, now departed, taking along, as the perquisites of his office, the dead felon's clothes. These, with the fatal rope, he exhibited for a fee in some tavern. A surgeon made an incision in the chest of the cadaver. This sufficed to satisfy the City Marshal that the law had been complied with, and he withdrew to prepare an official report. The dissection then proceeded in earnest, one surgeon working on the brain, another on the viscera, a third on the bones. Later in the century, as the surgeons grew more sensitive to the indignity of their position, this was no longer done publicly in Surgeons' Hall. After the ritualistic incision, the body would be sewn up and transferred to a hospital. In rare instances an anatomical school received it—how rare may be judged from the fact that between 1749 and 1756 only 306 criminals were executed in the London-Middlesex area, and not all of those were consigned to dissection.

"In a country where liberty disposes the people to licentiousness and outrage," William warned his students in a characteristically contemptuous vein, "and where anatomists are not legally supplied with dead bodies, particular care should be taken to avoid giving offense to the populace, or the prejudice of our neighbors. Therefore, it is to be hoped, that you will be upon your guard, and, out of doors, speak with caution of what may be passing here."

What occurred in William's school, as in most British anatomical schools, was the dissection of stolen bodies. Every responsible anatomist deplored the practice; none could dispense with it. The students did a lot of the stealing. Sir Robert Christison, an Edinburgh toxicologist, recounted a typical escapade in his memoirs: "The time chosen in the dark winter nights was, for the town churchyards, from six to eight o'clock; at which latter hour the churchyard watch was set, a d the city police also commenced their night rounds. A hole was dug down to the coffin where the head lay—a canvas sheet being stretched around to receive the earth, and to prevent any of it spoiling the smooth uniformity of the grass. The digging was done with short, flat, dagger-shaped implements of wood, to avoid the clicking of iron striking stones. On reaching the coffin, two broad iron hooks under the lid, pulled forcibly up with a rope, broke off a sufficient portion of the lid to allow the body to be dragged out; and sacking was heaped over the whole to deaden the sound of cracking wood. The body was stripped of the grave-clothes, which were scrupulously buried again; it was secured in a sack; and the surface of the ground was carefully restored to its original condition—which was not difficult, as the sod over a fresh-filled grave must always present signs of disturbance. The whole process could be completed in an hour, even though the grave might be six feet deep, because the soil was loose, and the digging was done by frequent relays of active men. Transference over the churchyard wall was easy on a dark evening; and once in the street, the carrier of the sack drew no attention at so early an hour."

Hardy students did not hesitate to hunt anatomical material at Tyburn itself, where, by bribing the hangman, or in the heat of a free-for-all, they might bag a prize. "As soon as the poor creatures were half dead," Fielding wrote of a mass hanging he witnessed, "I was much surprised before such a number of peace officers to see the populace fall to hauling and pulling the carcasses with so much earnestness as to occasion several warm encounters and broken heads. These, I was told, were the friends of the persons executed, or such as, for the sake of tumult, chose to appear so, and some persons sent by private surgeons to obtain bodies for dissection. The contests between these were fierce and bloody and frightful to look at, so that I made the best of my way out of the crowd."

Now and then, some layman would bequeath his body to an anatomist. Ninety-nine Dubliners signed a testament in the interests of the "more rational, benevolent and honorable purpose of explaining the structure, functions and diseases of human beings." The destitute occasionally offered their bodies for future delivery as security against a loan. Among medical men it was considered only proper to leave one's remains to one's confreres. In a letter notable for its detachment, a dying London physician by the name of Messenger Monsey wrote to a colleague: "Mr. Foster, a Surgeon in Union Court, Broad Street, has been so good as to promise to open my Carcass and see what is the matter with my Heart, Arteries, Kidneys, &c. He is gone to Norwich and may not return before I am [dead]. Will you be so good as to let me send it to you, or if he comes will you like to be present at the dissection? I am now very ill and hardly see to scrawl this & feel as if I should live two days, the sooner the better." He lingered seven months.

John Hunter left a similar bequest, and he derided members of the profession who neglected to do likewise. William was one of them. He instructed his executors to bury him intact in a vault, feeling, no doubt, like the surgeon in Robert Southey's ballad, *The Surgeon's Warning*:

> *All kinds of carcasses I have cut up,*
> *And the judgment now must be!*
> *But, brothers, I took care of you,*
> *So pray take care of me!*

The son of a dead patient so infuriated John by refusing to let him perform an autopsy, which might have illuminated the nature of the disease, that he roared at him: "I heartily hope that yourself and all your family, nay, all your friends may die of the same disease, and that no one may be able to afford any assistance!"

But neither the forays of daredevil students nor the beneficence of sympathizers could begin to fill the anatomists' needs, and there arose a highly specialized vocation. Variously known as "sack-'em-up men," "resurrectionists," "body snatchers" and "inhumanists," its practitioners sowed terror up and down the land for more than a hundred years.

Few graves were safe. With experience the body snatchers developed an ingenuity hard to foil. If spring guns were mounted in the cemetery, female confederates decked in spurious widow's weeds would, while pretending to pray, detach the trip-wires. Bodies had to be snatched soon after burial or not at all, for once putrefaction set in they were unsalable. Some bereaved families built small stone houses where the departed's remains could be kept under lock and key. The resurrectionists would pick the lock. Patent coffins enriched a number of manufacturers. "Many hundred dead bodies will be dragged from their coffins this winter," ran one of their advertisements. "The only safe coffin is Bridgman's Patent wrought-iron one." But venal undertakers could be persuaded to leave the lid unlocked. Iron cages cemented to tombstones, known as mortsafes, proved to be impregnable. Only the rich, however, could afford them. Those were palmy days for sextons. The bereaved paid them generously to keep out the resurrectionists, and the resurrectionists paid them still better to let them in.

Although cemeteries were the main source, enterprising body

snatchers snatched bodies wherever they found them. If they saw a man die out of doors, as often happened in the gin-soaked, disease-ridden city slums, they would fling themselves down beside the corpse, tearfully claiming to be relatives, and bear it off to some ready purchaser. By such impostures they also sneaked bodies out of hospitals, morgues, and almshouses. The custom of hiring professional watchers to "wake the dead" fell into disfavor. Too many watchers yielded to bribery.

Body snatching had its folklore, its poetry, and its humor. Sack-'em-up man (to cite a popular joke), returning from the cemetery in a carriage, stops at a tavern and orders a bottle. Potboy, spying an inert figure in the corner of the carriage: "What's the matter with your friend? Don't 'e want no drink?" Sack-'em-up man: "Damn 'im, no— 'e's sulky!" There were mock pathetic ballads like Thomas Hood's *Mary's Ghost*:

> *The body-snatchers, they have come,*
> *And made a snatch at me;*
> *It's very hard them kind of men*
> *Won't let a body be!*

The body snatchers and their clients had more to fear from the public than from the law. A mob was apt to lynch them. William Hunter's school was repeatedly stoned. But no statute covered body snatching, and taking a body was not, until the last quarter of the century, a criminal act. With their highly developed sense of property, the British jurists of the epoch held the view that nobody owned a dead body and therefore taking one could not be theft. To take shrouds or coffins was another matter, for they belonged to the heirs. This was why prudent body snatchers always reburied them. Even after the courts declared body snatching to be "indecent and *contra bonos mores*," they treated it as a misdemeanor. There were no less than two hundred offenses, punishable by death, among them stealing to the value of five shillings and destroying a turnpike, but for body snatching the courts inflicted a fine, a whipping, or at worst, a few months' imprisonment.

Toward the anatomists they showed even greater leniency; few went to trial. There were compelling reasons. The army needed surgeons, and rather than undermine the anatomical schools, the courts tended to look the other way.

The body snatchers prospered. Discreet at first and moderate in their terms, they became arrogant and extortionate. Gangs of them, organized under ruthless leaders, would brook no competition. To discourage it, they would raid a dissecting room and hack to bits any bodies they themselves had not supplied. The gangs continually betrayed each other to the authorities. At the same time, they maintained reciprocal trade agreements with out-of-town resurrectionists. If public indignation waxed too hot to risk a delivery in London, the gang would ship the body in a barrel of brine, labeled "ale" or "salts," to affiliates in, say, Liverpool, who would dispose of it there and remit part of the profits. Or, if a Liverpool gang had locally undeliverable stocks, London would take them. Such shipments occasionally strayed, with startling results. In Edinburgh an anatomist opened a barrel in which he expected to find a body. Out rolled some smoked hams. It is not known what happened when the purchaser of the hams opened his barrel.

Prices soared. At the mid-century cadavers averaged a guinea apiece. In 1820 Sir Astley Cooper, the best customer the body snatchers ever had, who liked to review his work by reopening his patients when they died, ordered the exhumation, "cost what it may," of the body of a man he had operated on twenty-four years before. The mission was accomplished, and Sir Astley noted in his account book: "Coach for two there and back, £3, 12s.; guards and coachmen, 6s.; expenses for two days, £1, 14s, 6d.; carriage of subject and porter, 12s, 6d.; subject, £7, 7s.; total, £13, 12s." The surgeon once boasted: "There is no person, let his situation in life be what it may, whom if I were disposed to dissect, I could not obtain."

At the start of each semester most gangs exacted a retainer from the schools they supplied and, between times, hush money. To defy them invited dire reprisals. Joshua Brookes, who ran a school in Blenheim Street, tried it. A few nights after, a gang deposited a decomposing corpse at his front door. The first to come upon it were two young girls. They had hysterics. The police arrived barely in time to save Brookes from being beaten to death by his neighbors. But more than threats to life and limb, what kept the anatomists subservient to the body snatchers was the fear of losing their pupils to schools better supplied.

Among the most successful body snatchers were Ben Crouch, a former prize fighter, who dressed in silks and velvet, consistently cheated, as treasurer of his gang, the other members, and silenced complaints with his fists; Jack Hartnett, who left an estate of £6,000; Butler, short, round, and a hearty laugher, who specialized in bones;

Murphy, who had a duplicate key to a graveyard; Joshua Naples, a navy veteran and, for a body snatcher, a mild man. Naples kept a diary:

"At night went out and got 3, Jack & me Hospital Crib [cemetery] Benjn, Danl & Bill to Harpers [probably the name of a sexton]. . . ."

"Intoxsicated all day; at night went out and got 5 Bunhill Row. Jack all most buried."

"At 2 A.M. got up, the Party went to Harps, got 4 adults and 1 small [a child's body under three feet long; there were three categories of smalls—a 'large small,' 'small' and 'fetus,' and the price was calculated by the inch] . . . sold small for £1, 10, 0. Recd. £4, 4, 0. for adult. . . ."

"Work'd two holes one bad, drew the C. ns. [meaning he opened two graves, found one body too decomposed to sell, and extracted the canine teeth]. . . ."

At those prices it was inevitable that some body snatcher would sooner or later try to replenish his stocks by murder. In Edinburgh, Burke and Hare accounted for at least fifteen victims. But it took a trio of Londoners, Bishop, Williams, and May, to shock Parliament out of its complacency. Usually they killed women and children—exactly how many was never determined—by drugging them or knocking them senseless with a blow on the nape of the neck, then suspending them head down in a well. They came a cropper in 1831, when a porter at King's College was struck by the freshness of a boy's body. May was sent to a penal colony for life, Bishop and Williams hanged and anatomized. The following year Parliament passed the Anatomy Act, which provided that all unclaimed bodies be distributed among the anatomical schools in proportion to the number of students. Almost overnight the sack-'em-up men went out of business.

When William Hunter taught anatomy, however, body snatching was booming. His classes came to number as many as a hundred students, which meant that in order to make good his prospectus he had to procure scores of bodies within a nine-month period. He delegated his rough-and-ready brother to handle the negotiations. It was a wise choice. John could talk a language the body snatchers understood. If he despised them, he never showed it. He was incapable of condescension, least of all to those who served him. He stood them drinks and accepted drinks in return. Almost certainly he snatched bodies himself. He acquired, moreover, a clinical interest in the abnormalities of his fellow creatures, psychological as well as physical, which could be mistaken for friendly approval. The body snatchers liked dealing with Jock Hunter, and they gave him preferential treatment.

It was not every anatomical school that, having turned to a study of venereal diseases, would be able to find out that two condemned felons had gonorrhea and the next day receive the bodies in its dissecting room. "We were," John recalled years later, "very accurate in our examination."

When William began the investigation that culminated in his masterwork, *The Anatomy of the Gravid Uterus,* few obstetricians had ever dissected the body of a pregnant woman. One died in a hospital and, as William remarked in his book, "the body was procured before any sensible putrefaction had begun." There is little doubt how he procured it.

8. THE LITHOTOMIST

> SWIFT *to* POPE: *Pray put me out of fear as soon as you can, about that ugly report of your illness; and let me know who this Cheselden is, that has so lately sprung up in your favor.*
>
> POPE *to* SWIFT: *I wondered a little at your quere who Cheselden was? It shows that the truest merit does not travel so far any way as on the wings of poetry; he is the most noted and most deserving man in the whole profession of chirurgery and has saved the lives of thousands by his manner of cutting for the stone.*

In the late spring of 1749 there was sad news from Scotland. Janet Buchanan had died. She was thirty-six. Of the ten Hunter children only three were now living.

Dissecting rooms, which, with their gagging stenches, were in all seasons offensive, in the heat of summer became intolerable. Teachers and students either retreated to the country or applied for a different sort of work in the hospitals. William was needed at Long Calderwood. There were legal papers to be signed and repairs to be supervised.

Although Mrs. Hunter still rode horseback around the farm and drove a cart to market, she was, in her sixty-fourth year, beginning to fail. So William journeyed north. It was his last visit. In fact, except for short professional trips, he never again left his "darling London."

Cullen was overjoyed to see him. He had not given up the hope of sharing a practice with him in Scotland. William was often to revive the project, especially when he felt that the English were not appreciating him. "Could you . . . join with me to raise a school of physic upon a noble plan at Glasgow?" he asked Cullen fifteen years later, after the government rejected his petition for a grant of land on which to erect a museum. He added: "[We] could not fail of making our neighbors stare." But it is unlikely that he ever seriously thought of leaving his snug perch in London.

The two friends were strolling through the fields below Long Calderwood, when Cullen, gazing up at the farmstead, remarked how conspicuously it stood out against the landscape. "Well," said William, "if I live, I shall make it more conspicuous."

Before he left Scotland the University of Glasgow awarded him an honorary doctorate of medicine.

John had not accompanied William. Impatient to get on with his studies, he had spent the summer in the Royal Hospital at Chelsea, where, at William's request, the great Cheselden accepted him as a pupil.

John was in luck. At the age of sixty-one William Cheselden had few peers as a surgeon. He was a kindly, merry, high-living man of diverse talents. An amateur architect, he had designed London's Fulham Bridge. He loved sports. In his youth he had been a boxer. His physique was still powerful, but he could not resist the pleasures of the table and they had given him a paunch and an extra chin. He affected a turban that made him look still rounder.

He treated the poor free, but the rich he charged as much as five hundred guineas for an operation. A good deal of his earnings he spent on art and literature, in both of which he dabbled gracefully. At his home in Fleet Street gathered some of Europe's brightest spirits. Among his warmest admirers he had counted Isaac Newton, whose deathbed he attended, Voltaire, and Pope. In *Imitations of Horace* Pope linked his name with that of Dr. Richard Mead, as celebrated in physic as Cheselden was in surgery:

Weak though I am of limb and short of sight
Far from a lynx and not a giant quite
I'll do what Mead and Cheselden advise
To help those limbs and preserve those eyes.

Cheselden returned the compliment. When asked to contribute money to the Foundling Hospital, of which Pope was a patron, he enclosed with his donation a couplet of Pope's:

'Tis what the happy to the unhappy owe;
For what man gives, the Gods by him bestow.

Cheselden's fame rested principally on his skill at lithotomy, or cutting for bladder stones, a drastic operation that, in the absence of anesthesia, required great speed lest pain kill the patient. Nobody submitted to the ordeal, however skillful the surgeon, except in desperation, when his suffering had become unendurable. Normally Cheselden completed a lithotomy within two or three minutes. "Mr. Cheselden," reported the *Gentleman's Magazine* for April 10, 1731, "took from the body of Mr. Hartwel Buck . . . a large stone of seven inches and a half round, weighing five ounces and a half; in the space of a minute." His record was thirty seconds.

Of the first hundred lithotomies he performed, while attached to St. Thomas's Hospital, only six were fatal. He was so widely reputed for his dexterity that people with stones came to him from all over Europe. From the bladder of the Swedish Baron Carlsen, Minister of State to King Frederick I, Cheselden excised two stones, each "as big as a large walnut," and three smaller ones, in two minutes and four seconds.

But lightning lithotomies were not his only claim to fame. He was also an opthalmic surgeon, the first to make an artificial pupil, cutting windows in the irises of a thirteen-year-old boy blinded by cataracts. The boy completely recovered his vision.

But for the pressure of public opinion, Cheselden might have done as much for the deaf. Queen Caroline, who appointed him Surgeon-Extraordinary, was hard of hearing. Cheselden conceived that he might cure her by removing part of the eardrum. He cast about for a guinea pig. A deaf criminal named Charles Ray had been sentenced to death. At Cheselden's request the court agreed to commute the sentence if Ray would submit to experimental surgery. But hearing of the bargain, the public howled for Ray's head and the court reversed itself. The surgeon never got another opportunity to test his theory.

Cheselden wrote a textbook, the *Anatomy of the Human Body*, which was not superseded for almost one hundred years. He was one of the first anatomists to challenge the monopoly of the Barber-Surgeons. As early as 1710, when only twenty-two, he taught anatomy privately, purchasing cadavers directly from the hangman. His teaching was so superior that students stayed away from the Barber-Surgeons in droves. The Barber-Surgeons suspended punishment only on his promise "never to dissect at the same time as the Company had its lectures . . . nor without the leave of the Governors."

It was under this prodigy that John learned the fundamentals of surgery, and as the son of a man who had been crippled by bladder stones, he must have watched with more than ordinary interest a lithotomy performed by its foremost exponent.

There was no operating theater. Any room in the hospital might be used, even a ward full of other patients. Only those who could not afford to be operated on at home went to hospitals.

Brawny assistants bore in the patient, who wore a loose nightgown. Under a window, in strong light, stood a table three feet high with a stool at one end. After administering a stiff draught of brandy or laudanum, the assistants laid the patient face up on the table, his torso kept higher than his head by layers of blankets. They drew his ankles back until they touched his buttocks and with strips of linen tied them to his wrists. They held his knees high and wide apart to expose the perineum—the area between the scrotum and the anus. One of the assistants produced a watch.

Intensely sensitive to the suffering of others, Cheselden always had a struggle to compose himself. Often, before operating, he vomited. A visiting French doctor once taunted him for this frailty. By way of rejoinder Cheselden took him to a bare-knuckle prize fight. At the first flow of blood, the Frenchman paled and had to be led away.

But once he had begun the operation the surgeon was all steel and ice. "If I have better success than some others," he said, "I do not impute it to more knowledge, but to the happiness of a mind that was never ruffled or disconcerted and a hand that never trembled during any operation."

He doffed his coat, rolled up his shirtsleeves, and lowered his massive frame onto the stool. In a pouch strapped to his side he carried five instruments—a catheter, or hollow tube, some ten inches long; a scalpel, its edges swathed in linen so that only the point would cut;

forceps; a gorget, or grooved rod, for channeling the forceps into the bladder; a threaded needle. Close at hand was a jar of oil and bandages. As the assistants tightened their grip, Cheselden arranged his instruments in the order of their use.

He tried to find a word of comfort for his patient, and by his gentleness he robbed surgery of some of its horror. Occasionally, he wrought a miracle. Obliged once to open a child's bladder, he promised him a sweetmeat if he held perfectly still and made no outcry. The child never budged, and as soon as it was over, claimed his reward.

Cheselden dipped the catheter in the oil to ensure smoother passage, and slipped it up the urethra, into the bladder. With the tip he probed for the stone. Finding it, he signaled an assistant to hold the catheter in place. He reached for the scalpel. Wielding it like a pen, he made a long, swift, vertical cut in the perineum. Through the incision he advanced the scalpel until, with his forefinger, he could feel the outline of the catheter above it. With the catheter to guide the scalpel, he cut straight into the bladder, the two instruments meeting. He returned the scalpel to his pouch and manually dilated the incision so that it could accommodate thicker instruments. He next inserted the gorget. The catheter, having served as guide and marker, went back into the pouch. Cheselden then slid the forceps along the gorget, into the bladder. The instant they made contact with the stone he withdrew the gorget. He opened the forceps inside the bladder, closed them upon the stone and extracted it.

After suturing and dressing the wound, Cheselden examined the stone, memorizing its contours for future reference. He turned to the assistant with the watch. The assistant called out: "Two minutes, forty seconds, sir."

When John returned to Covent Garden for the fall term, he showed such proficiency at dissection that William made him an instructor. That year William rose to still higher distinctions. At Middlesex Hospital he had associated himself with a minority group of staff doctors who wanted to convert the institution into an obstetrical clinic. Overruled, they resigned to found their own. William became one of four surgeon-accoucheurs in attendance.

About this time he adopted a custom from which he never departed, that of maintaining two separate professional establishments. In rooms in the Little Piazza he conducted his private practice, now chiefly obstetrical, and for a while he lived there instead of at Mrs. Douglas's. The Great Piazza house he reserved for the school and for resident student quarters. John went to live there.

An interesting reason for this arrangement was suggested by Peachey: William may have sensed the septicemic character of child-bed fever, which killed mothers by the thousands, and hesitated to attend his maternity patients on the same premises where cadavers were dissected. Certainly he had cause to fear the dangers of the dissecting room. He had seen anatomists, after accidentally pricking a finger with a knife that had probed diseased or decaying tissue, sicken and die. If William did so reason, he anticipated Semmelweis by ninety-eight years.

John took a second summer course under Cheselden. There was no third. The master had a stroke that partially paralyzed him. Another stroke, in 1751, killed him. Chelsea Hospital had its own cemetery, and there he was buried.

John continued to be lucky in his teachers. William arranged for him to resume his surgical studies at St. Bartholomew's Hospital, the oldest in England, founded in 1123, where Harvey had lectured on the circulation of the blood. Its surgical staff included a slight, quiet man named Percivall Pott, who, though only thirty-eight, was by way of replacing Cheselden as the leading figure in British surgery.

Pott lacked Cheselden's inventiveness. He was nevertheless a superb operator. He was the first of his profession to receive an honorary diploma from the Royal College of Surgeons of Edinburgh. Four morbid conditions Pott described still bear his name. *Pott's puffy tumor* is a soft swelling of the scalp, indicating a local inflammation inside the skull; *Pott's gangrene,* a senile ailment due to a failure of circulation in the extremities; *Pott's disease,* a type of spinal curvature resulting from tuberculosis (the cause Pott did not identify); and *Pott's fracture,* a fracture of the fibula above the ankle. Pott also recognized cancer of the scrotum in chimney sweeps as an occupational disease, what the sweeps themselves called "soot-wart," and what other doctors insisted was venereal. "The fate of these people," Pott wrote, "seems singularly hard. In their early infancy they are most frequently treated with great brutality, and almost starved with cold and hunger; they are thrust up narrow, and sometimes hot, chimneys, where they are bruised, burned, and almost suffocated; and when they get to puberty, become peculiarly liable to a most noisome, painful, and fatal disease . . . which seems to derive its origin from a lodgment in the rugae of the scrotum."

Pott was galloping down an icy road one winter morning, on his way to a patient, when his horse stumbled and threw him. He fractured his leg. It was a compound fracture, the broken bone ends tearing through flesh and skin. A crowd gathered and wanted to lift him into a coach. Pott forbade it, knowing that careless handling would aggravate the injury. Lying motionless on the road, he calmly issued directions. Two porters were sent to find poles such as were used to support sedan chairs. Pott persuaded the owner of a nearby house to take the front door off its hinges. This he told the porters to fasten to the poles, lay him slowly upon it, and slowly carry him to his home. A group of his colleagues arrived and promptly split into two camps, the one favoring splints, the other amputation. Pott, feeling that no surgeon could objectively diagnose his own case, took no part in the debate, but stoically awaited the majority decision. Fortunately, it was for splints, and after weeks abed, the bone knitted. Pott did not waste the interval. He wrote a treatise on ruptures and outlined another on fractures.

From Pott, John learned the value of simplicity not only in surgery, but in medication and bandaging. The mode of the epoch was to employ numerous complex instruments for each phase of an operation, whereas a few simple ones would have sufficed; to ply the patient with a witch's broth of "suppuratives," "digestives" and "scarotics"; and to prescribe dressings beautiful to behold, but difficult to keep on. Pott deplored such embellishments. When trying to alleviate what became known as *Pott's disease,* doctors would imprison the sufferer in wooden collars and steel corsets. Pott got better results with a few strips of sticking plaster and a support for the back. He relied as much as possible on the restorative powers of nature, a principle that formed the cornerstone of John's medical philosophy.

Toward the end of the summer, William received a letter from Cullen, telling him that his mother, that woman of iron, had been forced at last to take to her bed. He suspected cancer of the stomach. "She says nothing now about Johnie's coming down; but I know, in her present temper, it would have pleased her much if he had." If left to himself, John would have hurried to his mother's side. But William demurred. There was the expense; St. Bartholomew's was too valuable a training to curtail; and in the fall he would need John's help more than ever. John owed his brother a good deal and he stayed.

William elaborately thanked Cullen for taking care of Mrs. Hunter, and begged him to continue. He also wrote to the patient, chiding her for entertaining "a whim begot of sickness and low spirits." Apparently, he found little else to say to her, because six weeks later Cullen was urging him to write to his mother before it was too late. A month after, she was dead.

William's reply to Cullen's letter of condolence was a model of sanctimony. "I was very unhappy," he said, "when I thought of the pleasure it would have been to her could I have been with her; but as that was impossible, the only comfort I could procure myself upon such a melancholy occasion, was recommending her to my friends, and particularly to you. . . ."

Then, with a brisk "the past is unavoidable," he gave a thought to Dorothea, now alone, whom Cullen had offered to take into his home. "Our next care," William wrote, "must be about my sister, who has recommended herself strongly to me by her indefatigable tenderness. Poor girl, I pity her from my soul. Your offer with regard to her is generous and friendly. I leave her to be determined by you and her friends."

He suggested that she come to live with her brothers in London, but not until the following spring, "both for the sake of good weather, and that my great hurry may be over, and that we may have some time to consider how our little affairs are to be managed in Scotland after she leaves the place." He added that he might even send John to escort her.

9. BROTHERS EMBATTLED

When spring came, William did send John to Scotland. For the younger brother, too, the first visit home was the last.

Agnes Hunter had been buried beside her husband in the "God's acre" of the parish kirk. The epitaph on the brownstone slab covering the grave read:

THIS IS THE BURIE
ALL PLACE OF IOHN
HUNTER OF CADER
FIELD AND AGNES PA
UL HIS SPOUSE
1751

In early September, John and Dorothea, having completed arrangements for the upkeep of Long Calderwood, boarded a stagecoach for London. By the end of the month, Dorothea was keeping house for William, while John, reinvigorated by his only vacation in four years, was hard at work again in William's dissecting room. Shortly after, he embarked upon his first bit of original research. The idea was William's, but the execution John's.

The seat of procreation in man is a mass of coiled, whitish, hair-fine tubules, completely filling the testicles. They are lined by several layers of cells, and it is these cells that secrete semen. That the testicles enclosed some such manufactury, anatomists had surmised long before the Hunters. The simple observation of loss of potency in eunuchs would have led to that conclusion. It had long been obvious, too, that where a duct existed, like the *vas deferens*—the excretory duct of the testicles —there must exist a secretory cavity emptying into it. No anatomist, however, had been able to delineate such a cavity or the sequence of passages through which semen flowed into the main genital tract. To have done so would have necessitated injecting them with a dye or other defining agent, that would not rupture the fragile walls, a delicate procedure.

Pondering the problem in November 1752, William decided to try mercury. He injected the *vas deferens* and through it the *epididymis*, that segment of the seminal duct lying directly behind the testicles. For some moments after these parts were replete, the mercury continued to run and the testicles to grow turgid and heavy. This confirmed William's belief that the testicles, *epididymis* and *vas deferens* formed a single, continuous passage, and he believed that should he now open the testicles he would find tubules likewise full of mercury. But, cautious and thrifty, he shrank from extending the experiment until he had another cadaver on hand, lest he spoil a valuable preparation. The ultimate proof of his theory he left to John to establish as soon as the fresh material could be obtained.

75

"In some such time as a week or fortnight," William recounted later, "my brother made the trial and succeeded. He showed me the *testis* opened, and the tubular internal substance very generally filled with mercury. This preparation, which I still preserve, I showed at my public lecture that very evening, with marks of being pleased with the discovery. In my next course of lectures, viz. Feb. &c 1753, and in every course since that time, I have shown the same, and some other preparations of the same kind; and always gave the history of the discovery, to avoid taking that share of it from my brother which belonged to him."

This demonstration embroiled the Hunters in the first of numerous ferocious wrangles with members of the profession over the question of priority. The enemy was another pair of gifted Scottish brothers, Alexander, junior, and Donald Monro, the sons of William's old teacher at Edinburgh, and in their territory, cocks of the medical walk.

To Donald Monro, a friend and physician named Garrow, who had attended William's first lectures on the seminiferous tubules, communicated the gist of them. Two months after, Alexander, junior, then only twenty years old, made the identical demonstration; the following year he published an account of it. In neither instance did he so much as nod in the Hunters' direction. Whether, as the Monros insisted, they had been thinking independently along the same lines before receiving Garrow's letter and therefore saw no reason to credit anybody else, or whether they picked the Hunters' brains, was never conclusively established. Whatever the truth, William could scarcely have been more outraged had he been defrauded of title to the discovery of the microscope. Neither he nor John had the equanimity that enabled James Watt to remark, when a friend reported that he had been anticipated by Cavendish in formulating the composition of water: "It matters not whether Cavendish discovered this or I. It *is* discovered."

At first in lectures and private correspondence, then in the *Critical Review,* William denounced the Monros as plagiarists. They retorted in kind, and hostilities raged for the next ten years not only about who first demonstrated the seminiferous tubules, but several other claims.

The medical ethics of the day did not inhibit such public wrangles. Savage paper warfare among scientists persisted until well into the next century. Personal vilification became an art, practiced by the intelligentsia with pride and zest, as when young Samuel Taylor Coleridge likened the venerable Erasmus Darwin to "a pigeon picking up peas, and afterwards voiding them with excrementitious additions."

The Hunters never attained quite such virulence, but they had a secret ally who gave them a stylistic advantage over the Monros. This was Tobias Smollett. Although the debt-ridden satirist opened the columns of his *Critical Review* to both camps with a show of impartiality, he edited a good many of William's diatribes and wrote some of them in their entirety. There is no evidence that he received any fixed payment for this service; yet it did not go unrewarded. William made Smollett several substantial loans. On the back of a letter from Smollett, promising to repay £50, William noted: "In case of my death, I desire my executors will not make any demands upon Dr. Smollett, because I sent the money to him as a present, never meaning to take it again."

There is a Smollettian flavor to such attacks as the following: "Shall we call the year 1753, *fortunate* or *unfortunate* for Alexander Monro, jun. Professor? Surely it was a remarkable year. He was then a *student* of anatomy, and in that *one year* made three discoveries; viz. filled the *Tubuli Testis* with quicksilver, found out that the lymphatics were absorbents, and saw the orifices, and introduced bristles into the ducts of the lachrymal gland in the human body. If he goes on at the same rate, he will become a prodigy. But it was rather *unfortunate* that Dr. Hunter should have done, and publicly taught, the very *same three things* before that time. . . ."

Concerning the tear ducts, the Hunters were on somewhat shaky ground. While William had explained them both verbally and by dissection in the first course of lectures he ever delivered, and John had reinforced his findings with more refined specimens, the whole line of investigation did not originate with the Hunters. The presence of tear ducts in animals was well recognized, and countless efforts had been made to trace them in the human anatomy. What doubtless annoyed the brothers was that when Alexander, junior, published his account in 1753, he neglected to mention that he had attended William's lecture on the subject.

The Hunters' work on the lymphatics, the vessels through which much of the body's nutriment is transported to the blood, was another matter. Here they achieved a discovery ranking not far below Harvey's discovery of the circulation of the blood, and it altered medicine and surgery in method as well as theory. For just as Harvey had done a century earlier with the movement of the blood to and from the heart, so the Hunters charted the corollary system of the lymphatic vessels.

When we eat a slice of bread, gastric juices attack it as soon as it enters the stomach, reducing it to a semi-fluid. Passing into the bowels, it is further liquefied. Waste residue is excreted; the nutritious elements, such as vitamins, fats, carbohydrates, are absorbed by the intestinal lymphatics known as lacteals. Lymphatics—translucent, flexible tubes, somewhat resembling a tangle of miniature, plastic hosing —permeate the entire body, forming a closed network. They run alongside the veins, and drain into a channel connected to a vein in the upper chest. Through this branch the food products enter the veins, which convey them to the heart, the blood acting as a sluice. From the heart, blood and food products are pumped into the arteries and thence to the various organs, nourishing en route all the tissues.

Thus, the lymphatic flow is afferent—toward the heart; the arterial flow, efferent—away from it. Most of the pre-Hunterians had this relationship backwards. They attributed to the veins the role of absorbents and believed the lymphatics to be mere continuations of the arteries— in short, efferent vessels. When applying this misbelief in his daily practice, the early eighteenth-century doctor was like a plumber trying to repair faulty drains under the delusion that the water ran up into a spout instead of out of it.

Drastic purging, for example, was a common treatment for a variety of toxic conditions, the theory being that the poison could be got rid of through the bowels. So it might, provided the lacteals, which originally absorb the poison, led into the bowels. But they do not. They lead away from them. Again, doctors commonly treated an infected hand or finger by tapping a vein in the arm, as if the progress of the infection could be interrupted at that juncture. But the true absorbents, the lymphatics, bypass the veins until they reach the chest.

During his first lecture course, William arrived at a true perception of the lymphatic system, and expounded it to his pupils. He spoke somewhat tentatively, for he lacked sufficient data, so much so that he dared not commit himself to publication. He did, however, deduce the essentials. It was John who, in a series of exquisitely precise dissections occupying him at intervals for almost seven years, confirmed and further elucidated the discovery. (In advancing it, however, the Hunters went too far, denying to the veins any absorbent power whatever, when, as later research showed, they have a good deal. Proteins, for example, pass directly into the veins.)

Terrible was the brothers' fury when they learned that once again a Monro had appropriated the first fruits of their labors. In 1753, while studying for his M.D. degree at Edinburgh, Alexander, junior, published an abstract, with a promise of more to follow, indicating the absorbent character of the lymphatics. By then William had been lecturing about them for five years. Alexander maintained that he would have published his findings extensively as his doctor's thesis, were they not too voluminous for that purpose. Disarmingly, he sent a copy of what he had written to William, at the same time saying he wanted to attend his next course of lectures.

William yielded to the flattery and for once chose to forget past injuries. "I looked it [the abstract] over and must own [it] struck me, and gave me some suspicion that he was going to treat me unfairly about the lymphatics. However, he was the son of my old master and he bore the character of an ingenious young gentleman, and he was appointed conjunct professor of anatomy at Edinburgh, and his coming to study with me was surely a particular honour conferred upon me; I therefore wished from my heart to procure his friendship."

He lived to regret it. Two years later young Monro published his extended treatise on the lymphatics. "And though from my own mouth," William stormed, "and in the presence of a great number of students, that I had taught the same doctrine, and supported it by the very same arguments several years before, he did not mention my name, even in a marginal note. . . . That he should thus expose himself to the world! That his father should suffer him to do so!"

While the Hunters were still locked in combat with the Monros, they opened fire on another front. The new adversary was Pott, and the *casus belli*, a type of hernia occurring in the groin. The rights of the matter were forever hopelessly confused.

In 1754 Haller had suggested that the hernia resulted from a congenital defect, not, as hitherto supposed, from strain or a blow after birth. He referred to it, in fact, as "congenital hernia." During the embryonic life of the male, the testicles develop in the abdomen, gradually descend to a canal in the groin—what is now called the inguinal canal—and through it pass into the scrotum. Before they enter the canal, a small fold of the peritoneum, the lining membrane of the abdomen, projects downward and precedes them into the scrotum. Against this fold the testicles come to final rest. The tip of the fold is pinched off to form a protective sheath for the testicles. Normally, the upper portion of the fold closes and atrophies. If, however, it remains open, a danger exists. After birth a slight pressure, owing perhaps to the infant's coughing or crying, may force a loop of intestine down through the opening into the scrotum, pushing through the walls of the inguinal canal. (Inguinal hernias are far rarer in the female, for the canal, not being required to receive the testicles, is smaller than in the male and so less likely to admit the intestinal loop.)

Haller's description of the phenomenon was fairly accurate. Reading it a year after publication, William had John test it on the dissecting table. A lengthy investigation confirmed the Swiss's observations and in one important respect improved upon them. Haller's understanding of how and when the testicles descended was sketchy and inaccurate. According to him, they did not enter the scrotum until after birth. John traced the migration in detail, proving that it normally ended during the last weeks of gestation. This furnished the subject of his first written work, which William published in 1762 as part of his *Medical Commentaries*. Other researchers have since added minor details, but John's description has never been superseded. His theory of why the testicles sometimes fail to descend is also, in many cases, correct. "I am inclined to suspect that the fault originated in the testicles themselves. When both testicles remain through life in the belly, I believe that they are exceedingly imperfect, and incapable of performing the natural functions of those organs, and this imperfection prevents the disposition of their descent taking place."

All this William disclosed in a general way during his lectures of 1755–56, bestowing due credit upon Haller, his brother, and, not least, himself. That summer, while John was still organizing his findings, Pott came out with his *Treatise on Ruptures*. Although he later claimed that he had not read Haller, he gave a similar account of congenital hernia. Since both the Hunters and Pott had been anticipated by the Swiss, William for the moment held his tongue. He was, however, enraged by the appearance of Pott's work before John's investigation had progressed far enough to warrant publication.

One morning in November, Pott called to exchange ideas with the Hunters on a topic of mutual interest. William was absent. The younger brother showed the surgeon a few fetal specimens in which the testicles had partly descended, and they discussed them briefly,

John with what struck Pott as "the most cautious apprehensive reservedness." The visit aroused William's darkest suspicions, and when, not long after, Pott issued an addendum to his *Treatise*, he exploded. "Mr. Pott called at my lecture-rooms in the morning, because he knew that I was there only in the evening. . . . In this production of Mr. P., the doctrine being transplanted from its native soil and nursed up in the dark, was imperfect; the pamphlet was a *time-serving* composition, which was hurried into the world, to snatch the only possible moment for raising reputation."

Pott contented himself with a denial. John, he declared, had shown him nothing he did not already know and had told him less. In view of Pott's immaculate professional standing, it seems unlikely that he would have stooped to theft. Moreover, if he did steal, he missed the significance of the loot. His treatise contained all the old errors about the descent of the testicles, and was in every way inferior to John's work. But the implacable William repeated the accusation. Pott ignored him.

By these onslaughts the Hunters made it clear that no considerations of sentiment or delicacy could deter them from lashing out when they felt that anyone had arrogated credit that belonged to them, let the offender be an honored colleague, an old teacher, or a friend. In a rare flash of self-mockery, William once observed by way of explaining his own contentiousness that "the passive submission of dead bodies, their common objects, may render them [anatomists] less liable to bear contradiction."

10. BROTHERS TRIUMPHANT

During their twelve years under the same roof, the brothers kept up a rate of activity that defied the limitations of time and human energy. Working sometimes in collaboration, sometimes independently, they undertook seventeen major investigations and innumerable minor ones, invented surgical procedures, taught ever-increasing numbers of students, pursued their own professional education, and treated patients.

William started what grew into the deepest anatomical study of pregnancy yet attempted. It was in 1751 that he got his first chance, thanks no doubt to John's excellent relations with the resurrectionists, to anatomize the body of a pregnant woman. The Scottish engraver, Robert Strange, executed twelve plates under William's direction, and William planned early publication. Then he came by two more specimens, each illustrating a different stage of gestation. They determined him to wait until he had examined bodies at every stage and could present a definitive account. He waited twenty-three years, during which he assembled approximately four hundred specimens. The resulting masterwork, *The Anatomy of the Gravid Uterus*, containing thirty-four life-size plates from drawings by Strange and another fine draftsman, the Dutchman, Jan Van Rymsdyk, remains unsurpassed, most of it as valid today as when William published it.

He produced the first accurate descriptions of various parts of the uterus, among them the mucous membrane lining subject to modifications during pregnancy. To this modified lining he gave the name *decidua*. He described for the first time the retroverted uterus, an abnormal condition in which the organ is tipped backwards instead of forwards, making conception difficult. As a treatment for large ovarian cysts, which were so little understood that midwives sometimes mistook the symptomatic swelling for pregnancy, William suggested, almost a hundred years before it became common practice, simple tapping, that is, making a small abdominal incision, driving a tube through it and into the cyst, and draining off the fluid, thereby reducing the swelling.

In these revelations William kept interjecting little notes of self-congratulation at the expense of his colleagues. Referring to the relatively meager attention the pregnant uterus had received from other anatomists, he wrote: "Let it not be objected to them that they neglected what in fact was rarely in their power to cultivate. Few, or none, of the anatomists had met with a sufficient number of subjects, either for investigating or for demonstrating the principal circumstances of utero-gestation in the human species. But let what cannot be praised in others be passed over in silence."

One of William's most important discoveries was the nature of the connection between mother and embryo, and of the placenta which forms that connection. It was generally believed that the fetal heart, veins and arteries did not begin to function independently until birth. The placenta, moreover, was thought to develop mainly from the uterus. Tracing the connection in a dissected, dye-injected pregnant uterus, he concluded that the placenta developed simultaneously from the chorion, or membrane enclosing the fetus, and from the decidua of the uterine wall. He went on, in later explorations, to prove that the circulatory system of the fetus operates independently of the mother's throughout gestation.

From these findings the whole mechanics of fetal feeding could be inferred: how the mother's blood passes to the fetus through the placenta, supplying oxygen and nourishment; how blood flows out through the umbilical cord, carrying waste matter.

The same year John ventured upon an inquiry which so engrossed him that he continued to pursue it in the heat of summer after most anatomists had fled the fetid air of the dissecting room. Steeping a brain in hydrochloric acid to delay putrefaction, he began the ticklish task of dissecting the nerves. He completely traced out the olfactory nerves, educing in the process some of the fundamental operating principles of the nervous system, notably, that different areas of the brain control different nervous functions; that each of the five senses has, besides nerves in common with the others, its peculiar nerve; that at whatever point a nerve may be stimulated, the sensation produced is the same.

With a third investigation begun in 1754, and to which he often returned, John fell wide of the mark. The error committed when he and William stated that the lymphatics were the only absorbent vessels, he now compounded. He had noted, quite correctly, that two other kinds of absorption take place in the body—the first, of diseased, atrophied or waste tissue, such as the roots of deciduous teeth; the second, of portions of a bone, a sculptural process that gives the bone its final shape. These powers, too, John attributed to the lymphatics. "This, at least, I may assert," he wrote, with that disregard of both scientific phraseology and grammar for which he became notorious, "that when any solid part of the body undergoes diminution, brought on in consequence of disease, it is the absorbent system that has done it; they are the thieves."

John harbored this notion to the end of his days. (Only with the development of microscopy was it possible to recognize the absorption of tissue as a cellular process.) But the mistakes he made did not invalidate his method, which was chiefly that of the inductive or Baconian reasoner, who from particular observations formulates general principles. John's observations were rarely faulty, and when sufficient examples presented themselves, his generalizations were sound. Only when his material was too thin or his tools too crude did he err. As Henry Buckle argued in *The History of Civilization in England*: "Since [Hunter's] death, the rapid advance of morbid anatomy and chemistry has caused some of his doctrines to be modified, and some of them to be overturned. This has been the work of inferior men, wielding superior chemical and microscopical resources."

Under the bylaws of the Corporation of Surgeons, anyone wishing to practice surgery in London had first to be apprenticed for seven years to a master surgeon. As a prerequisite to apprenticeship, he was supposed to know Latin, and before being freed from bondage and receiving a license, to pass an examination before the Corporation's Court of Examiners.

John, hopelessly deficient in Latin, did not trouble to petition the Court of Examiners. For almost twenty years he practiced without a license, and for the first two or three without having finished his hospital training. He was not unique in this. London abounded in unlicensed practitioners of every stripe, from quacks to surgeons able enough, but unwilling to recognize the corporation's authority. That authority was at best theoretical, and the accompanying police powers, feeble. Moreover, the Court of Examiners was under constant pressure from the army and navy to relax its regulations so that greater numbers of surgeons might be available to their understaffed medical corps.

John's first surgical patient was a chimney sweep with gonorrhea, whom he attended in 1752. The almost invariable effect of the disease was to constrict the urethra, causing the victim pain when he urinated. There was no specific treatment; John had to improvise. He tried to dilate the urethra by passing up it a slender, cylindrical instrument called a bougie. He repeated this at intervals for six months with bougies of different diameters, but had no success. He then smeared the tip of the bougie with an adhesive salve and dipped it into mercuric oxide, hoping so to burn away the stricture. He managed only to rub the caustic off on the walls of the urethra, inflaming the whole tract and inflicting fearful agonies upon the wretched chimney sweep. At the next attempt he protected the tract by first introducing a silver tube and passing bougie and caustic through that. The stricture would not yield. Was mercuric acid not strong enough? He tried instead lunar caustic, a concentrated, solid form of silver nitrate, fastening it to a wire with sealing wax, and sliding the wire through the tube. Following the third application, the patient was able to urinate more freely.

With the fourth, the wire breached the stricture. Taking up another bougie, John widened the urethra further. Not long after, the chimney sweep was cured.

But John could not forget the pangs he had caused when he first applied caustic, and he hastened to devise a more efficient instrument. It consisted of a silver rod of the same length as the cannula, but with the addition of a plug at one end to give a smooth, rounded edge, and at the other, tiny pincers to hold the piece of caustic. In later operations he passed the rod into the tube smooth end foremost, using it as a guide in somewhat the way Cheselden used a catheter to perform a lithotomy. When he came to the stricture, he withdrew the rod, reversed it, and reinserted it, bringing the caustic to bear directly upon the stricture without touching any other part of the urethra. For strictures located in a bend of the urethra he developed a set of curved, flexible rods and tubes.

In the summer of 1754, John Hunter was admitted as a surgeon's pupil to the hospital with which his name would be forever associated —St. George's.

11. ST. GEORGE'S

The voluntary hospital movement, an expression of the humanitarian feelings stirring in the national conscience, had barely begun when St. George's was founded in 1733. There were only two other hospitals in London supported entirely by private philanthropy—the Westminster Public Infirmary and Guy's. Both St. Thomas's and St. Bartholomew's, which operated under royal charters granted by Henry VIII and were controlled by the government, demanded not only an admittance fee but a deposit to cover the cost of burial should the patient die and no relative claim the body. Though the amount was small, it excluded the neediest invalids for whose aid these institutions had been primarily intended.

The first voluntary hospital was the Westminster Public Infirmary, which admitted its first patient in 1720. Its founders, led by a banker, Henry Hoare, and a schoolteacher, Samuel Wesley, the older brother of John Wesley, chose to shoulder the entire financial burden rather than petition the crown for help, as the founders of St. Thomas's and St. Bartholomew's had done. Meeting in St. Dunstan's Coffee-house on December 2, 1719, they ratified a statement of purposes beginning:

"Whereas great numbers of sick persons in this city languish for want of necessaries and too often die miserably, who are not entitled to parochial relief from their respective parishes, many suffer extremely and are sometimes lost, partly from want of accommodations and proper medicine in their house or lodgings (the closeness and unwholesomeness of which is too often one great cause of their sickness), partly by the imprudent laying out of what is allowed and by the ignorance and ill-management of those about them: We, whose names are underwritten, in obedience to the rules of our holy religion, desiring so far as in us lies to find some remedy for this great misery of our poor neighbours, do subscribe the following sums of money to be paid by us yearly (during pleasure), by quarterly payments, for the procuring, furnishing and defraying the necessary expenses of an infirmary or place of entertainment for such poor sick persons, inhabiting the parish of St. Margaret, Westminster, or others who shall be recommended by any of the subscribers or benefactors. . . ."

The trustees agreed that no subscriber should have the right to recommend more than two patients at a time—one outpatient and one inpatient—and that the length of any patient's hospitalization be limited to one month, though they made provision for care at home. Incurables and victims of infectious diseases they ruled out altogether.

The founders of St. George's were seceders from the Westminster board. As the need for a bigger building arose—in thirteen years the infirmary had treated almost four thousand patients—dissension broke out over the location. The majority wanted to lease three buildings in Castle Lane, by the wharf slums, whose population had the greatest need of free hospital service. But a minority of 16 out of 130 preferred to accept the offer of Lanesborough House, the estate of the late James Lane, Viscount Lanesborough, at Hyde Park Corner, in the parish of St. George. This parish, they reasoned, stood in the path of the city's rapid westward expansion and would therefore soon require its own hospital. Furthermore, although the parish swarmed with the needy, such sections of it as Hanover Square and Grosvenor Square were inhabited by the rich, who, it was hoped, frequently passing the hospital as they rode through the park, would take pride in it and support it.

Eventually Westminster's entire medical and surgical staff joined the seceders. They signed a twenty-four-year lease on Lanesborough House at £60 a year, began soliciting donations, and retained Isaac Ware, a leading London architect, to remodel it. A plate was affixed to the pediment with the inscription: ST. GEORGE'S HOSPITAL FOR THE SICK & LAME SUPPORTED BY THE VOLUNTARY SUBSCRIPTIONS OF SEVERAL OF THE NOBILITY GENTRY & OTHERS. The earliest of these supporters included Queen Caroline and Frederick, Prince of Wales; the Prime Minister, Sir Robert Walpole; the whole bench of bishops; seventeen dukes and their duchesses; Beau Nash, Lord Chesterfield, David Garrick, and a Sir Dudley Rider, who contributed £30 "to prevent prosecution for laying rubbish in the streets."

On Sunday, December 30, in St. George's Church, Hanover Square, the rector, the Rev. Andrew Trubeck, delivered a sermon exhorting his parishioners to be charitable. Two days later, punctually at nine o'clock in the morning, as announced in the *Daily Advertiser,* the new hospital, with thirty beds available, admitted its first patients. There were four of them—three men and a woman.

By the end of the month the number of beds had been doubled and sixty-five patients treated—ten for ulcers of various types, three for syphilis, ten for consumption, eight for intermittent fever, five for rheumatism, four for tumors (one of them malignant), three for fractures, two for chlorosis (a form of anemia), two for diarrhea, and one for herpes (an acute skin inflammation), albugo (an opacity of the cornea), ringworm, rupture, bladder stones, kidney stones, worm fever, asthma, dropsy, cancer of the spine, and colic. Only two of the sixty-five died, both from tuberculosis.

Lanesborough House was a square, three-story building of red brick, with its face to the broad sweep of Hyde Park Corner roadways and its back to a flat, green stretch of the park. Though but a few yards beyond the western gates of the city, the terrain lay as open as farm land, a situation that had led Viscount Lanesborough to inscribe over the entrance:

> It is my delight to be
> Both in the town and the country.

When, twenty-one years after its founding, John Hunter first traveled the mile and a half to St. George's from his quarters in Covent Garden, the hospital was almost four times its original size. Huge wings had been added at both ends, giving it an H-shape, which, according to prevailing medical opinion, made for the freest circulation of air through the wards. With its 250 beds, each costing £30 a year to maintain, St. George's was, after Guy's, the largest of the voluntary hospitals. (Two general—London City and Middlesex—and seven special hospitals, such as Queen Charlotte's Lying-in and the Lock Hospital for venereal diseases, had been founded since St. George's opened its doors, bringing the total number of hospitals in London to sixteen.) New housing had sprung up on all sides of St. George's and traffic swirled ceaselessly around its palings, so that it no longer looked out upon untrammeled bucolic vistas.

The new surgical student, arriving to report to his instructor, David Middleton, a fellow Scot and friend of William's, climbed three low steps and passed through a narrow door with an iron knocker into a lofty, stone-flagged hall. On his right hung a poor box with two locks. At the next weekly board meeting the hospital's two treasurers, each of whom retained a key, would open it, and the contents would be applied to the relief of the most destitute patients to redeem their clothing from pawn, buy them trusses and artificial limbs, and pay for their after-care. On John's left, at a table behind a wooden screen, sat the porter, holding his silver-headed staff of office, surmounted by a figure of St. George and the Dragon. Guarding the door was but one of numerous duties that devolved upon this Cerberus and his assistant. They also prepared the surgical dressings and maintained the boxes in which they were stored; helped the patients bathe; drew the daily quart ration of small beer allowed to every patient with the strength to drink it; prevented inpatients from leaving the premises without authorization from their surgeon or physician; kept the key to the charnel house, surrendering it to no pupil or apprentice without a surgeon's orders; carried out the dead.

The ground floor was given over mainly to administrative offices. The treasurers, the secretary, the physicians, the surgeons and the nurses' matron, all had their own separate quarters. The board room faced south, with tall glass windows through which the deliberating directors could gaze out upon a flower garden and beyond that upon the trees and soft, green fields of Hyde Park. A dispensary opened off the entrance hall, its floor covered with sailcloth that could be readily changed and washed after a bleeding or other minor surgery. On the second floor, directly above the board room, was the operating theater, a recent installation and a great improvement over the practice of operating in the wards in front of other patients.

After John had reported to the senior surgeon and obtained an entry certificate, he was directed to a broad wooden staircase rising from the center of the entrance hall to the gallery. Off this gallery opened the operating theater and the wards. To reduce the tracking of dirt from the street a foot-scraper had been installed at the bottom of the staircase. The walls of the gallery were freshly whitewashed and the floor sprinkled with sand.

There were fifteen wards, each named after a different patron of the hospital. In nine of them medical and surgical patients lay side by side, regardless of the nature of their ailment or the degree of their suffering. The only distinction was sex, the women being bedded in the west wing, the men in the east. Of the remaining six, two were segregated wards for accident cases, two were "cutting" wards for lithotomy convalescents, and two—the women's, named the Princesses' Ward after three daughters of George II, and the men's, named the Burlington Ward after Richard, Earl of Burlington—were "salivating" wards for venereal patients. These last patients were segregated in order to spare others the harrowing sights and stenches produced by the standard treatment of rubbing massive quantities of mercurial ointment into the lesions. This stimulated an excessive secretion of saliva, causing the patient to dribble incessantly, befouling his breath, and loosening his teeth.

The general wards, where John received most of his tutelage in postoperative methods, held about fifteen beds each. They were four-posters, their canopies reaching the ceiling, with heavy curtains hanging down to shut out draughts. As a further precaution against draughts, the patients wore nightcaps. One sack of coal a day was allowed to each ward in winter, half a sack in summer. By way of disinfection the floors and walls were washed down with vinegar. Twice a year a bug-catcher, assisted by the nurses and able-bodied patients, tried to rid the beds of roaches. ("In the hospitals at London," wrote the surgeon, Samuel Sharp, after he had seen an iron-framed bedstead designed to discourage the vermin in a Florentine hospital, "bugs are frequently a greater evil to the patient than the malady for which he seeks a hospital, and could I have interest enough with the Governors to bring about an imitation of this frame, I should be exceedingly rejoiced in the comfort it would afford so many thousands of miserable wretches that are tormented, sometimes even to death, by these nauseous vermin.")

The patients' eating utensils were kept, along with a box for soiled linen, underneath the bed. Hospital fare, whether the full diet fed to the stronger patients or the low diet, was simple. According to the menus posted in the wards, a typical day's victuals would consist, in addition to the beer ration and fourteen ounces of bread, of one pint of milk soup for breakfast, one pint of barley broth and four ounces of pudding for lunch, and for dinner two ounces of cheese. The low diet ran to milk soup at all meals, with minute portions of meat four days a week and pudding the other three. The salivating diet was all liquid, since the patients' loosened teeth could not chew solids, usually milk and the broth from half a pound of mutton, with a pint of warm beer every hour during the day and half a pint during the night. Neither diet included fish, fresh fruit, tea, or coffee, and in John's early days at St. George's greens had only recently been added. For a time the greens were supplied by a Mrs. Hoare, who superintended the Brompton Cemetery, a mile away, where the hospital's unclaimed dead were buried. A thrifty woman, she grew them herself in the richly fertilized soil among the graves.

One nurse served an entire ward, and she was not likely to be of the highest character or ability, for nursing had no professional standing whatever. Doctors and laymen alike looked down upon nurses as the lowliest of menials. They received no training, no special skills were expected of them. Most of them were hired by priority of application, though the board gave consideration to women who were, or had been, patients themselves and so had some idea of the work.

At St. George's, where she slept either in the basement beneath the board room or in one of the adjoining outhouses, a nurse's day began at 6 A.M., when she emptied the coal grate, carried the ashes down to the porter, sifted them under his supervision, and returned with the fresh supply of coal he doled out to her. For an hour she dry-rubbed and swept the ward, enlisting the help of all patients fit for it. Regulations prohibited the use of water lest it increase the dampness.

About seven o'clock the house surgeon arrived to change dressings. Frequently, he left it to the nurse to finish the task. A little later the staff physician, carrying a cane with a vinegar-soaked sponge in the head as a protection against noxious effluvia, seated himself at a table in the middle of the room and bade the nurse parade the ambulatory patients before him to be examined and prescribed for. He then passed among the bedridden patients.

At eight the nurse ladled the milk soup into the patients' porringers and breakfasted in the ward with them. The meal over, she made the beds and removed the dishes to be washed, again recruiting the able-bodied patients as helpers. Any scraps of food remaining she returned to the kitchen to be served again. The patients lunched at 1 P.M., and an hour after, placing one of them in charge of the ward, the nurse joined the servants in the kitchen for her own midday meal. From the lunch table she carried away a platter of food she would eat cold for her supper. At frequent intervals the matron, herself classed as a mere servant, would issue to the nurse a copper oil lamp and a tinderbox, and assign her to night duty, a long, murky watch when she might find herself in solitary attendance upon all the wards.

A nurse got no vacation, not even a day off. She was not permitted to set foot outside the hospital before six in the evening and then only after showing the porter a pass signed by the matron. On the three days a week when patients were given hot baths she could not leave at all. Her salary was £6 a year, with an extra pound if she worked in the accident, cutting or salivating wards.

"She must," the regulations at St. Thomas's ordained, "stupe as often and in such a manner as the doctors shall direct, and shall attend to the workings of all vomits.

"She is to make all the beds on one side of the ward, and to scour and make clean the beds and floors of the whole ward, the passages, stairs, etc.

"She must keep clean scoured the cans for beer, and the dishes fouled at dinner.

"She must attend the butler at the ringing of the beer bell and of the bread bell . . . and at the ringing of the cook's bell must receive from her the exact amount of provision appointed for each patient."

The women willing to accept such conditions were, with rare exceptions, kindly illiterates at best and at worst brutish sluts who saw a chance for plunder. The latter robbed the patients, browbeat them into drawing wills in their favor, demanded tips for performing their normal duties, neglecting and maltreating those who could not pay, smuggled gin into the wards, prostituted themselves. Even the best-intentioned nurses had low standards of health and hygiene. Uniforms were unheard of; they dressed as they pleased, most of them unkempt and dirty. Many were riddled with venereal diseases.

Sir William Blizard of the London Hospital once protested to the board of directors that two of his patients, convalescing from lithotomies, were being attended by an infirm crone of seventy.

In reply to a circular letter from a committee investigating hospital conditions, one doctor wrote: "If I can but obtain a sober set of nurses, it is as much as I can hope for."

"I inquired from Dr. —— about the character of the nurses," wrote another, "and he says they always engage them without any character, as no respectable person would undertake so disagreeable an office. . . . I know that a respectable woman was declined the other day, as being too good for the situation."

But if the patients' material comfort was frequently ignored, no efforts were spared to improve their moral and spiritual outlook. Visiting ministers held daily religious services, which all ambulatory patients had to attend. For those too ill to leave their beds a sermon would be delivered in the wards, each of which had a lectern with a Bible chained to it. To these captive congregations the ministers distributed inspirational literature. A widely circulated homiletic, written by the Rev. Dr. Stephen Hales, a physiologist as well as a divine, was entitled *Admonition to the Drinkers of Gin, Brandy, etc.*, and it warned the patients that brandy "by coagulating and thickening the blood and contracting the narrow vessels produces obstructions and stoppages of the liver . . . burns up the lungs, depraves the natural temper and breeds polypuses in the heart."

John stayed at St. George's all spring and summer and would have returned after the winter's work, had not William, still hoping his brother might acquire some cultural polish, persuaded him to enter Oxford University. He matriculated at St. Mary's Hall.

12. "THESE SCHEMES I CRACKED . . ."

John's introductory act was ominous. Required by tradition to register on the matriculation list in Latin, he misspelled the genitive of Mary in St. Mary's Hall, writing: *Johannes Hunter, ex aula Santae Marae.*

. . . Within a few weeks he was back at St. George's. "They wanted to make an old woman of me," he told one of his own pupils many years later, "but these schemes I cracked like so many vermin," and he pressed the ball of his thumb down hard on a table as if to crush an insect.

As he grew older, he became increasingly defensive about his academic shortcomings. "Perhaps, sir, you have read a great deal?" he was once asked by a bibliophile, who had invited him to inspect his library.

"I turn over the volume of nature," replied John, whose own library was estimated, after his death, to contain £160 worth of books, most of them presentation copies he had scarcely glanced at.

"Then, sir," retorted the collector, "let me tell you that you have not turned over more than the title page."

John's cultural deficiencies became the despair of men who valued him most. Because he found it so hard to express himself clearly, many of his ideas were garbled or lost to posterity altogether. Few scientists have ever been so poorly equipped with the tools of communication. "This of signs [to quote at random an example of his muddy style from his posthumously published *Essays and Observations*] although natural in themselves, yet are arbitrary in their modes, therefore varies," which the editor tried to clarify, with only partial success, thus: "This [subject or system] of signs, [which signs], although natural in themselves. . . ."

"If we were capable [John wrote elsewhere in *Essays and Observations*] of following the progress from the number of parts of the most perfect animals, as they first formed in succession, from the very first state of full perfection, we should be able to compare it with some one of the incomplete animals themselves, of every order of animals in the creation, being at no stage different from some of the inferior orders. Or, in other words, if we were to take a series of animals, from the more imperfect to the perfect, we should probably find an inferior animal, corresponding with some stage of the most perfect."

That passage Charles Darwin probably had to reread several times before he realized that John had anticipated him by almost a hundred years in enunciating the principle that the human embryo at each stage of development resembles the mature form of some lower species.

Having read so little, even in his own field, John could seldom refer to a source or quote an authority. The shortcoming cost him a vast amount of needless effort. He might spend weeks struggling with a problem, unaware that it had been solved before by other investigators.

When the house surgeon at St. George's ended his term of service, the board would choose a successor by seniority among the students. The duties involved were arduous and unpaid—the house surgeon, in fact, had to pay £10 a year for bed and board and supply his own linen—but so rewarding in clinical experience that every student wanted the appointment. A vacancy occurred that summer, and in the ordinary course of events the choice should have fallen on John Gunning, an apprentice to Caesar Hawkins and a student of three years' standing. But the board favored John. Although Gunning became house surgeon the next year and later attained an influential position in the affairs of the hospital, he never forgot the slight nor forgave John. The Scotsman's unvarnished candor, his aggressive self-confidence and flashes of arrogance, did nothing to soften Gunning's enmity.

During certain hours of the day and almost the entire night, the house surgeon would be in sole charge of all the surgical patients, his alone the responsibility to carry out the instructions left by the staff surgeons and to meet any surgical emergencies.

Awed by the burden he had assumed, John walked the dim halls from ward to ward those first nights with eager ears and taut nerves, the fresh sand rasping under his heels, the lamp in his hand casting jagged shadows on the pale walls. . . .

An old soldier, his leg amputated, cries out in sudden terror. John hurries to him, sees by the lamplight the dark stain spreading under the blanket. He flings aside the bedclothes. The stump is hemorrhaging. He calls to the nurse for a crooked needle and waxed thread. Swiftly, he draws the thread around the exposed, spurting end of artery and pulls it tight. The bleeding stops, the frightened patient sinks into sleep. . . . An uproar by the porter's table below brings John on the run. He finds two battered youths supporting a third between them. They have been attacked by footpads. The third youth's arm dangles at an unnatural angle suggesting a broken bone. John gives him a dram of brandy, then gripping his elbow with one hand and his wrist with the other, moves them in opposite directions. The youth howls, but John has heard the telltale sound he was listening for—the crepitation of bone as the broken ends scrape each other. He immobilizes the arm between heavy logs and so leaves the youth to rest until the arrival of a surgeon qualified to set and splint it. . . . Returning to the wards, he changes the dressings on purulent ulcers—to spare them the reek of their own bodies some patients have been given flowers to smell—on carbuncles, gangrenes, and venereal sores. With warm wine he washes out the wounds inflicted by lithotomies, the extirpation of tumors, the cutting for hernias, and salves them with balsam. There are torments he can calm a little with spirits of opium. But many, whose cause and cure no surgeon understands—the rack of tuberculous joints, the fires of septicemia, the deep clawing of bone cancer—death alone can relieve. John tarries awhile by each bedside, offering such comfort as his willing presence can give, muttering words of courage in his rough Lowland burr, while inwardly cursing his own ignorance . . .

Despite the pressures of his duties at St. George's, John somehow found opportunities for private experimentation. He resumed his studies of the blood, of which the incessant cuppings and bleedings ensured a plentiful supply. He demonstrated—or rather demonstrated anew, for the Irish physicist, Robert Boyle, had done it at Oxford in 1660—the oxidation of blood. A dual process common to all living organisms is the intake of oxygen and the output of carbon dioxide. As the lungs draw in air, oxygen passes through the thin membrane of the air sacs into the blood, whose red cell pigment, the hemoglobin, has the property of combining with it. In this new form the oxygen proceeds through veins to the heart, thence through arteries, where the hemoglobin releases it. The arteries now convey the oxygen to the tissues, which consume it. Thus nourished, the tissues give up, along with other waste, carbon dioxide, which travels via the veins to the heart, thence to the lungs, and passes out in the exhaled air. The entire cycle recurs with each breath in a few seconds.

The clue that led John to an understanding of the blood's affinity for oxygen or "vital air," as he called it, was the difference in color between the venous blood flowing towards the heart and the arterial blood flowing away from it. The former is dark red, the latter bright. Yet John had noted, while watching patients being bled, that venous blood turned bright red in the pan receiving it. Was it exposure to air that caused the change?

"I covered the mouths of vessels filled with venal blood with gold-beaters' skin [the membrane of an ox's intestine, used to lay between leaves of gold as they were hammered out in ornamental work], touching the surface of the blood, and the blood constantly became of a florid red on the surface, and even for some depth. I put some dark venal blood into a phial, till it was about half full, and shook the blood, which mixed with the air in this motion, and it became immediately of a florid red."

And conversely: "I took a phial, and fixed a stop-cock to its mouth, and then applying an air-pump to the cock, exhausted the whole air: in this state, keeping it stopped, I immersed its mouth in fresh blood flowing from a vein, and then turning the cock, allowed the blood to be pressed up into the phial. When it was about half full I turned the cock back, and now shook the phial with the blood, but its colour did not alter as in the former experience; and when I allowed the blood to stand in this vacuum, its exposed surface was not in the least changed."

Having thus established the effect of "vital air" on the blood—and then the opposite effect of "fixed air" (carbon dioxide)—John went on, in a bizarre experiment on a dog, to observe the phenomenon in conjunction with the mechanics of respiration.

"I invented a pair of double bellows, each of which had two openings, but their actions were reversed: two of the openings were inclosed in one pipe or nozzle, and the other two were on the sides. The lower chamber had its valve placed exactly similar to that of the common bellows; but it also had a valve at the nozzle, which did not allow any air to enter there. The upper half had a valve placed at the nozzle, which allowed the air to enter but not to escape, and the opening on the upper side allowed the air to escape but not to enter; so that, on dilating the bellows, the upper side or chamber drew in its air by the nozzle only, and at the same time the under chamber drew in its air by the side only. On closing the bellows, or expelling this air, the air drawn in by the nozzle passed out at the opening on the upper side, and the air that was drawn in by the under side passed out by the nozzle. By this means I could, by fixing the nozzle into the trachea, draw the air out of the lungs into the upper chamber of the bellows, and at the same time draw fresh air into the lower chamber: on emptying these cavities of their air, the pure air in the lower chamber passed into the lungs, and that which had been just taken from the lungs into the upper chamber passed into the open alternately. The action of these bellows, though double, is exactly as simple as breathing itself; and they appear to me to be superior to any invention made since for the same purpose. I fixed the nozzle of these bellows into the trachea of a dog, and immediately began the artificial breathing. I then removed the sternum and the cartilages, and opened the pericardium. While I continued the artificial breathing, I observed that the blood in the pulmonary veins, coming from the lungs, the left auricle, the aorta, &c., was florid or dark just as I threw the air or not into the lungs.

"I cut off a piece of the lungs, and found that the colour of the blood which came from the wound corresponded with the above effects. When I threw air into the lungs, so as to render the blood florid in the pulmonary veins, two kinds of blood issued from the wound; and when I left off blowing, the whole blood which passed out by the wound was of the dark colour."

John was to have remained at St. George's as house surgeon for a year, but after five months he abandoned the post to Gunning. He gave no reason. Possibly William, who now had a hundred pupils, pressed him for help. It is also possible that the symptoms of failing health, which beset him four years later, forced him to leave that polluted atmosphere. When the fall term opened in the Great Piazza, he was at work again with his brother.

13. WILLIAM ONWARDS AND UPWARDS

Despite the low regard for men-midwives held by the rest of the medical profession, William was prospering. Between the tuitions of seven guineas each from his pupils, whose instruction he shared with John, and the fees from his obstetrical practice, his annual income reached several thousand pounds. "Every man should be held a criminal who locks up his talent, whatever it may be," he vaunted himself. "Mine, from nature was small; but by application and perseverance it has grown to be considerable."

For the time being, moreover, the silkily elegant Scot had the field of man-midwifery largely to himself. Many of its leading figures were either dead or retired and the best of the active ones were, like Smellie, an earthy lot with a no-nonsense approach to their patients.

"Physic," William wrote to Cullen, "is in a strange ferment here.

The practitioners in mid-wifery have been virulently attacked, but by a madman [a reference to Dr. Frank Nicholls and his *Petition of the Unborn Babes*]; and in the scuffle I have had a blow too, obliquely:— the reason is, we get money, our antagonists none. May the dispute, therefore, long continue."

He decided to give up almost entirely the practice of surgery, though he would always teach it, in favor of obstetrics, a move entailing certain financial penalties. For six years he had been an honorary doctor of medicine of the University of Glasgow, but to practice any form of medicine legally in London, membership was required in the College of Physicians. If the applicant already belonged to the Corporation of Surgeons, he had first to be disenfranchised. He could not belong to both; such was the surgeons' jealous and monopolistic attitude.* For his certificate of disenfranchisement the corporation assessed William forty guineas. One of its bylaws further stipulated that a resigning member who wished to join another company must obtain prior leave from the Court of Assistants. This William neglected to do, and they fined him an additional £20.

The Physicians admitted him on September 30, 1756, but only with the secondary rank of licentiate. Not until the last years of the century would the Physicians deem obstetricians worthy of full fellowship. Gestating ladies of fashion were nevertheless eager to engage William's services.

"Loo is mounted to its zenith," reported Horace Walpole in a mischievous letter to his friend, George Montagu; "the parties last till one and two in the morning. We played at Lady Hertford's last week, the last night of her lying-in, till deep into Sunday morning, after she and her lord retired. It is now adjourned to Mrs. Fitzroy's, whose child the town calls *Pamela* [after the opportunistic heroine of Richardson's novel]. I proposed that instead of receiving cards for assemblies, one should send in a morning to Dr. Hunter's, the man-midwife, to know where there is loo that evening."

Before the birth of his second son, the majestic elder Pitt majestically wrote to William: "The knowing persons here think it proper to desire your assistance." And William's delivery of the future Prime Minister, William Pitt the younger, won him the favor of one of the most illustrious families in England.

* Then as now, British surgeons carried the title Mr., physicians the title Dr.

William foliated like a tropical bloom after rain. He bought land adjacent to Long Calderwood. "I cannot get it out of my head that I shall one time or other live there," he wrote to Cullen, "and, in that case, I should like to possess both, that I might have a little bit all round me that I could call my own."

He registered a coat of arms: "Vert, 3 dogs of Chace Argent, Two and One, collar'd Or. On a chief of the Second a Hunting Horn of the Frist Stringed gules." And for his crest, "a Hawk riseing proper with the motto Arte et Industria." John, at the peak of his fame, displayed no insignia more impressive than a brass plate nailed to his door, bearing his name without even the prefix "Mr."

William also began to form, after the current vogue, a "Gentleman's Cabinet" of miscellaneous precious objects. His taste was eclectic but sound, and his sense of values acute. Among his earliest acquisitions were two landscapes by the seventeenth-century Dutch masters, Philips de Koninck and Philips Wouwerman, for which he bid at auction one pound, eight shillings, and seventeen pounds, six shillings; a print of Hogarth's riotous *Election Entertainment;* and a first edition of Hogarth's book, *The Analysis of Beauty,* which he purchased directly from the artist. Collecting became a vice. "What say you of Mead's auction of books?" he wrote to Cullen. "I am afraid I shall ruin myself in the winter with it." He eventually acquired, in addition to an immense gallery of anatomical specimens, minerals, fossils, and shells, forty-three paintings and drawings, including a Rembrandt, a Murillo, a Rubens, a Titian, and three Chardins (William was the only collector in England to esteem the French portraitist); thirty thousand ancient coins, costing him approximately £23,000; a library of more than six hundred manuscripts, many of them medieval, and twelve thousand books, including such rarissimi as the Aldine edition of Plato's works printed on vellum in 1515 and a 1455 edition of Cicero's *De Officiis.*

He was the terror of the dealers, inflexible in his terms, vindictive when thwarted. "It is my rule," he announced, "to offer at once what I will give when I treat with gentlemen. Gentlemen shall always do so." When a coin dealer agreed to lower his price on a series William coveted, William bought them, but afterward wrote him pettishly: "In answer to your note to Mr. Combe [his executor] I beg leave to put you in mind that you refused my offer when the press [which printed his catalogue] stood still, waiting for some of your coins. I told you that

I would give no more and that it was a *generous* price. But you would not accept; thinking perhaps that I would give more money. The transaction was declared to be *at an end,* and the printing went on without your coins. A great while after I was told you would part with your coins for the sum which I had offered. I wished not to take them; but Mr. Combe urged me, and went to you with my express order not to thank you, nor to admit the least matter of favour to mix with the bargain."

John, too, in later years, when his means permitted it, collected, but like a magpie and with utter disregard of values. Fascinated by the random element in life, by the *outré* and the anomalous, he amassed a roomful of oddments worth a fraction of what he paid for them—waxworks, portraits of freaks, Oriental scrimshaw, exotic weapons, scraps of tapestry, electromechanical novelties, things embalmed, stuffed and pickled. From these must be excepted a few fine contemporary engravings and canvases—he had a grateful eye for line and form—and his museum of comparative anatomy, his masterwork and the most important of its kind before or since.

The size and quality of William's practice, not to mention his abundant Gentleman's Cabinet, demanded a more imposing frame than the Little Piazza apartments, and leaving John and the resident students to occupy them, he removed, in the spring of 1756, to a large house at No. 42 Jermyn Street. Dorothea returned to Scotland and two years later married a theologian, the Reverend James Baillie, who succeeded to the Chair of Divinity at the University of Glasgow.

The neighborhood perfectly suited William's pretensions. A few doors below stood the Church of St. James's, where George II's eldest daughter, Princess Anne, had worshiped and of which Defoe complained that a seat in the pews was "almost as dear as to see a play." The lordly houses surrounding William's had been inhabited at one time or other by the Duke of Marlborough, the Pitts, Bishop Berkeley, the poets Thomas Gray and William Shenstone, Sir Isaac Newton. St. James's Street, running into Jermyn Street, was the heart of London's "Clubland," embracing Boodle's, the Cocoa Tree, frequented by Tories, St. James's Coffee-house, by Whigs, and White's, a favorite of gamblers, for which Horace Walpole designed a coat of arms emblazoned with dice-boxes, where £180,000 were once staked on a single card, and long odds were offered that a hell-bent member, Sir Winston Burdett, would be the first baronet hanged in England (he was not). As they passed to and from their pleasures, such clubmen as Lord Chesterfield, the Prince of Wales, the Duke of Queensberry and David Garrick became familiar figures to William and he to them. With a number of them he came to enjoy a social as well as a professional relationship.

William himself, who was no gamester, patronized the British Coffee-house in Cockspur Street, a tranquil port of call for Scotsmen sojourning in London, kept by a bishop's sister. "Hunter was lively and gay to the last degree," a fellow habitué recalled, "and often came to us at nine o'clock fatigued and jaded. He had no dinner, but supped on a couple of eggs, and drank his glass of claret; for though we were a punch club, we allowed him a bottle of what he liked best. His toast was 'May no English nobleman venture out of the world without a Scottish physician, as I am sure there are none who venture in.'"

When William played host at home, the wine flowed less freely. The butler filled each guest's glass only once. Nor were more than two courses served. When dining alone, William limited himself to one course. "A man who cannot dine on this," he said, "deserves no dinner."

William wanted John to take some of the lecture classes, but if the younger brother was a halting writer, as a speaker he was chaotic. The prospect of addressing an audience unnerved him, and no inducement William offered could move him to attempt it. Only in the dissecting room, where he could teach by showing, did John feel secure, and there he stayed.

Through colleagues who corresponded with friends in the American colonies, reports of the brothers' work crossed the Atlantic, and among their students in 1759 was a twenty-three-year-old Philadelphian, William Shippen, Jr. He proved to be a retentive receptacle for Hunterian precepts, and the consequent effect upon the development of American medicine, then in its infancy, was enormous.

The Shippens were a large, wealthy and public-spirited Presbyterian family, originally from Yorkshire, influential in the political and educational affairs of not only Pennsylvania, but also New Jersey, Maryland, and Virginia. William Shippen, Sr., a physician, and his older brother, Edward, a jurist, who served a term as mayor of Philadelphia, helped establish the College of New Jersey (later Princeton University). As valedictorian of its graduating class, in 1754, when he was seventeen, William, Jr., according to one listener, "attracted the eye of every beholder by the elegance of his person, the ease and gracefulness of his whole deportment."

After serving a four-year apprenticeship to his father, Shippen sailed for England. He attended William Hunter's spring series of lectures and during the summer walked the wards of St. Thomas's and Guy's Hospital as a pupil-at-large. ". . . took off a man's leg very elegantly," he wrote in a journal of his London period.

In the prim vein of many another youth far from home, seeking familial approval and a larger allowance, he wrote to his Uncle Edward: "I find the ways of Vice and Wickedness as many and various as I expected; but can with pleasure and without boasting say, I find very little difficulty shunning them; nothing necessary but a little Resolution and a constant call to more necessary Business; I now and then by accident amuse myself with Garrick's inimitable playing; by accident because Dr. Hunter's anatomical lectures begin at the same time [5 P.M., a sore point with Dr. Hunter, who, when Garrick was appearing at the Drury Lane Theatre nearby, often found himself addressing a half-empty room; to avoid the conflict, he started his lectures at two]. . . . Your instructing lessons upon the frugal use of Time and Money are always in my mind and influence my conduct much. My Father will inform you, Sir, how I spend my Time and I flatter myself to convince the World at some future day that I do not spend it trifling about Play Houses, Operas, reading idle romantic Tales or trifling Newspapers at Coffee Houses, &c, &c, as I find many have done before me, but in the right Improvement of those advantages which are not to be had in my own country, which are peculiarly great in my Way of Surgery and Anatomy. I live with the best practical Anatomist in Europe, I think I may say . . . I shall always, Sir, take pride in executing your Commands with Care and Punctuality. My Money I think I spend very cautiously, yet as you observed, it melts faster than I imagined; nothing done in London without Pay; else how could a Million of Souls be supported? . . . N. B. I find as many fools in England as in America. . . ."

But William Shippen's life abroad was not as Spartan as all that. He went to the theater eighteen times in three months and saw Garrick as Lear, Macbeth, and Richard III. He played skittles, weekended on baronial estates, wined and dined in style. He missed few public spectacles. His fellow Philadelphian, Benjamin Franklin, the official agent of Pennsylvania in England, took him to a meeting of the Royal

Society, a rare privilege for a mere medical student, and presented him to the Court. He cut a dashing figure at high society balls and assemblies, which he did not, however, consider up to Philadelphia standards. "No proper decorum or Regularity in Assembly," he wrote in his diary, "some sitting down as soon as they have danced to the Bottom." With his dancing partners he was more indulgent. ". . . very fine were Miss Innocent, Watson, Seaton, Jepson, Coit and Thomas etc. . . . 40 young ladies most of them pretty and genteel, elegantly dressed in flounced Trollopes . . . Miss S. Church a very pretty soft agreeable girl . . . Miss Britton a very angellic figure!"

But the girl who captured his heart was an American orphan, Alice Lee, a Virginia Lee—her father, Colonel Thomas Lee, had been acting governor of the colony—"expressing upon all her features," as an unsuccessful suitor described her, "that heavenly mildness which is the characteristick of her Soul." Since her parents' death she had been staying with an uncle in London and going to school there. Before the visit ended William Shippen married her.

John Hunter gave special attention to his receptive American pupil. After the regular classwork, he would discuss anatomy and surgery with him until late at night. When Shippen went home in 1762, with his bride and a medical degree from the University of Edinburgh, it was as a militant Hunterian, and he proceeded at once to adapt his teacher's ideas to the American medical scene.

On the grounds of Shippen House, his father's estate, at the juncture of Prune (now Locust) and South Fourth streets, where he passed his early married life, he launched the first private anatomical school in America "for the advantage of the young gentlemen now engaged in the study of physick in this and the neighboring provinces whose circumstances will not admit of their going abroad for improvement to the anatomical schools of Europe." Like the Hunters, he undertook to furnish his students with an adequate supply of human material to dissect, and, like them, he incurred a good deal of opprobrium, even though he had no truck with body snatchers, obtaining quite legally from hospitals and prisons the cadavers of paupers, suicides, and executed criminals. Mobs stormed the school, hurling stones through the windows. They once besieged a carriage he was riding in. He managed to slip down an alley in time to avoid a musket ball that ripped through the rear seat. Gradually, however, Philadelphians came to accept the necessity for dissections, and Shippen was able to advertise his courses without danger of being lynched.

In establishing America's first private school of obstetrics for students of both sexes, and the first private maternity hospital, he aroused furious opposition. Even more than in England was the layman's sense of propriety outraged by the idea of a woman in labor being attended by a male. Shippen somewhat pacified the prudes by a hardheaded statement of aims, with which he prefaced the announcements of his lectures: "Dr. Shippen, Jr., having lately been called to the assistance of a number of women in the country, in difficult labours, most of which was made so by the unskillful old women about them, the poor women having suffered extremely, and their innocent little ones being entirely destroyed, whose lives might have been easily saved by proper management, and being informed of several desperate cases in the different neighbourhoods which had proved fatal to the mothers and were attended with the most painful circumstances too dismal to be related, he thought it his duty immediately to begin his intended courses in Midwifery, and has prepared a proper apparatus for that purpose, in order to instruct those women who have virtue enough to own their ignorance and apply for instructions, as well as those young gentlemen now engaged in the study of that useful and necessary branch of surgery who are taking pains to qualify themselves in practice in different parts of the country with safety and advantage to their fellow citizens."

Shippen remained susceptible to pretty girls. One Philadelphia charmer gushed in her diary: "What a pity it is that the doctor is so fond of kissing; he really would be much more agreeable if he were less fond. One hates to be always kissed; especially as it is attended with so many inconveniences; it decomposes the economy of one's *handkerchief*, it disorders one's *high roll*, and it ruffles the serenity of one's countenance; in short, the doctor's or a sociable kiss is many times worse than a formal salute with bowing and curtsying, to 'This is Mister Such-a-one, and this is Miss What-do-you-call-it.' 'Tis true, this confuses one no little, but one gets the better of that sooner than to readjust one's dress."

The obstetrician never swerved from Hunterian principles, and never wavered in his loyalty to the brothers, neither during the events that led to the Revolution, when Shippen House was a hive of conspiratorial activity, nor during the fighting, when he served as Director-

General of the Military Hospitals. "I am sure," he wrote to William, "you will be particularly pleased to know that your sons [using the word in a symbolic sense] are engaged in the glorious attempt in America; may the genius of Hunter be ever with us to ensure success." A decade later William might have received such news with embarrassment, for although he professed to be a liberal and spoke sympathetically of the American cause when Shippen first knew him, he moved, as his fortunes rose in court, deep into the King's camp. In his library was a copy of Benedict Arnold's apologia, *To the inhabitants of America on the motives which have induced me to join the King's arms.*

John Hunter's political opinions remained as conservative as his scientific theories were radical. "I wish," said he, "that all the rascals who are dissatisfied with their country would be good enough to leave it." He compared Edmund Burke's speech in defense of the colonies to "a shrub full of flowers, which is pretty while viewed; but, strip it of its flowers, and it will hardly be taken notice of." To a request from a colleague that a foreign visitor be allowed to inspect his anatomical collection, he replied: "If your friend is in London in October (and not a Democrat) he is welcome to see it; but I would rather see it in a blaze, like the Bastille, than show it to a Democrat, let his country be what it may."

Shippen named his first son after William. The boy died in infancy, as did six of his eight children. Referring to his loss many years later, in a letter to William Cullen, under whom he studied in Edinburgh, he observed: ". . . before this time he might have been sitting at your Feet; I have but one, and he is reading Law, now 20 years old and 6 feet 2 inches high, a Boy no father need be ashamed of." This son, Thomas Lee Shippen, died of tuberculosis early in his career.

Shippen had stood at John's side during a crucial period in the anatomist's development, when his research was taking a new direction. Lacking refined tools of measurement and observation, he was frustrated in his efforts to probe certain minute and complex areas of human structure below a relatively superficial level. Van Leeuwenhoek, the Dutch microscopist, had ground short-focus single lenses of high quality almost a hundred years before, but, inexplicably, John does not appear to have been familiar with them, or, if he was, to have used them. It occurred to him to start his inquiries afresh as a comparative anatomist, exploring similar organs in simpler forms as they existed among lower species, and thus arriving at an understanding of functions shared by both man and animal. Among his first efforts was an investigation of the breathing apparatus of birds, in which he demonstrated how air is communicated from their lungs to numerous cavities of their anatomy through widely distributed air cells.

As John went on to compare such mechanisms with those of other animals and of man, and eventually of plants, he was carried far beyond his original intent. He soon found himself pondering a question that would obsess him ever after and form the underlying theme of his whole work. What is life? What are the quintessential elements common to all organic phenomena? Unlike such cataloguers of living things as Linnaeus, Buffon, and Cuvier, John was not content merely to classify a particular species. He tried rather to isolate manifestations of what he variously termed "animal fire," "the vital principle," "the life force." John Abernethy, a follower of his later years, reported: "When he met an animal he had never dissected, he cared little by what name it was called and to what family it belonged. . . . He wished to know how its food was digested, how its blood circulated, how it secured and defended itself from injury, how the multiplication of its species was effected and insured." He adopted the Baconian method. "No natural phenomenon," wrote the Elizabethan philosopher, "can be adequately studied in itself alone, but to be understood must be considered as it stands connected with all nature."

An example of this spirit was an early experiment, which has been described as the most brilliant use made of a hen's egg since Columbus. Having observed that a hatching egg, kept at a temperature of 103° Fahrenheit in the hen's nest, retained its vitality to the moment of the chick's birth, but that an egg which failed to hatch rapidly putrefied like any other dead animal matter, he attributed to the former a self-preservative element. To prove it, he embedded a fresh egg in a mixture of salt and ice, registering a temperature of zero. Unthawing it, he found that the yolk and albumen were dead. He replaced it in the mixture, along with a new-laid egg. The live egg took seven and a half minutes longer to freeze than the dead one. He repeated the process at varying freezing temperatures. The live eggs invariably froze more slowly. "From these experiments," he concluded, "it appears that a fresh egg has the power of resisting heat, cold and putrefaction in a degree equal to many of the more imperfect animals which exhibit exactly the same phenomena under the same experiments; and it is more than probable that this power arises from the same principle in both." He also submitted to such experiments fish, eels, frogs, the muscles of bullocks, the sap of trees.

John came no closer to unraveling the ultimate riddle of life than any thinker after him, and in the attempt he adopted a philosophy, tinged with mysticism, that finds no acceptance among modern scientists. He conceived of life as having an existence independent of structure and organization, a force like magnetism or electricity, which was mysteriously superadded to organic matter, whereas life is now seen to be inherent in organic matter, and growth inseparable from cell development. John leaned towards a form of teleology, now discredited, that explained as the causes of phenomena not the actions producing them but the end purposes they were assumed to serve. "Many of the effects both in animals and vegetables," he reasoned, "might at first appear to be chemical, or the consequences of fermentation. The production of many juices of plants, such as gums, acids, sugars, &c., would seem to be of this kind, but all arise from natural actions of the vegetable, and do not belong to chemistry. No chemist on earth can make out of the earth a piece of sugar, but a vegetable can do it. . . . The man, the oak and the mountain are but different modifications of the same elementary matter, mere composition does not give life, for the dead body has all the life it ever had. A seed put into a moist ground grows, but the moist ground is only a necessary attendant and not the immediate cause. The life of the seed stimulated to action is the immediate cause of its growth. All the water in the world would not make a dead seed grow."

Acknowledging that "in nature nothing is irregular, nothing is perturbed, nothing is disobedient, and everything is really regular, uniform and obedient to recognized principles," he postulated a guiding intelligence—"the Great Chemist," he called it—a view to which theologians, certainly, are committed, though John himself does not seem to have retained any profound religious convictions. Yet, that universal order does reflect a plan none but the most rigid mechanists would deny. Of that plan John uncovered countless facets, and from them drew practical inferences that affected almost every major branch of science, and laid the foundations for new ones.

Abnormality and disease, he saw, were neither—contrary to prevalent notions—products of blind chance, nor visitations of celestial wrath, but deviations from natural laws, whose origin should be sought in factors like excessive or retarded tissue growth, inadequate nourishment, toxins. He saw, too, that nature, always regular in her normal operations, was no less so when she deviated. "In the regeneration of bone which was originally cartilage, as the long bones," said he by way of illustration, "there when a fracture takes place she begins by forming cartilage, but in the head, where the bone was at first membrane, there membrane is formed." He demonstrated this principle further in a series of experiments, foreshadowing by a century and a half the efforts of modern embryologists to regenerate living tissue. From the leg of a young cock he transplanted the spur to the comb, where it resumed growth as a spur. He also successfully grafted skin to the ulcerated ankle of a child, an anticipation of plastic surgery.

It followed in John's reasoning that a study of monstrosities and morbid states could illuminate normal functions, "for the wrong action of a part often points out what the natural action was, and itself gives an idea of life." He never viewed any pathological symptom as an isolated aspect of disease, but always in connection with interacting phenomena. Delving into the problem of inflammation, which is a response of tissue to injury, he realized that he must concurrently consider changes in blood flow, the cycles of body growth, the actions of sympathy, that is, the relation between different parts whereby a modification in one affects the other. He was the first to describe the pus-producing inflammation of veins known as phlebitis, and to explain its cause as arising from the suppuration of surrounding tissue. Tracing the blood through every stage of embryonic development, he inferred that the red components formed later than the others, and that their main function was to reinforce the vitality of the system, discoveries later confirmed by hematologists with microscopes.

He early recognized the body's ability to marshal its own defenses against attack, as when the lymphs dissolve dead tissue, and he grew to rely as much on this natural property as on medication and the knife—perhaps his greatest contribution to surgery. In an age when virtuosos of the scalpel performed with the bravura of actors, John regarded surgery as an admission of defeat. "It is like an armed savage," he said, "who attempts to get that by force which a civilized man would get by stratagem."

In a fashion peculiarly his own, he applied pathology and physiology to surgery, transforming it from an empirical craft, guided by observation and experience alone, to a true science based upon general principles. To his ideas can be traced the roots of almost every major surgical advance made during the next fifty years.

For his pursuit of "animal fire," John required, in abundance and endless variety, experimental animals healthy and diseased, alive and dead, and he sought them with an avidity verging on mania. He ran up enormous bills in pet-shops. He bribed zoo keepers to let him anatomize some of their inmates, bought from the owners of circuses and raree shows any aged or ailing creatures they wanted to dispose of, badgered explorers bound for distant ports to bring him back fauna—among them, Captain James Cook, when he sailed to Tahiti, and Captain John White, when he was appointed Surgeon-General to the New South Wales Settlement. He offered a former pupil, John Sheldon, who had joined a whaling expedition to Greenland in order to test the efficacy of poisoned harpoons, £500 for a live bottlenose whale. "The only return I received," he complained, "was a piece of whale's skin with some small animals sticking upon it." His descriptions of several whales he did dissect later, on barges anchored in the Thames, provided Herman Melville with much of the cetology for *Moby Dick*.

He corresponded with hundreds of people traveling abroad, entreating them to send him descriptions of any animals they might encounter, and, if possible, the animals themselves, and he hastened to visit them the moment they returned to London. "Mr. Griffiths," was the distressing response to one such request, "presents his compliments to Mr. Hunter, and begs leave to acquaint him that the entrails, etc., of the Pangolin, or Ant-eater, from Sumatra, which he brought home for his inspection have been entirely spoiled from their long detention at the India House. Mr. Griffiths takes the liberty to send them, that Mr. Hunter may see the state they are in, and will do himself the honour to call in a few days with the aquatic snail that he mentioned. . . ."

During a study John undertook of tumors, many a London slaughterhouse worker learned to recognize melanomas, benign skin tumors of a dark-brown pigmentation, in steers, excise them, and deliver them to John. In a study of reproductive systems, lasting ten years, he spent £10 a year procuring the genitals of certain species.

A book dealer named George Nicoll, whom John had frequently treated, was startled one day when the anatomist burst into his store to ask: "Pray, George, have you got five guineas in your pocket? Because if you have and will lend it to me, you shall go halves?"

"Halves in what?" demanded Nicoll.

"Why, halves in a magnificent tiger which is now dying in Castle Street."

Friendly colleagues came to bear John's needs in mind. One of the friendliest was Dr. Maxwell Garthshore, a bumbling general practitioner, whom John never tired of baiting—"dear Tom Fool," he once greeted him—but who looked up to John with an admiration approaching idolatry. Wanting to send him a gift for his thirty-third birthday, Garthshore asked a mutual friend, Sir George Baker, if he thought John would fancy a basket of table delicacies. "He cares not what he eats or drinks," replied Sir George, "and I am sure that a curious case, or some anatomical curiosity would be more agreeable to him than all the wine and all the venison in the Country."

"If you will step in at Banks' in Soho Sq.," Joseph (later Sir Joseph) Banks, a noted naturalist, apprised John, "you will find the corpse of the fine Sierra Leone cat, the inside of which is at your service. The skin is to be stuffed for the British Museum." When the oldest elephant in the royal menagerie died, George III notified John that he might do as he chose with the carcass. It was the first elephant ever to be thoroughly dissected, and the first to have its skeleton mounted.

In time, John managed to dissect at least one specimen of most classified genera, and a good many unclassified ones, from bees to bears, from alley cats to exotic marsupials like the poteroo, the hepoona roo and the tapua tafa. If he heard of an animal unfamiliar to him, he knew no peace until he had a specimen under his scalpel. When a Dr. Clarke refused to part with an unusual anatomical preparation, John warned him with mock ferocity: "Well, then, take care I don't meet you with it in some dark lane at night, for if I do, I'll murder you to get it."

John planned to establish a menagerie of his own, from which he could select subjects at will. As a beginning, he leased, in 1760, a plot at Earl's Court, in the hamlet of Kensington, forming part of a manor formerly owned by the Earl of Warwick and Holland. The amount John paid was not recorded, but the annual tax came to £8. The property lay roughly six miles from Covent Garden, about an hour's carriage drive, and in the same direction as St. George's Hospital. John's tenancy, however, was postponed. The year before, he had contracted pneumonia. Pains in his chest persisted, and, mindful of his family

medical history, he took alarm. With the exception of his brief visit to
Scotland in 1752 and his month at Oxford in 1755, he had spent
twelve years in dissecting rooms and hospital wards, and he felt the
need for more healthful surroundings. He hit upon a somewhat dubious
solution. He decided to join the army, preferably as a staff surgeon.

The Inspector-General of Hospitals, upon whose recommendations
the King made appointments, was at this time Robert Adair, an Irishman whose dash and good looks moved his wife, the former Lady
Caroline Keppel, to compose:

> *What's this dull town to me?*
> *Robin's not near—*
> *He whom I wish to see,*
> *Wished for to hear;*
> *Where's all the joy and mirth*
> *Made life a heaven on earth*
> *O, they're all fled with,*
> *Robin Adair!*

Adair knew the Hunters well, having worked in hospitals with both
of them. John's credentials were impressive, since he had just been
named to St. George's board of governors. The commission he applied
for was granted in the fall of the year, with a daily pay of ten shillings.

England was then in the fifth year of the Seven Years' War, which
she had entered as an ally of Prussia against a coalition of France, Austria, and Russia. Among her objectives was the capture of Belle Isle,
a rocky island off the coast of Brittany, which she meant to use as a
naval base in large-scale assaults against the mainland. Early in 1761,
seven thousand troops were mustered under the command of Major-
General Studholme Hodgson, and to transport them, a flotilla under the
command of Commodore Viscount August Keppel, Adair's brother-in-
law, of one hundred vessels, including ten of the line, eight frigates, and
an assortment of sloops, bomb-ketches, and fireships. In addition, a
covering squadron of four sail under Commander Matthew Buckle was
to hover off Brest.

John was one of three surgeons assigned to the expedition. He sailed,
flamboyant as a macaw in a double-breasted red coat and cocked hat,
from Spithead on March 26, amid thundering choruses of *Heart of Oak*,
the patriotic chanty popularized by David Garrick in his musical play,
Harlequin's Invasion:

Heart of oak our ships,
Heart of oak our men,
We always are ready,
Steady! Boys! Steady!
We'll fight and we'll conquer again and again.

"The sea," John wrote to William after a voyage lasting eleven days, "plays the Devil with me."

III. WAR
1762-1763

◊◊◊◊◊

14. OF FISH, LIZARDS, WOUNDS, AND ROCKS

The initial attack on Belle Isle added little luster to British arms. Against His Majesty's armada stood a garrison of less than three thousand ill-equipped defenders, part of them militia, under the command of the island's courtly military governor, the Chevalier de Sainte-Croix. The natural defenses of the island, however, were formidable. Twelve miles long, its coast presented a towering, almost unbroken escarpment of rock, hewn by lashing seas and gale winds into a frieze of gargoylish shapes. Two fierce currents, clashing at the center of a sea cave called the Apothecary's Grotto, because the cormorants nesting in tiers along the walls resembled rows of apothecary jars, hurled geysers up to the ceiling with a roar like a cannonade that carried miles.

To delude the enemy on the horizon as to his real strength, Sainte-Croix ordered the island farmers to mount their dray horses, and their women, clad in red capes, to sit cows, and ride the coastal ridge. But so confident were the British that many of the officers had brought along their wives or mistresses to watch the campaign, and to organize afterwards a victory ball.

On April 6 at daybreak, the fleet, led by Keppel's flagship, the *Valiant,* rounded the southern end of the island. It sailed close inshore for a time while Keppel and Hodgson peered anxiously through their spyglasses for a break in the palisade. They finally discerned a sandy cove, which was Port St. André. Sainte-Croix had installed there a battery of cannon. Two ships of the line opened fire and crippled it. Four thousand of Hodgson's men then piled into flatboats and forced a landing. But so sheerly rose the surrounding hills and so heavy was the hail of musket shot from the heights that they soon fell back, leaving four hundred and fifty of their companions dead or wounded. That night a gale blew up, wrecking half the flatboats.

Keppel dispatched a report of the disaster to Pitt, adding that no landing was possible. "The coast," Hodgson agreed in an accompanying letter, "is the most inaccessible I ever saw, the whole island is a fortification." The Prime Minister's response was to ship four more battalions, and a quantity of flatboats and stores, with orders to seize Belle Isle at all costs. On April 22, nine thousand troops launched a two-pronged attack in the south, while a party of dragoons created a diversion to the north. The main body advanced three miles to the town of Bangor, where the French held them for twenty-four hours. The next day, Sainte-Croix, his forces now reduced to eighteen hundred, retreated into the citadel of Le Palais, on the west coast, to await reinforcements from the mainland. None could breach Keppel's blockade. Yet the French commander held out for six weeks, despite the arrival of more British troops, bringing the total to 17,800, while the ships' cannon raked the interior. Learning from a British prisoner of the presence of ladies aboard the ships, Sainte-Croix returned him to his lines with a message tendering them all safe conduct to the citadel where he would protect and entertain them until the hostilities ended.

On June 8 Sainte-Croix hoisted a white flag, and the invaders took possession of Belle Isle. The cost in British lives had totaled seven hundred. Two years later Pitt traded the island for Minorca.

To judge from what seasick John wrote to William, the quality of the medical services was poor. "My fellow Creatures of the Hospital are a damn'd disagreeable set. The two Heads are as unfit for employment, as the devil was to reign in Heaven." Years later, in a book on gunshot wounds, he commented: "It was hardly necessary for a man to be a surgeon to practice in the army."

Once ashore, however, he found compensations. The coves teemed with marine life strange to him, and shortly, when he could spare the time from official duties, he was splashing happily about at low tide, gathering for dissection netfuls of squirts, squid, starfish, sea nettles, anemones and conger eels.

The abundance of the eels enabled him to solve a little puzzle that had eluded a good many naturalists. How did they propagate? Earlier investigators had fallen so wide of the mark as to assume that eels were viviparous. But John, after dissecting scores of them, traced the passage of roe, showing them to be, like most fish, oviparous.

On Belle Isle he extended his studies of tissue regeneration. The island abounded in lizards, many of whose tails he observed to have regrown after mutilation. In one lizard he caught, regeneration was nearly complete. He severed the tail again, and before long it grew back a third time.

As winter approached, the lizards further served John in an experiment to test his surmise that during hibernation the life processes of animals slow down almost to a halt. "I conveyed worms and pieces of meat down the throats of lizards when they were going to winter quarters, keeping them afterwards in a cool place. On opening them at different periods I always found the substances which I had introduced, entire and free from any alteration; sometimes they were in the stomach, at other times they passed into the intestine, and some of the lizards that were preserved alive voided them towards the spring with but very little alteration of their structure."

John anatomized, embalmed and bottled organs from about two hundred animals, each preparation illustrating a principle of the relationship between structure and function. The imagination is taxed to conceive how, amid the disorders of military occupation and his routine hospital chores, he maintained the singleness of mind essential to such finicky probings, how he laid hands on chemical preservatives and containers, which he lugged around with him for a year before he could get them to England.

To the sick and wounded in his care, meanwhile, he applied revolutionary methods of therapy. The accepted treatment of a gunshot wound, for example, unchallenged since the sixteenth century, when the French surgeon, Ambroise Paré, recommended it, was to enlarge the passage and extract the bullet. No distinction was made between one wound and another, though bullets can cause injuries as diverse as any other penetrating blow. The resultant pain, loss of blood, and shock, especially in the field remote from a hospital, often proved deadlier than the bullet itself.

The cardinal error of the Paré school, as John did not hesitate to proclaim, was its underestimation of nature's curative powers. From his studies of anatomy he knew that organs could sometimes adjust them-

selves to the presence of a foreign body, obviating the necessity of prob-
ing for it, and that, in other instances, a bullet would work itself harm-
lessly to the surface. Only in relatively few gunshot wounds, as when
the bullet exerted pressure on a vital spot or a part became gangrenous,
did he prescribe surgery, and then not always immediately, but after
inflammation had subsided and the patient's resistance rallied. "I think
we should be very quiet," he counseled. "We often find more difficulty
in keeping up the strength than we find in lowering it."

"This treatment of gunshot wounds [dilation]," he wrote many years
later, "is diametrically opposite to the principle which is generally
adopted in other cases, although not understood as a general rule, which
is, that very few wounds of any kind require surgical treatment at their
commencement, excepting with an opposite view from the above, viz,
to heal them by the first intention [the primary union of a wound when
the broken edges of the skin are lined up and so held until union occurs
through the natural granulation of tissue]. It is contrary to all rules of
surgery founded on our knowledge of the animal oeconomy to enlarge
wounds simply as wounds. No wound, let it be ever so small, should
be made larger, excepting when preparatory to something else, which
will imply a complicated wound, and which is to be treated accordingly;
it should not be opened because it is a wound, but because there is
something necessary to be done which cannot be executed unless the
wound is enlarged. This is common surgery, and ought also to be military surgery respecting gun-shot wounds."

As if to corroborate this doctrine, four wounded French soldiers sur-
rendered shortly after Hodgson's second landing. The first had been
wounded in the thigh by two musket balls, one of which passed clear
through, the other lodging there; the second, in the knee joint; the
third, in the chest; the fourth, in the arm. They had been hiding for
four days in a farmhouse, and had received no treatment of any kind.
John dressed the wounds lightly. Only from the fourth soldier did he
extract the bullet. All of the Frenchmen recovered.

It was not surprising that, as John wrote to his brother, "I have had
the eyes of all the surgeons upon me, both on account of my suppos'd
knowledge, and method of treatment." But their curiosity was mixed
with resentment. Tactless and cocky, John poorly concealed his contempt for classical surgical procedures and for those who slavishly adhered to them. During a subsequent tour of duty in Portugal he so
enraged one Francis Tomkins, a military surgeon with ten years' ex-

perience, that he drew his sword. Cooler heads averted bloodshed, but the adversaries were never reconciled.

Not all of John's relations with his army colleagues were acrimonious, however. For an older surgeon and fellow Scot named Robert Boyne Home he developed a warm regard. An unassuming and amiable man, Home had been gazetted a surgeon in 1760 to the 16th Dragoons, General Burgoyne's regiment, a detachment of which had been those dispatched to Belle Isle and later to Portugal. He was a Border Scot, resident in London with a large family, and he pressed John to call on him as soon as they should both be out of the army.

Rumors of an impending expedition to the West Indies reached John in the summer of 1761. The prospect of another long sea voyage appalled him, and he wrote to William: ". . . if there is anything to it, I would beg you to see if I could possibly avoid it, and be put upon some land service. . . . I would rather stay here in this place (if a surgeon is to be left with the Troops) than go to the west or east Indies; but if there was no chance of going to either, I would come home with the forces that comes home; as I can have it in my power to do either, I'll beg that you'll inquire of Mr. Adair. . . ."

He reiterated his fears in another letter, together with concern over his meager pay. "My scheme at present is this: If we are order'd home, and a surgeon is to stay here, I propose staying (if there is any chance of another expedition) and if I do stay, I propose applying for the deputy parveorship, which is ten shillings a day, and if I get that I can give my Prentice a place of five shillings a day, so that I can make it worth my while, this is my present plan."

No expedition materialized, nor did the Belle Isle contingent depart. John's application was granted, and a hospital budget allocated to him. But his relief was short-lived. In 1762 Spain invaded Portugal, a British ally, and Parliament voted to support her. The regiments chosen for the campaign included four from Belle Isle. John was of two minds. He had grown to loathe the place; yet he hated to give up his perquisites as deputy purveyor, even though he had not been paid for months. "I am told that our arreas are to be paid in two months . . . I think that it should amount by that time to £160 for my Prentice and myself."

Perhaps he might secure a similar or even more remunerative appointment in Portugal? He petitioned the Deputy Secretary of War,

Thomas Tyrwhitt, to appoint him deputy director of the military hospital to be set up in Lisbon. He received no direct reply, but William, having spoken to Tyrwhitt, assured John that he could count on it. So, resigning himself to another siege of seasickness, John sailed for Lisbon on July 6 aboard the hospital ship *Betty*. His gloom was scarcely lightened by the news that two of the men whose abilities he deplored, a Dr. Blythe and a Mr. William Young, were already in Lisbon as staff physician and Surgeon-General. "God help the Hospital," he wrote to William, "when directed by such two."

A crushing blow befell him on landing. No sooner did he claim the deputy directorship than another surgeon, William Madox, produced a warrant signed by the aged, ailing commander of the British forces in Portugal, Lord Tyrawley, and approved by his second in command, the Earl of Loudoun, conferring the post upon him. Tyrawley undoubtedly favored Madox because Madox was treating him. Thunderstruck, John demanded an explanation. What of Tyrwhitt's order? No formal notification had arrived, but with a fair-mindedness that led John to acknowledge him as "my stanch friend," Young, the Surgeon-General, admitted he had been told of it before leaving London. Tyrawley then declared that he had intended his warrant to be effective only in case John remained on Belle Isle. Madox stepped aside, and when debility forced Tyrawley to sail home, he went with him as his personal physician.

But all this candor availed John nothing. Loudoun, a stickler for formalities, refused to sanction anybody in the post without written instructions from England. None ever came, and the post was never filled. As the front advanced, John, after weeks of subordinate duties in Lisbon, was shunted from field hospital to field hospital on the Tagus River. Learning of a vacancy in the Lisbon hospital, which would pay the incumbent £1 a day, he wrote in desperation to Loudoun from São Domingos:

"I take the liberty to throw Myself upon your Favour. I have been informed, that your Lordship has given Dr. Cadogan [the head physician, who had fallen ill] leave to return to England. I therefore presume that a Phisiciane will be wanted in that Hospital. If so I take the liberty to recommend myself, and I hope that the following reasons will plead some excuse for troubling your Lordship. First, my Lord I have the oldest commission on this Staff. In the second place I came here with the promise of My ten shillings a day being continued, which your Lordship know I have not got. Thirdly I have your Lordships promise . . . that your Lordship would serve me the very first opportunity. . . . I hope that my Education in Physick will be no objection to me.

"I know that your Lordship has Natural objections to the increasing the Hospital Expences but I hope that this can be done without any additional Expence for I should not have the least objection to my acting as a surgeon in the Same Hospital, or indeed in any capsity that the Service required, as I have done all along Since I came to Portugal. . . ."

The appeal was doomed to failure, since John, though competent to handle both medical and surgical emergencies, had no medical degree, a requirement for the vacated post. For the rest of the war he tried in vain to better his rank and financial position.

The Portuguese campaign was a dim sideshow to the main action at sea and in the Western Hemisphere. The Anglo-Portuguese forces pushed steadily forward along the banks of the Tagus, fortifying bases as they went, and the Spanish, having overextended their lines of supply, retreated after feeble skirmishing. There were few wounded. But dysentery and ague raged through the camps, felling more men than the sketchy medical facilities could cope with. At Santarem, forty miles from Lisbon, in a base hospital John helped to establish, four hundred patients were packed into wards barely big enough to contain two hundred and fifty.

Transported from camp to hospital on muleback or in wooden carts, over boulder-strewn paths, hundreds died en route. As the front moved still farther from Lisbon, the stocks of drugs, bandages, instruments and food dwindled. Foraging parties clashed constantly with the natives. "I'm left here," one surgeon reported from Cabassa in a dispatch to his commanding general, "with twenty-nine of your sick, eleven of the 75th, and one of Lord Blaney's, Being in a melancholy situation to get provision for them, have took the liberty to detain Nicholas Mc-Colly of the Major's company in your regiment to interpret for me, that I may get them to Santarem as soon as possible, otherwise the poor sick must inevitably suffer through want of common sustenance."

In their idleness and dejection, the convalescents deserted, looted, and drank themselves senseless. "Refractory and disobedient patients," read an order from headquarters, "are to be confined on bread and water as long as the Doctor shall direct and a Black Hole and Irons are to be provided. The Guard will also send frequent patroles to Tipling houses in the neighborhood to prevent any man drinking and quarrelling with the inhabitants." Two inmates of the Lisbon hospital murdered a Portuguese and were sentenced to 116 days in the Black Hole.

By November the fighting had ceased, and the Treaty of Paris, signed the following February, ended the Seven Years' War. But the removal of patients lingering in the base hospitals, to Lisbon and thence to England, dragged on. John's duties during this period consisted mainly of touring the field to determine which patients were fit for the journey. He returned to Lisbon himself early in 1763, and stayed there until May.

Physical discomfort, daily drudgery, and the embittering feeling that he had been cheated of rightful promotion did not dampen John's ardor for research. Portugal offered opportunities as enticing as Belle Isle. An autumn evening finds him by a lavishly stocked fishpond in the gardens of a Portuguese nobleman, who carries a musket. He commands his companion to retire behind a bush "so that there might not be the least reflection of light," and to fire the musket in the air. To the astonished man's questions, John replies that the fish have recalled to him an inquiry begun before the war. Can fish hear? If they can, what organs constitute their ears and where are they situated? In London he had exposed these organs in all their ramifications, and injected the canals with liquid colored wax for permanent exhibition—a work he believed to be original. (The literature on the subject, which John, with his distaste for academic study, did not trouble to consult, would have shown him that at least three earlier investigators had anticipated him.) He now proposed to ascertain the reaction of fish to sound, a point on which any angler could have enlightened him, but he must observe it at first hand.

His bemused companion pulled the trigger. "The moment the report was made the fish seemed to be all of one mind, for they vanished instantly, raising a cloud of mud from the bottom. In about five minutes afterwards they began to appear, and were seen swimming as before."

When, twenty years later, he submitted to the Royal Society *An Account of the Organ of Hearing in Fishes*, having belatedly compared his findings with those of earlier ichthyologists, he inserted a somewhat sheepish little disclaimer of originality, a painful gesture for a man as touchy as John about priority of discovery. The paper was nevertheless important in its own right as a statement of the pre-

Darwinian principle that underlay so much of John's thinking. "I am still inclined," he wrote, "to consider whatever is uncommon in the structure of this organ in fishes as only a link in the chain of varieties displayed in its formation in different animals, descending from the most perfect to the most imperfect, in regular progression."

Of greater value was a geological investigation John ventured upon while in Portugal. As an exercise of pure observation and reason it has seldom been surpassed, for he had no previous experience of the subject. Encamped on the immense plain stretching east from Lisbon known as the Alentejo, he fell to speculating about its curious composition. Gravel covered the surface, with numerous hills of similar loose material rising steeply in the shape of inverted pyramids. From these hills John deduced one of the chief mechanisms of land formation, namely, the action of retiring seas upon an emergent continent.

"The most striking evidence of the sea having once covered this tract," he wrote, "and afterwards having left it gradually, is the peculiar shape of the remains of those elevations of gravel; for it would appear that as soon as the sea left their tops exposed, the pebbles were washed off by the motion of the surface of the water where this motion is greatest; and, as the sea subsided, the lower parts of such risings, beyond the general surface or basis, were longer washed by it than the top; consequently more of the gravel was washed away, till at last they became a pyramidal figure standing on their apex . . . and all round, on the flat surface, is strewed the gravel washed off the rising part which now forms the inverted pyramids. . . . If the sea was to leave the Isle of Wight, the Needles would exhibit something of this kind."

He later applied the hypothesis to the Thames Valley. The river flowing between its flanking hills, he reasoned, must once have been an arm of the North Sea, which became shallower, reducing the arm to a river. He insisted that the composition of the surrounding land, for a great depth, would prove it: there would be strata of gravel, then of sand, then of clay, with fossil shells in the clay two hundred to three hundred feet deep, deposited when the sea covered it, and in the upper strata, the bones of land animals where the sea level fell—a surmise later confirmed.

Before John's time geologists were committed to a search for the methods whereby the Almighty ordered the globe from chaos and made it habitable; futilely, they tried to explore the primordial cosmos. When the French naturalist, Buffon, advanced his theory of earth without regard to Mosaic cosmogony, the Sorbonne demanded a retraction of his "reprehensible opinions." He obediently announced: "I abandon everything in my book respecting the formation of the earth, and generally, all which may be contrary to the narration of Moses."

Among the first geologists publicly to repudiate this stultifying dogma was the Scotsman, James Hutton. "Geology," he stated in the Edinburgh *Philosophical Transactions* of 1788, "was in no way concerned about questions as to the origins of things. The ruins of an older world are visible in the present structure of our planet; and the strata which now compose our continents have once been beneath the sea, and were formed out of the waste of pre-existing continents. The same forces are still destroying, by chemical decompositions or mechanical violence, even the hardest rocks, and transporting the materials to the sea. . . ."

John reached the same conclusion independently, had, indeed, been guided by it since his observations on the Alentejo plain. In notes scribbled before Hutton's publication, but not assembled in a manuscript until four years after, he wrote: "[Geology] had nothing to do with the original formation of the earth, but had only a connection with the changes on the surface. Our mode of reasoning on this subject may be termed retrograde; it is by supposing from the state of the earth now, what must have taken place formerly."

Hutton and Hunter helped to free geology from its theological trammels to progress as a science. John, moreover, moved ahead of his contemporaries by stressing the importance of fossil remains as clues to the changes of the earth's crust. "We should be unable," he said, "to consider the causes of the operations affecting the surface of the earth, if we had not the preserved parts of sea-animals. Just as we would trace the remains of former actions in any country, by the monuments left; judging the past from the present."

Although geology for John was only a bypath off the main road of his lifework, he did not leave it without erecting some towering guideposts along the way. Among the basic principles he enunciated were the coevality of fossils with the mineral strata containing them; the geographical distribution of animals as evidenced by their fossil remains ("In considering animals respecting their situation upon the globe, there are many which are peculiar to particular climates; others that are less confined; and others again which, probably, move over the whole extent of the sea, as the shark, porpoise- and whale-tribes; while many shell-fish must be confined to one spot"); the alternations of sea and land in the same place; the animicular formation of calcareous earth, such as coral islands.

John did not approach geology as a study distinct from his attempt to establish a unified theory of nature, but as an integral phase of it. He collected minerals and fossils primarily to illustrate the fundamental differences between organic and inorganic matter.

Laden with bones, rocks, animal specimens, and notebooks, John sailed back to England in the spring of 1763, and retired on half pay.

15. PHYSICIAN-EXTRAORDINARY

William's star was still rising. He owed his latest triumph to Caesar Hawkins. The St. George's surgeon, whose reputation as a fast and painless bloodletter enabled him to charge fees for that service alone totaling £2,000 a year, had been attending Queen Charlotte in her first pregnancy. Towards the end of the fourth month, April 1762, she began coughing and running a slight fever, symptoms the phlebotomist felt called for his specialty. But hesitating to act without a second opinion, he requested the King to summon Dr. Hunter. Overwhelmed by the honor, William entered the Queen's bedchamber in St. James's Palace for the first time on May 3.

He concurred in the proposed treatment, but recommended bleeding *ad defectionem*, that is, not beyond the first signs of faintness, rather than *ad plenum*, or full bleeding. "She consented," he recorded later, "tho she disliked bleeding."

Hawkins covered the Queen's face with a kerchief to spare her the sight of her own blood, had her clench a ball of worsted in her fist so that the basilic vein would swell and stand out, and with a light flick of his lancet opened it. To William, as physician, fell the duty of holding a basin under the arm to catch the flow. It was a point of professional pride not to let a drop spill. When five ounces had been drawn, Hawkins applied a tourniquet. As a restorative he gave the Queen a glass of Rhenish wine in which had been steeped some petals of borage. She rallied quickly.

(According to court gossip, William, upon meeting the King nervously pacing outside the bedchamber, calmed his anxiety by reminding him, "Her Majesty is with bairn." But it seems unlikely that the studiously Englished Scot would have stepped so far out of character as to revert to his native Doric.)

William continued as Physician-Extraordinary to the Queen throughout her pregnancy. Although she progressed normally, without any effects worthy of medical note—which, in any event, could not be published with propriety—he kept for his own gratification a journal of the case.

"Mr. Hawkins," it began, "informed me that her Majesty before her marriage had had very good health, and had been very regular in her menses. That the last were Octr. 27th from which therefore reckoning was to commence. . . . From that time to this her health had been in pretty good order, except that at different times she had a cough; but without any pain and without any considerable heat. She had taken at times Wormwood Draughts with Sp. Cet. and occasionally a little Tinct. Rhubarb Bakena at night, so as to keep the body open; and it had answered the intention very well."

With the common sense and conservatism that typified his practice, he restrained Hawkins from overindulging his penchant for bleeding. "As Labour is not a disease," he cautioned him, "it does not require that the constitution should be reduced, by way of preparation; and therefore when the patient is cool & has no marks of having too much blood.—and taking it away cannot do good & may do harm."

Shortly after four o'clock on the morning of August 12, a palace courier rode into Jermyn Street and roused William by shouting through the speaking tube that hung by his front door. The Queen had gone into labor. William hurried back with him to the palace, but did not see his patient for several hours, for no man-midwife could be permitted to deliver a Queen of England. That function was performed by a Mrs. Draper, an aged and at times negligent midwife, while William and Caesar Hawkins waited in an anteroom where she could consult them if an emergency arose. None did.

"At 1/2 after seven," William's journal continued, "when I little expected it from what Mrs. Draper told us, the Prince [George Augustus Frederick, later King George IV] was born. Soon after we examined him all over, and found him perfect, with every mark of health, and of a very large size. Then we examined the Placenta which was sound &

very compleat; and Mrs. Draper told us that the Queen had had a very good time and was very well."

(To Cullen he wrote the same day: "I have just time to congratulate you on the Queen's happy delivery of a fine boy.")

Thereafter William divided his attention between mother and son. "At 6 in the evening the Q. had slept an hour & was remarkably well. She had eaten with appetite—had made water plentifully & with ease —the cloaths were of a full colour & in plenty. She now took a 2d Haustus [fluids] and was ordered a spoonful of Wine in each half pint of Caudle [a mixture of wine or ale with eggs, gruel, sugar, and spices].

"At this time . . . the Prince was quite well, had had another stool & had sucked several times."

In an age when highborn infants were usually entrusted to wet nurses lest they impair their mother's figure, he insisted that Charlotte suckle her son for their mutual benefit. The breast, he decreed, should be the babe's main source of nourishment, supplemented by two light feedings a day. "The milk," he noted, "ran out freely from both breasts which were quite easy." So incensed was Mrs. Hester Thrale, the friend and patroness of Samuel Johnson, who had herself borne eleven children, when William rejected a wet nurse she had recommended to the Queen, that she wrote him two letters of rebuke.

Again, contrary to the prevalent view of early motherhood as a state of semi-invalidism, requiring prolonged bedrest, William urged the Queen to take exercise on the fifth day after her confinement.

During his second week of life the Prince of Wales created panic in the palace by tumbling into a faint on his mother's bed—the results, William conjectured, of having been deposited, after feeding, with his head lower than his feet. Turned right side up and administered a little peppermint water, he was soon restored to bawling well-being.

Anxiety beset the royal couple again, not long after, when a rash erupted upon the heir apparent's face. William assured them that it was merely "the common scabby humour which attended teething," and would subside when the suckling had cut a few teeth.

William doctored the Queen again through her second pregnancy and the birth of Frederick, Duke of York and Albany, a year almost to the day from Prince George's birth. His journal of that attendance suggests that he had the sweet satisfaction of reproving Mrs. Draper. "I was called at eleven in the forenoon, and was informed first by Mr Hawkins & then by the King who presently came to me, that the

Queen, after complaining for about two hours lightly, was delivered—with 3 pains of a fine Boy so that there was not time to call the proper people together. He said that he had ordered Mrs. Draper to give him information when the Labour seemed to be near; but that instead of receiving such information in good time as he expected, the screaming of the Child was the first notice he received. Then, accompanied with Mr Hawkins I saw Mrs. Draper who told us that she was called from St. James', where she had been in waiting some days, at nine o'clock in the morning,—that she upon her arrival found the waters broken, and that the Queen was wet even to her stockings; upon which she immediately got the Bed properly made, and put her Majesty into it—that the pains continued so trifling that she did not imagine the Queen was near delivery, till three strong pains came suddenly and close together and finished it. This she *said*."

He closed the record on a self-congratulatory note. ". . . her Majesty . . . regulated herself in all things by what she had done in her first lying-in, which she said she chose to do because she had succeeded so well."

In 1764 Charlotte miscarried while sojourning in Richmond out of William's care. The following year the man-midwife was at hand when she gave birth to William Henry, Duke of Clarence [afterwards King William IV]. With her fifth pregnancy [Princess Charlotte Augusta], the year after that, she defied precedent by dismissing Mrs. Draper and letting William deliver her. ". . . it was kept as great a secret," wrote Lady Mary Coke in her diary, "as if the fate of the Country depended on the change."

Charlotte was pregnant for the sixth time in 1767. The King wanted another daughter. To prepare him for a possible disappointment, William remarked, "I think, Sir, whoever sees these lovely princes above stairs must be glad to have another."

"I did not think I could have been angry with you," the King retorted, "but I am. I say whoever sees that lovely child, the Princess Royal, above stairs, must wish to have the fellow of her."

Charlotte produced Edward Augustus, the Duke of Kent, father of Queen Victoria.

"I forgive you," the King told William.

Altogether, the fecund Queen bore, within twenty years, nine sons and six daughters, of whom William delivered ten.

Under this royal patronage William's prestige soared. Attired in velvets of richly somber hues, ruffled, laced and beribboned, his cameo-delicate features framed by a full silvery peruke, coldly witty and austerely graceful, he moved through London's glossiest salons as confidently as he attended the confinements of his hostesses. The journals, diaries and correspondence of ladies of rank twittered with allusions to the elegant accoucheur. "Duchess Hamilton & Mrs. Fitzroy are both past their reckoning," wrote Lady Coke, "but I have not heard they are brought to Bed. Doctor Hunter, I am told, sometimes attends the Lu table, which is not an unnecessary precaution. . . . I think Doctor Hunter perfectly right to persuade Lady Sarah not to suckle her child, there are reasons that ought to make it prejudicial to her health."

The Duchess of Argyll, reputed to be the fairest woman in England, and Lady Diana Beauclerk, one of the cleverest, Lady Cork, Lady Douglas, Lady Maynard, the Duchess of Westmoreland—all gratefully submitted themselves to William's suave and tactful ministrations. "Lady Di Beauclerk sends her comp to Doctor Hunter and is extremely oblig'd to him for his offer of venison, which she will send for Saturday morning. Mr. Beauclerk and Ly Di wish vastly to see Doctor Hunter at Muswell Hill [the Beauclerk estate] & think if he wish'd as much to come he might find a day."

While his practice remained chiefly obstetrical, he also numbered among his patients Thomas Coutts, the leading banker of his day, and David Garrick; the artists, Reynolds, Hogarth, and Gainsborough; Charles Burney, the scholarly musician, whose first wife he attended on her deathbed; Henry Fielding, whom he treated for dropsy. When Fielding died, his half brother, Sir John, wrote to William:

"Sir John Fielding presents his Compliments to Dr. Hunter and acquaints him that the Comedy of the Good-Natured Man written by the late Henry Fielding will be performed at Drury Lane next Monday being the Author's Widow's Night.

"He was your old & sincere friend. There are no other of his works left unpublished. This is the last opportunity you will have of shewing any respect to his Memory as a Genius, so that I hope you will send all your pupils, all your patients, all your Friends & every body else to the Play that Night, by which Means you will indulge your benevolent feelings & your Sentiments of Friendship."

Earlier in his career William had advised Cullen, "Get the world on your side, as I find you do, and your rivals will humble themselves and confess your merit." And William could now count on his side many a powerful Georgian statesman. The Earl of Bute, successor to Pitt as Prime Minister, begged him to accept "as a trifling mark of his regard . . . a curious fish." Lord North, Chancellor of the Exchequer, besought his presence at a meeting of the East India Company so that he might add his respected voice in favor of a contract offered by the government.

When William refused to accept a fee from the Earl of Suffolk, after Lady Suffolk died in childbirth—the result of his failure to remove the placenta soon enough—he received a letter possibly unique in the annals of doctor-patient relations:

"Sir—You forbid me addressing you as I meant: you restrain my Gratitude from flowing in the only channel which is open to it at present. How am I to return the greatest of obligations? You gave up everything to us! You risqued your own health to restore Her's! . . . Indeed, indeed, Hunter! She bore her illness in a manner to make Men blush!—But no more of that—my busyness is to beg of you, if *Reward* is an irksome word, to let me substitute *Regard* in its room: and when I come to London to entreat an opportunity of seeing you, and marking that Regard. I will say no more of it now, save to insist, if hereafter, in Life, at any time, in any case, I may ever be so fortunate as to have it in my power to indulge my own wishes by being able to shew my gratitude to you essentially, as I ought, and owe it, that you will do me the pleasure & favour, I will call it Justice, freely to command it; for I shall esteem myself *dum memor ipse mei!* Your much obliged tho' most unhappy friend & servant, Suffolk."

The prospect of lifelong favor from a man who had been appointed Secretary of State for the Northern Department was more attractive than any payment William could demand, and he replied in equally highflown vein:

"I am now by your Lordship's kind sympathy, as happy as I can be, after taking such a share in so great a calamity. I feel an inclination to say a thousand things which I must suppress. I wish to talk upon a subject which you must forget. We will take it up in Heaven. At this moment I fancy that I have a Friend there who listens to my thoughts, and bids me say to you in a little time we shall all be happy again; who bids me tell you, to take care, for her sake, of yourself and of your child. . . ."

Professional kudos, foreign and domestic, accompanied William's social apotheosis. He was elected a fellow of the Royal Society, Professor of Anatomy to the Royal Academy, an associate of the French Academy, and President of the Society of Physicians.

With such lofty connections William became an intermediary of favor-seekers. Dr. John Fothergill, a prominent Quaker, implored him to use his influence with the Earl of Hertford, the Lord Chamberlain, to ban performances of a comic opera, *The Quaker,* which poked fun at Fothergill. The Bishop of Down and Connor wrote asking William to dissuade David Hume from a proposed visit to Ireland, where he was detested for his heretical ideas. Hume did not go. He himself later bore witness to William's high standing, when a protégé of the doctor's sought election to the Chair of Divinity at the University of Glasgow: "It seems Dr. Hunter supports a friend of his and nothing can be refused him by the University."

When Samuel Johnson published his *Journey to the Western Islands of Scotland,* he asked William to draw it to the King's attention. ". . . I have not the courage to offer it myself, yet I cannot forbear to wish that He may see it, because it endeavours to describe a part of his Subjects seldom visited and little known, and His Benevolence will not despise the meanest of his people. . . . I have sent you a book to which you are very justly entitled, and beg that it may be admitted to stand in your library however little it may add to its elegance and dignity."

William had no objection to performing such a service for a book that ridiculed the country of his birth.

IV. HARD TIMES
1763-1771

CRXE03

16. AT THE SIGN OF THE PAINTED HAND

For John, back from the war more bluff and bearish than ever, there was no place in the society to which William enjoyed such easy access. Nor did he show any inclination—and William did not encourage him —to storm its portals. On the professional level, too, the brothers' paths diverged. In John's absence William had engaged as an assistant a former pupil, William Hewson, and John was not reinstated. He abided for a time obscure, solitary, grubbing among his specimens and incessantly seeking new ones. His only income was his army pension of five shillings a week.

A coolness arose between the brothers. A letter from Smollett to William alludes to a quarrel: "I cannot help expressing an eager Desire that your Brother's future may entitle him to a revival of those favourable sentiments in you, which he has indiscreetly forfeited."

(Yet, despite his indebtedness to William, it was for John that Smollett seemed to have the warmer regard. When he lay dying of a neglected ulcer in Leghorn, Italy, in 1771, at the age of fifty, he wrote to him: "With respect to myself, I have nothing to say, but that if I can prevail upon my wife to execute my will, you shall receive my poor carcase in a box, after I am dead, to be placed among your rarities. I am already so dry and emaciated, that I may pass for an Egyptian mummy, without any other preparation than some pitch or painted linen; unless you think I may deserve the denomination of a curiosity in my own character, I mean that of your old friend, and affectionate servant, Ts. Smollett." John never received the bequest. When Smollett died on September 17 of that year, his wife buried him in Leghorn's English Cemetery.)

At thirty-five John faced the problem of building up a private practice with few helpful connections in or out of the profession. He held no hospital appointments. He had no diploma. As a governor of St. George's Hospital he was privileged to express a voice in its management, but the title carried no monetary benefits, called, in fact, for an annual donation. Hopeful of a post on the staff, John faithfully attended board meetings and recruited other subscription-paying governors. But no post was forthcoming.

The cream of London's surgical practice was shared by Percivall Pott of St. Bartholomew's, Caesar Hawkins and William Bromfield of St. George's, Samuel Sharp and Joseph Warner of Guy's. Army officers usually consulted either Robin Adair or Francis Tomkins, the regimental surgeon who had drawn his sword against John on Belle Isle. What clientele remained the lesser lights disputed with a horde of quacks. One struggling practitioner complained that the profession failed "to procure its members bread until they have no teeth to eat."

For a Scottish surgeon the obstacles had not been as formidable since Bonnie Prince Charlie led an army against London, when any Scot caught in the streets was likely to be beaten to death. The heads of two Jacobite officers still moldered on spikes above Temple Bar. Boswell, who came to London in 1762, wrote of an evening he spent at the Covent Garden Theatre:

"Just before the ouverture began to be played, two Highland officers came in. The mob in the upper gallery roared out, 'No Scots! No Scots! Out with them!', hissed and pelted them with apples. My heart warmed to my countrymen, my Scotch blood boiled with indignation."

But prejudice was not confined to the vulgar. "It is not so much to be lamented that old England is lost as that the Scots have found it," quipped Johnson to the delight of his Cheshire Cheese cronies. When Boswell, whose adulation of the Grand Cham exceeded his pride, apologized that he couldn't help it if he came from Scotland, he was told, "Sir, that, I find, is what a very great many of your countrymen cannot help."

No man created blacker resentment of the Scots than the postwar Scottish Prime Minister, the Earl of Bute. He had been the King's mentor in the art of politics since George was Prince of Wales. It was rumored, but never proven, that George's mother, Princess Augusta, was his mistress. After the coronation he became the chief architect of schemes to wreck Whig prestige. Weak, ineffectual, and vengeful, he proposed no major policy that did not infuriate the public. The forced resignation of Pitt, who was idolized as the hero of the war, alone would have made Bute unpopular. His peace policy made him despised. His concessions to the vanquished were denounced as cowardly. He was accused of accepting foreign bribes, though later exonerated. He tactlessly promoted a disproportionate number of Scots to government offices. To edit a party periodical defending the Government, he chose Smollett, who rubbed salt into English wounds by naming it *The Briton*. When, through bribery and intimidation, Bute secured a parliamentary majority for his Tory policies, he proceeded to wreak vengeance on every Whig adherent, not sparing the widows of Whig civil servants, whose pensions he abolished.

In Bute and in Scotsmen generally, John Wilkes, the malevolent Whig demagogue, found choice whipping boys. Through the *North Briton*, a periodical that he launched as a counterblast to Smollett's *Briton*, he kept animosities boiling. With the collaboration of Charles Churchill, who wielded one of the most venomous pens in England, he perpetuated the slanders against Bute and Princess Augusta. He warned that the minister was opening the halls of government to a locust plague of lean and hungry Scottish office seekers. The rabble made bonfires of jack boots, a pun on the Premier's name, together with petticoats, symbol for the Queen Mother. Bute dared not venture out of doors without a bodyguard of prize fighters. A mob once demolished a coach carrying him to an official banquet, and but for the prize fighters would have torn him to pieces.

It was in this hostile atmosphere that John Hunter strove to secure a firm professional footing. He lived for a time in Golden Square, formerly known as "Pest House Field" after the plague victims buried there, but which had since become, its bubonic phantoms exorcized, a pleasant and quiet residential area. Susannah Cibber, the eminent actress, was a neighbor of John's. Angelica Kaufman, the painter, lived nearby with her father, and David Hume occupied an apartment behind the square in Brewer Street.

John longed to open an anatomical school of his own, but he could not compete for pupils against the entrenched teachers, of whom

William was now foremost. In his financial extremity he resorted to a type of practice that undoubtedly appalled his fastidious brother, and for which his enemies ever after gleefully derided him. He allied himself with a family of Scottish barbers and tooth-drawers, the Spences.

Dentistry in eighteenth-century England ranked lowest among the healing arts. There were no dental schools, no body of principles or precedent. Each practitioner evolved his own methods, guarding them as trade secrets to be divulged only for huge sums. One novice paid fifty guineas for a single day's instruction in filling teeth with gold. Rivalries between dentists were savage. Thomas Patence, of Great Suffolk Street, a former dancing master, and Jeremiah Wallach of Church Lane schemed endlessly to steal each other's patients. When Wallach took a trip abroad, Patence circulated the rumor that he had died there.

With few exceptions the "Operators for the Teeth," as they termed themselves, conducted their practice as an adjunct to other trades. They were barbers, hairdressers, corn-cutters, cuppers, vendors of cosmetics, ivory-carvers, gem-polishers, blacksmiths. One D. Ritchie of Rupert Street introduced a towering coiffure for women (as disfiguring, according to Hannah More, the theological writer, as smallpox). He also confected a styptic, advertising it with a testimonial from a maidservant to the effect that it had instantly stopped the bleeding when she sliced off the tip of her finger. For years Ritchie's Styptic was supplied to the British Navy by royal warrant. Whatever its effectiveness as an anti-hemorrhagic, it probably caused less distress than the traditional red-hot iron.

For a toothache, which the dentists thought to be not a symptom but a disease in itself, the standard treatment was extraction, though some variously favored singeing an earlobe, lancing a vein in the neck, applying a calf's bladder filled with milk. If the condemned tooth was situated in the lower jaw, the operator would seat the patient on a stool or the floor, and attack either with his bare fingers or one of a series of massive iron implements—the odontagra, the clavis, the pelican. At that oblique angle the tooth frequently broke off at the root. The Bills of Mortality attributed an average of six hundred deaths a year, somewhat cryptically, to "teeth."

Dental quacks, trailing robes emblazoned with cabalistic symbols and driving garish chariots, touted painless extraction at fairs and market places. A confederate, groaning piteously, his jaw bandaged, would be awaiting his cue in the crowd. When "the Professor," to the accompaniment of brassy music, had arrayed his paraphernalia on a stand, the spurious sufferer would burst forth, begging for relief. A flourish of forceps, a thrust, a twist, and out would pop an enormous molar without a whimper from the patient. The Professor would then drop it hastily into a box lest close inspection expose it for what it was— a paste model that the confederate had concealed under his tongue. Thus reassured, the genuinely afflicted would surrender themselves to surgery. A bugler would muffle their screams.

The tooth-drawers derived a substantial part of their revenue from patent toothbrushes, dentifrices, and dentures. The dentifrices ran to powdered crab's teeth, hare's brains, coral, and oil of vitriol, and they eroded enamel. False teeth ranged in quality from the bones of oxen and calves, which, being porous, soon disintegrated, to more durable materials like the teeth of asses, goats and hippopotamuses, ivory, and gold. The most sought after were human teeth. The demand for them pushed the price up to £300 a set, and gave rise to a special line of body snatching. Enterprising resurrectionists followed armies to war. "Oh, sir," replied one of them, when asked how he proposed to fill a large order, "let there be a battle and there'll be no want of teeth. I'll draw 'em as fast as the men are knocked down."

As showmen, the Operators for the Teeth had few equals. There was, for example, Bartholomew Ruspini. The Chevalier Ruspini, he styled himself, and claimed kinship with Roman nobility. He had emigrated from Italy to Bath, where his manly beauty and *grandezza* commended him to the vacationing bon ton. His business card depicted Venus escorting a swollen-jawed Cupid to Aesculapius, who holds a scroll inscribed with the dentist's name and address.

"The Chevalier Ruspini [his early brochures set forth] begs leave to acquaint the Nobility and Gentry that he cures scurvy in the Gums, first cleans the Teeth from that corrosive tartarous graty substance that hinders the Gums from growing, infects the Breath, and is one of the principal causes of the Scurvy. His dentifrice (which is free from any corrosive preparation) will restore the Gums to their Pristine State, will preserve the Teeth, and render them perfectly white; will fasten those that are loose, and prevent them from further Decay: He fills up with Lead or Gold those that are hollow, so as to render them useful, and prevents the Air from getting into them, which generally aggravates the Pain. He makes and fixes in Artificial Teeth, which cannot possibly be distinguished from natural ones, with the greatest Ease and Elegance. He will wait upon Gentlemen or Ladies in Town or Country, by directing a line for him at his lodgings or at Mrs. Badham's in the Square, or at the Coffee House, Bath."

To his credit, Ruspini deplored indiscriminate extraction. "I flatter myself," he said, "that I have introduced a mode of cure by which those persons who are so unfortunate as to have bad teeth and diseased gums are easily relieved, and the injurious practice of tooth-drawing considerably decreased."

His nostrums enjoyed an immense vogue. Ruspini's Toothpowder, a mixture of orris root, Armenian bole, crabs' eyes, pimento, and rose pink, cost three shillings a pot and could be purchased "with proper Directions and Brushes" at "Mrs. Broderip, Milliner, near the Parade Coffee House and Mr. White, Hair-Cutter in Bath; and at Miss Logan's, at the Ladies Tea-Room, near the Hot-Wells, Bristol . . . Likewise at George's Coffee House, in Coventry Street, London." His Tincture for the Gums consisted of rectified spirit of wine, essence of scurvy grass, distilled water, orris root, cloves, ambergris, alum, and sage, blended in a bottle for ten days and filtered through blotting paper. The popularity of his Balsamic Styptic survived him by a hundred years.

Under the patronage of his most influential patient, the Queen Mother, Ruspini moved to London in 1766, leased an opulent house at 32 St. Albans Street, and married the heiress of a wealthy surgeon. A compassionate man, he treated the poor without charge, endowed an orphans' home, and, for all his fanfaronading, contrived some useful operational procedures. He was one of the few members of his profession whom reputable medical men did not dismiss as an utter charlatan.

In sheer flamboyance none of the dentists surpassed Martin van Butchell, an erstwhile pupil of the Hunters, whose antics amused and endeared him to John. A small, keg-shaped, owlish man of Flemish origin, he wore blue-tinted spectacles, allowed no scissors to touch his flowing reddish beard and locks on the theory that hirsuteness was conducive to vigor, carried a bleached human femur as a cudgel to protect himself against ruffians, and bounced up and down Rotten Row astride a pony dyed purple. The pony, whose embellishments he occasionally varied with polka dots and stripes, was never clipped either.

At the height of his hairy glory Van Butchell described himself as a

"British Christian man, with comely beard, full eight inches long," and he offered for sale as fertility charms, at a guinea each, the strands that came loose when he combed it. "Of use to the fair that want fine children:—I can tell them how; it is a secret. Some are quite auburn; others silver-white:—full half quarter long, growing (day and night). . . ."

In addition to dentistry, Van Butchell treated ruptures and anal fistulas. (His son, to whom he imparted his techniques, was the first surgeon in England to be sued for malpractice following the death of a patient.) A prolific inventor, he devised trusses, a fire extinguisher, cork-lined stirrups guaranteed not to slip, spring saddles for girdles, and rubber carriage wheels. People treasured his handbills for their distinctive literary flavor.

> The First Magistrate [ran a typical effusion]
> And other sincere lovers of this State
>   Are now informed most respectfully
> That some years ago MARTIN VAN BUTCHELL
>   had an appointment to meet
> (—At Lady Hunloke's house in Strafford Place—)
>   his able teacher JOHN HUNTER, Esq.,
> Who overtook him in Grosvenor Square, and
>   Bade him get into his chariot: Soon as he was seated
> John said. What mischief are you up to now?
> Martin. Curing the king's evil [scrofula].
>   John. I can't cure the king's evil.
>   Martin. I know you can't cure the king's evil. If you
> could cure the king's evil, I should not trouble myself about
> the king's evil: but I want to do
>   What you cannot do!
>   John. That is right. Do you try to get first (we know
> nothing, compared to what we are ignorant of,) make yourself
> of consequence, and then everybody will make you of consequence;
> but if you don't make yourself of consequence, nobody else will.
> I do assure you many are in very high esteem and very full
> practice that (comparatively) know no more about healing than
> dray-horses: they have not the powers.
>   You try to be first!

Of his medical skill Van Butchell later proclaimed, with no protest from John:

EMPERORS,—PRINCES,—DUKES AND MARQUESSES
  May want our aid. We are paid, as others are not:
  We have said, what others dare not.
The great JOHN HUNTER Taught Me to Get First:
  Excentrically:—in Neat Healing-Art!
To SAVE Feeling Blood—is the GIFT of GOD:
And the Will of Man:—Conquering Himself:
  So we do much good:—curing fistulae
Without Confinement, Fomentation, Risk;
  Injection, Poultice, Caustic, or Cutting.
FEE is Two per cent.—On Five Years' Profit.
  All the money down:—Before I begin.
Ananias, Fell!—Dead: for KEEPING back!

  MARTIN VAN BUTCHELL.

He advertised his saddle girths thus: "His Serene Highness of Orleans encourages the author more than anyone in Britain, except the discerning John Hunter, Esq. . . . Price four guineas ready cash for Martin Van Butchell's new invented Spring Band Regulators (but not such as the Duke of Orleans had.) At home from ten till two. Churls may be so good as to stay away. Venez les Gens de la Liberati Sentir le douceur de grand Liberte? Ici cheze moi. Five brave lads should be fed. Nos enfants bien faits come les fils d'Hercule."

When his request to be appointed dentist to George III was ignored, he published an open letter to the Earl of Salisbury: "But now, my Lord, the very pleasing prospect and earnest desire of extensive impartial usefulness to His Majesty's good subjects, makes me humbly hope that the King will not call me to that honorable appointment."

For nearly forty years Van Butchell's home was in Mount Street, near Berkeley Square, and he refused to treat patients anywhere else. "I go to no one," said he. He once rejected an offer of one thousand guineas to attend a bedridden invalid. He married twice, and was twice bereaved. Before each wedding he obliged his bride to declare her choice between white and black apparel. The first chose white, the second black. He permitted neither of them ever again to wear any other color. It was also his humor to dine alone in sepulchral silence, wife and progeny being relegated to distant quarters.

At the time of the second Mrs. Van Butchell's death, William Hunter was lecturing on the art of embalming as exemplified by the ancient Egyptians. The subject appealed to one of William's assistant lecturers,

John Sheldon, a dissolute but capable anatomist, with a penchant for bizarre adventures, he who had sailed to Greenland to test the efficacy of poisoned darts on whales. He was the first Englishman to make a balloon ascent. His mistress, an Oxford Street whore, had succumbed to consumption, and he proposed to William that they mummify her experimentally. Sheldon liked the results so much that he kept the body in his bedroom until he married and his wife objected.

Upon hearing of the experiment, Van Butchell wanted to have his departed wife preserved above ground, and he applied to William, undaunted by the doctor's warning that "considering the trouble you must have during all these Processes now laid down you ought not to undertake it under 100 guineas." The transaction occasioned this doggerel from the pen of Sir Richard Jebb, surgeon:

> To do his Wife's Corps peculiar honour
> Van Budgell [sic] wish'd to have it turned to stone;
> Hunter cast his Gorgon Looks upon her,
> And in a twinkling See the Thing is done.

Londoners presently learned through their newspapers that the late Mrs. Van Butchell, attired in choice linens and lace (presumably black), could be viewed any day except Sunday between 9 and 1 P.M. under glass in the widower's reception room. A friend of the dead lady reported that she had never looked healthier. Van Butchell continued to exhibit her to the day he died, at the age of seventy-seven.*

Compared to this gaudy blossom, the Spences, father and son, were shrinking violets. Their Soho Square establishment flaunted no ensign more ostentatious than a painting of a lace-ruffled hand daintily holding a tooth between thumb and forefinger. Inside the accouterments were sumptuous and neat. Spotless baize covered the floors, "green as the carpet of nature in the month of May." The barbers' blocks were snow-white, the blood basins like mirrors from constant scouring, the specimens of human teeth on display the pearliest money could buy. To divert nervous patients there was an electrical machine that animated dancing dolls, rang bells, and exploded small charges of gunpowder.

Under their stiff caste system medical men seldom had direct dealings with dentists. Though they regarded them, in most instances

---

* Both Sheldon's mistress and Mrs. Van Butchell now stand side by side in the Royal College of Surgeons museum. They have greatly deteriorated.

justifiably, as mechanics at best, not fit to make sound independent judgments, they would not deign to proffer them advice in person concerning a mutual patient. When dental care appeared unavoidable, they would send the sufferer with written instructions to some practitioner whom they felt to be at least honest. The Spences received a large share of these grudging referrals. ("Toothache easier," noted Boswell on May 6, 1773. "Went to Spence: two stumps drawn and teeth cleaned; agreeable to see thing well done.") But what the astute elder Spence wanted was a surgical consultant on his own premises, if one so unorthodox could be found. He broached the idea to John Hunter, who forthrightly consented, and for the next five years spent three mornings a week at the sign of the painted hand, diagnosing dental diseases and sometimes treating them himself. It was his chief means of livelihood.

John never tried to keep the arrangement dark nor to apologize for it. He always spoke of the Spences with respect, acknowledging himself indebted to them for the opportunity of pursuing the "vital principle" in a new channel. And, indeed, he had no cause for shame. Largely through his contributions, dentistry, a crude patchwork of empiricism when he entered the field, was, when he left it, by way of becoming a science. In 1799 a pupil of John's, Joseph Fox, joined the staff of Guy's Hospital as dental surgeon—a theretofore unimaginable appointment.

The fruit of John's labors in Soho Square was the first scientific treatise on dentistry in English, his two-volume *Natural History of the Teeth,* and up to that time the most extensive in any language. (The only comparable work had been *Le Chirugien Dentiste,* written forty-three years earlier by a Frenchman, Pierre Fauchard.)

Behind the treatise lay a comparative study of practically every species in the animal kingdom that grows teeth. Earthworms whose gullets are lined with them, whelks that have them in their stomachs, lobsters, insects. John added 583 dental preparations to his collection, illustrating structure and development from infancy to old age. He explained occlusion—the meshing of upper and lower cusps—the complex mechanics of the jaw, the masticating muscles, the alveolar processes. He accounted for the disappearance of useless, decaying or dead parts, like the socket remaining after extraction, by postulating an absorptive agent. Though he could not prove it, he surmised that the bony component of teeth, what we call dentine, is living tissue, nourished through a modified vascular system.

John was the first to suggest the biological interdependence of the teeth and the body as a whole, perhaps the most important single principle of dentistry. Diseased teeth, he cautioned in the second volume of his *Natural History*, devoted to pathology and treatment, can produce diseases of other organs, can become, as dentists now know, a focus of infection. He described gingivitis and pyorrhea. The latter he believed to be incurable, wryly noting, "At last the tooth will drop out, which will put an end to all further trouble." Modern dentists cannot offer patients with advanced pyorrhea much more comfort. John saw how teeth developing in abnormal positions can damage each other, and the correctives he prescribed—removing some teeth to relieve the pressure on others, straightening malformations with wires and plates—scarcely differ from those prevailing today.

But no explorer of so much uncharted territory, equipped with the primitive research tools then available, could have avoided going astray. John's worst misstep was to revive and popularize the transplantation of teeth, a deadly procedure that had been first attempted centuries before by a Moorish surgeon, Abulcasis of Cordova.

In view of John's reliance on nature's regenerative powers, it is understandable how he came to favor transplantation. He felt that there was "a disposition in all living substances to unite when brought into contact with one another, although they are of different structure, and even although the circulation is carried on in one of them." If teeth grafted to a cock's comb would take root, why would they not thrive in the human jaw? The reasons are manifold. True, superficial adhesions might form, but the "living substance" of teeth is so tenuous that, once disrupted, it can rarely maintain a permanent union. They would loosen and, by an action still not wholly comprehended, be resorbed. That was not the least hazard. The constant pressure of the scion tooth against bone would inflame the surrounding tissue. If, furthermore, the original possessor of the tooth happened to harbor an infectious disease, such as syphilis—in John's day an overwhelming statistical probability —the patient would almost certainly contract it.

But John, not yet suspecting any of these perils, recommended and performed the operation. He moored the scions to their new neighbors with silk thread. He preferred to transplant living teeth immediately after they had been pulled, though he often used dead ones, believing that the socket tissues alone would effect the union. He was on somewhat sounder ground when he reimplanted teeth that had been knocked out in accidents or brawls, and of those he saved several.

Dentists everywhere adopted John's method. They charged bigger fees for a live transplantation than for a complete set of the best dentures, because they had to pay donors heavily. There was no dearth of starvelings, however, willing to undergo mutilation. In a Rowlandson caricature two edentate wretches slink out of a tooth-drawer's parlor, a third submits to the odontagra, while a pair of high-coiffed beldames recline in chairs waiting to receive the sacrifice. An army subaltern was once compelled to render the service gratis to his commanding officer.

In the first flush of enthusiasm John announced that transplanted teeth should last for years. But the cases he was able to follow up dashed his hopes. By the turn of the century most dentists, after inflicting dreadful agonies and causing innumerable deaths, had abandoned the practice. Long before, John had penned a contrite marginal note in a copy of the *Natural History:* "I may here remark that the experiment is not generally attended with success. I myself succeeded but once out of a great number of trials."[b]

17. ANNE

John remembered with affection his fellow surgeon-in-arms of the Belle Isle campaign, Robert Boyne Home, who had since gone into private practice in London, and shortly after he returned from Portugal, he called at his house in Suffolk Street. The Homes were a cultivated and attractive family, intensely proud of their Lowland lineage. They claimed descent from the ancient Border chieftains, the Earls of Home—Alexander, the fifth Lord Home, died a captive after fighting in defense of Mary, Queen of Scots—and were distantly related to David Hume (the spellings were interchangeable). Robert Home showed no exceptional skill as a surgeon. His eldest daughter, Anne, who wrote poetry, appraised him as a man

Of soul too high to act a dubious part,
With modest talents and a feeling heart;

While worth and honour our respect shall claim,
Rever'd shall be thy fair unspotted name.

The Homes had married with scanty means on both sides. Mrs.
Home, nee Mary Hutchinson, was the dowerless daughter of an army
officer. She bore seven children, four sons and three daughters, who
proved to be of no ordinary intelligence and abilities. Robert, the first-
born, after studying art in Rome and hanging several canvases in the
Royal Academy, journeyed to the Indian state of Oudh at the invita-
tion of its Nawab, and was appointed court painter. He left two
portraits of John Hunter, one in surgical garb at his writing desk, the
second fondling a mastiff. Another son distinguished himself as a
colonial administrator with the East India Company. A third, Everard,
a precocious, cherub-cheeked tot of seven when John first set eyes on
him, who had been admitted to the exigent Westminster School, already prattled of becoming a surgeon like his father.

But the brightest star in the family constellation was twenty-three-
year-old Anne. Tall and slender, with a heart-shaped face framed by
pale golden curls, deep blue eyes, and a full, generous mouth, she had
a beauty at once ethereal and sensuous. A harpsichordist, composer,
and painter, as well as poet, she fitted effortlessly into London's little
coterie of bluestockings, without sharing their pedantry, affectations,
or malice. Her presence at a social gathering was catalytic. Though no
sparkling wit herself, she had the faculty of stimulating wit in others.
Her beauty, kindliness and good sense shed a glow in which the dourest
spirits tended to brighten.

Anne's poems, written chiefly for the diversion of her friends and
circulated among them in manuscript, never achieved any profundi-
ties of thought or emotion, but at their best they had freshness and
simplicity. A sequence of lyrics, *Adieu Ye Streams that Softly Glide,*
which she wrote at the age of twenty, appeared in an Edinburgh review, and most of her work was eventually collected in a small volume.
"I had no notion," declared Hester Thrale, "that she could write so well."
Robert Burns valued two of Anne's poems, *To a Nightingale* and *A
Sonnet in the manner of Petrarch,* so highly that he copied them out
in his daybook, the only verse beside his own he ever preserved there.
Of the nightingale Anne wrote:

Why from these shades, sweet bird of eve,
Art thou to other regions wildly fled?

Thy pensive song would oft my cares relieve,
Thy melancholy softness oft would shed
Peace on my weary soul; return again.
Return, and, sadly sweet, in melting tones complain.

At the still hour I'll come alone.
And listen to thy love-lorn plaintive lay;
Or when the moon beams o'er yon mossy stone,
I'll watch thy restless wing from spray to spray.
And when the swelling cadence slow shall rise,
I'll join the harmony with low and murm'ring sighs.

Oh, simple bird! where art thou flown?
What distant woodland now receives thy nest?
What distant echo answers to thy moan,
What distant thorn supports thy aching breast?
Who'er can feel thy misery like me,
Or pay thee for thy song with such sad sympathy.

Anne had surely heard a good deal about John Hunter even before her father met him on Belle Isle. She had gone to the same school as Alice Lee, who remained a close friend and christened her first-born daughter after her, and she had known William Shippen in the days of his courtship. "Compt to Mr (I believe I should say Doctr Shippen)," she wrote to the young couple after they settled in Philadelphia, "& my love to my little namesack, & I wish I may ever have it in my Power to make it of any use to her. I am heartily sorry for the disturbances which now reign in the Colonies & I hope the Doctr & Yourself will be no sufferers of them. . . ."

The American had undoubtedly entertained his betrothed and her entrancing schoolmate with tales of the strange Hunter brothers, whose teachings left such an indelible stamp on his mind, so that it must have been with warm curiosity that Anne greeted John when her father presented him to the family. He returned often to the house in Suffolk Street, and at length he asked her to marry him. To the stupefaction of her high-toned circle, she consented.

They made an incongruous pair—Anne taller, with her blonde, willowy grace, her gentle breeding and devotion to the arts; John, plain as salt, fourteen years older, heavyset and disheveled, ill-read, unused to the amenities of the salon, forever preoccupied by the problems of the dissecting room and the sick ward, whose interest in nightingales went no further than wanting to know how their insides were put together.

Yet Anne was a woman to be stirred by John's lonely, passionate search, to sense greatness in him, and she was able to bring into his turbulent life the repose and serenity he needed.

Though Mr. and Mrs. Home liked John, they could have wished for Anne a brighter financial prospect. They looked more favorably on the engagement of her youngest sister, Mary, to Robert Mylne, a Scottish engineer and architect, whose fortune had been assured when he won a competition for the design of Blackfriars Bridge, which he then built at a cost of £153,000. But they respected Anne's choice, and with good will accepted John as their future son-in-law.

No such benevolence animated John's brother, who professed to believe that marriage was incompatible with a scientific career. "I have now finished 20 years of lectures," he once told his pupils. "However, as I presume I am still approved of, I propose 20 more beginning next October, and after this is over, I propose to settle in the world and take to me a wife." When Hewson, who had succeeded John as second-in-command at the school, married,* William broke with him, appointing in his place William Cruikshank, as yet unwed. His pretext was that "Mr H would have used a body of Dr Hunter's Purchasing to make a Skeleton, who it could not be expected should purchase Bodies for him for such a purpose." If John must marry, William felt, at least it should be into a family of loftier station than the impecunious Homes. He took a dislike to Anne, which he scarcely troubled to disguise, and the breach between the brothers widened.

William, at this time, was hoping for the support of the Chancellor of the Exchequer, George Grenville, in an ambitious undertaking. He had requested a grant of land on which he would erect a museum of anatomy and a surgical school. He proposed to invest £7,000 of his own capital, to endow a professorship in perpetuity, and to bequeath all of his collections, both scientific and artistic, to the crown. Grenville never replied. Furious, William considered leaving London forever, and practicing in Scotland. The mood soon passed. But at Samuel Johnson's suggestion he willed his collections to the University of Glasgow, which in gratitude commissioned Sir Joshua Reynolds to paint his portrait. Grenville's refusal was later regretted

---

* He married Polly Stevenson, the daughter of Franklin's London landlady. Mrs. Stevenson had also been Franklin's mistress.

by the British Museum. After William's death the museum offered to pay for the coins alone £20,000. The university refused to relinquish any part of the bequest.[c]

William determined to realize his plan with or without governmental aid. Spending more than £8,000, he bought a three-story mansion in Great Windmill Street, and enlarged it to contain an amphitheater, dissection and lecture rooms, a hall for his collections, and a sumptuous private apartment where he lived during the rest of his life. John later took over the lease on the Jermyn Street house.

The Great Windmill Street School, as it was popularly called, opened in the fall of 1767, and flourished both in William's time and, under a succession of Hunterian exponents, for almost fifty years after.[d] A forerunner of the general medical colleges, assembling under the same roof all branches of medicine and surgery, it became world-renowned, and many of the practitioners who had received its diploma —bearing a portrait of William and certifying that the graduate "hath attended my lectures"—came to dominate their fields.

"The Dr.," wrote a pupil from Scotland, William Hamilton, in letters to his father, "asked me and G. Reid who was along with me to come and eat an oyster with him and we set till eleven. The Drs class meets from half after one till half after three on Saturday and he has two meetings a night one from six till eight at which I was. . . . I went to day to fee the Dr., we give the money to Mr. Cruikshanks [sic] but he said he would speak to me about that tomorrow when he gave me my ticket. The Dr. is particularly hurried this week as he is afraid his body won't keep, he is on Surgery just now, he explained lithotomy and passing the catheter to day. Bodies are vastly scarce at present some of the men have been taken up and tried but I hope this will soon be over. . . . The Dr. is an exceedingly good lecturer and vastly plain, he tells a story w grt. humour one or two of which he introduced into his lecture on Saturday. He was vastly chatty with us at supper. . . .

"I yesterday got my ticket for the Drs. lectures and I feed him and Mr. Cruikshanks for this course. I am afraid I shall not have much for my dissecting fee as bodies are not to be got and there are several before me. G. Reid had promised to get me one and John the servt who is a very necessary man to be great with, to whom G. Reid introduced me and spoke for me has promised me the first that comes. The way I am to have it is this, if a body comes to Mr. Reid (who has told the pupils he is going out soon to lift one) is to say he got it and of consequence it belongs to him and he is to chuse me for his partner and then we will see if I can get a head or a leg or an arm or any thing to be doing with. . . . The Dr. is very near done with surgery and has the nerves still to show and some principles of Midwifery they say his course will not be done before the 20 of next month.

"Bodies are vastly scarce two resurrection men are taken up and all the burying ground is watched so that I am afraid we shall have little dissecting for some time there is nothing but an arm and my leg in the dissecting room at present. . . ."

There was no scarcity of anatomical material in the caricature that Rowlandson drew of a class at the Great Windmill Street School. Under William's owlish gaze, Hewson is enucleating a cadaver's eye, while Cruikshank and two pupils dissect the lower organs. Off to one side Smollett watches a second cadaver being disemboweled, and, kneeling on the floor, a simpering, apelike figure rummages elbows-deep amid the entrails of a third.

An instinctive actor, William loved addressing an audience as much as John hated it. "A man may do infinitely more good to the public," he held, "by teaching his art than by practising it," and according to one of his contemporaries, nobody surpassed him as a lecturer. Although the school's instructors included Caesar Hawkins and for a time, despite his estrangement from William, John Hunter, its success was William's personal triumph. He brought to the rostrum a comic sense, a gift for anecdote and analogy, a theatricality that made the driest subjects exciting, and in that age when men of intellect sought to embrace the whole range of human knowledge, he attracted a lay as well as a medical following, including Edmund Burke, Walpole, Hume, Johnson, Franklin, Reynolds, and Gainsborough. "They opened a new and very entertaining scene within myself," said Adam Smith, after attending the school for three months. Gibbon postponed a trip to Paris and neglected his work on *Decline and Fall* all one winter rather than miss a single lecture by William. At the end of each session, which lasted two hours, he would bustle up to the platform, press the doctor's hand, and thank him effusively.

Even William's frequent comments of self-appreciation charmed his listeners, as when he passed among them a placental specimen and gloated: "Now let me set all modesty and all appearances of it aside, and say here is the finest preparation in the world. If you let it fall, you may as well knock me on the head, for I shall not be able to outlive it."

To illustrate obstetrical techniques he used Smellie's apparatus, which he had bought when his old teacher left London. Decrying instrument delivery, he would dramatically brandish a pair of forceps rusty from years of disuse, and declare: "I am sorry they were ever invented. Where they save one they murder 20."

Such dependence on natural processes, admirable when no crisis demanded artifice, belonged to a theory of which John was a staunch advocate. But William tended to carry it to extremes. He disapproved so strongly of extracting a stubborn placenta that he sometimes waited hours for it to work itself out of the uterus, with consequent infection and loss of blood. It was the error that killed the Countess of Suffolk. "There are but two things that have much effect upon me at labour," William nevertheless maintained, "hemorrhage and convulsions." Caesarean section he considered to be almost invariably fatal, and of abnormal presentations, he said: "Some advise turning, others reducing it to the natural presentation; but the great rule is to do nothing." This policy of masterly inactivity stemmed partly from fear of endangering his reputation. "If any misfortune happens," he said, "the accoucheur may entirely lose his credit."

William's lectures on anatomy, which drew the largest crowds of laymen, bristled with historical and literary allusions. "Herophilus has been said to have anatomized 700 bodies. We must allow for exaggeration. Nay, it was said, that both he and Erasistratus made it a common practice to open the living, that they might discover the more secret springs of life. But this, no doubt, was only a vulgar opinion, rising from the prejudices of mankind; and, accordingly without good reason. Such tales have been told of modern anatomists, and have been believed by the vulgar. . . .

"What contempt would the King of Prussia, or Prince Ferdinand entertain for any officer, who said that a moderate share of that sort of knowledge [topographical], is sufficient for a general? The famed retreat of the ten thousand Greeks from Persia, would have been easily effected, if their leaders had known the country through which they were to pass: their dangers, disappointments, and distresses arose principally from their ignorance of Anatomy of that part of the globe."

As a natural philosopher, William expounded one or two ideas far ahead of his times. The most striking was an anticipation of the Darwinian doctrine of the survival of the fittest. "The last conjecture," he set forth, "which we shall venture to make is upon the scheme which the Author of our nature has laid down for perpetuating animals. Particular evils are allowed to exist. Many animals, from the imperfection of their fabric, are necessarily to perish before the common natural period. This is compensated for by a great superfluity in the number, and so it is also in the Vegetable Kingdom. As in vegetables, too, the parent produces a species very like itself; but sometimes a different constitution, whether better or worse. Whatever may happen, in a particular instance or with regard to an individual, the most perfect and sound animal upon the whole, will have the best chance of living to procreate others of his kind: in other words, the best breed will prevail: and the monstrous constitution, and that which is defective, or of such fabric as necessarily to breed disease, will be cut off. The most perfect constitution will be preserved: it will be most susceptible to love, and most likely to meet with a warm return of that passion: so that, in every way, the sound constitution will have the preference in procreation, and the defective, weak or diseased line will be wearing out."

The wedding of John and Anne did not take place that year or the next. John postponed it, pleading poverty. His private practice and his work with the Spences, he told Anne, together failed to produce the income he had expected; not for a while yet would he be able to support a family decently. But it was not the real reason. That he could hardly confide to Anne.

18. THE ACCURSED SHEPHERD

On Friday, the twenty-second of May, 1767, John sat in his Golden Square dispensary fingering a lancet he had dipped into pus excreted from the sores of a venereal patient.

No maladies so confused the eighteenth-century doctor as syphilis, gonorrhea, and such localized venereal infections as chancroid. They had been epidemic for centuries. Rakes held with desperate bravado that never to have contracted a venereal disease was to be accounted "boorish and no gentleman." Folklore and superstition beclouded the whole subject. Some doctors correctly viewed syphilis and gonorrhea as two unrelated diseases, originating from different causes; others as symptoms of the same disease. But nobody suspected the gradual progression of syphilis through the entire system, with its general, irreversible destruction, long after the external signs had disappeared.

Gonorrhea had been known in Europe since antiquity, but it was probably Columbus's sailors who introduced syphilis to the Continent when they came home in 1493 from Hispaniola, where they had caught it from the aborigines. A Spanish physician, Roderigo Diaz de Isla, witnessed the disembarkation at Palos, tried to cure several sailors, among them the pilot, Martin Alonzo Piñon, of an ailment unfamiliar to him, and heard from Columbus himself a description of it as it existed in the West Indies. He later wrote a treatise on what he called "the Disease of the Island of Hispaniola."

Politics and war created an ideal breeding ground. A few months after Columbus completed his first voyage, Charles VIII of France, a preening, feeble-minded adventurer, intoxicated by the panopoly of conquest, claimed sovereignty over the Kingdom of Naples as his hereditary right. When the Neapolitans defied him, he led an army against them of six thousand mercenaries, recruited from many countries. Naples fell in February 1494 and Charles returned in swaggering triumph to France, leaving his troops in occupation. They did not long enjoy the victory. Ferdinand of Spain, allying himself with the Neapolitans, sent an army to their rescue. It included men fresh from the West Indies.

In the ensuing capture and recapture of towns, Charles's mercenaries lay with some of the same women who had favored the Spaniards, and the strange, new plague ravaged the garrisons. Relatively mild in the country of its origin, characterized there mainly by an itch, it took a virulent form like most diseases attacking organisms never before exposed to them. It corroded the flesh, the bones, the vital organs. It killed thousands.

When the surviving mercenaries drifted back to their own countries, they sowed the pestilence wherever they passed. By the turn of the century scarcely a corner of Europe had been spared, and as the Jews and Moors, fleeing persecution in Spain, reached Africa, as explorers like Cortes, Magellan and Vasco da Gama sailed the seven seas, the rest of the world was contaminated. History records no other instance of such a swift, universal spread of a new disease.

People gave it many names, usually derogatory of some nationality not their own—*mal franzoso, mala napoleta,* the Spanish scab, the Polish, German, and Turkish pocks. The mellifluous name under which it entered the medical lexicon was invented by Girolamo Fracastoro of Verona, physician, poet, astronomer, mathematician, and philosopher. In 1530, Fracastoro published a poem, *Syphilis, or the Gallic Sickness,* dedicated to Lucrezia Borgia's lover, Cardinal Bembo, which summarized, in the fate of a Greek shepherd, everything then known about the symptoms and medication.

The shepherd, beset by a drought that was killing his flocks, lost faith in the ancient gods and built an altar to a mortal king, Alcithous. For this sacrilege Olympus chastised him with a poison, which

> *Within the body, long its ferment rests*
> *To nourish at some hidden source of breasts.*
> *Then suddenly, beneath a langour's weight,*
> *The victim creeps about in fearful state,*
> *The heart defective and the slightest strain*
> *Tiring the limbs, while energies remain*
> *All sapped. A gloomy eye and saddened face*
> *Of sickly pallor bend to this disgrace,*
> *And soon a vicious ulcer eats its way*
> *Into the privates. And a vengeful sway*
> *Takes cancerous possession to remain.*
> *Extended to the groin is its fell bane.*
>
> *Soon is the body ulcerous and vile.*
> *The face becomes within a little while*
> *A mask of running pustules small and great.*
> *A horny shell will glands well imitate.*
> *Breaking and emptying an acrid humor,*
> *From pus-corroded skin, pours every tumor.*
> *And bloody ulcers deeply dig away,*
> *Gnawing the tissues that they make their prey.*
> *Then is man stripped until his piteous moans*
> *Come from a skeleton of putrid bones.*
> *The lips are torn to shreds for this vile ill,*
> *And, ere the voice dies, it is harsh and shrill.*
>
> *Gone is the brilliance of his youth and spring.*
> *Dying by inches, as his soul sinks, he*
> *Finds on his limbs a hideous leprosy.*
> *Upon his very bones would caries fling*
> *Its banner, till they open to the eyes.*

His lovely eyes that were so long alight—
Ulcers devour these—a hideous sight.
Purulent poison too his nose corrodes,
Until for viscous humors, it explodes.*

Victims of the disease, the poem went on to warn, should shun truffles, artichokes, leeks, cucumbers, vinegar, milk, and especially wine. As curatives, it prescribed lard ("Soon is repaired the ruin of the flesh"), oxide of lead, antimony, storax, frankincense, and mercury.

All men concede that mercury's the best
Of agents that will cure a tainted breast.
Each acrid mole will in its turn
Seize upon every humor that will burn
The scourge away. . . .

But Fracastoro was overoptimistic. While inunctions of mercury, in use since the twelfth century against various skin eruptions, relieved the gross early symptoms, they seldom arrested the spread of the poison through the tissues, an action of which Fracastoro had no inkling. (Mercury remained the specific remedy until the twentieth century, when Paul Ehrlich discovered Salvarsan.)

In the profusion of theories no effective control of the epidemic was possible. Astrologers attributed its origin to planetary influences. Nicolaus Leonicenzo, an Italian physician, the first to observe that syphilis produced visceral as well as cutaneous lesions, blamed floods. Others thought it due to intercourse with animals, pederasty, eating lizards. Pope Clement VII's physician maintained that the soldiers of Charles VIII imbibed poisoned wine that the retreating Spaniards had left behind after polluting it with the blood of pesthouse inmates. Francis Bacon propagated one of the most fanciful notions. "The French," said he, "from whom the Neapolitan Disease derives its Denomination say, that there were at the Siege of Naples, certain dishonest Merchants who sold human flesh, new killed in Mauretania, pickled and put up in Vessels, instead of Tunny; and that to this abominable and heavy Food, the Origin of the Venereal Diseases ought to be ascribed. Nor does this Opinion seem to be without just Foundation. For Cannibals in the West devour human Flesh; and this disease is very frequent in the West Indies when they were first discovered."

Yet, an intimation of the truth—the germ theory Louis Pasteur es-

* From the translation by William van Wyck.

tablished almost four hundred years later—was skirted by several medieval observers. In a resumé of existing theories, Jean Astruc, physician to Louis XIV (a victim of syphilis in early youth), wrote: "There are some, however, whom I forbear to spend time in imputing, such as Augustus Hauptman and Christian Langius, who think that the Venereal Poison is nothing else but a numerous School of little nimble, brisk invisible living things, of a very prolific nature, which when once admitted, increase and multiply in Abundance; which lead frequent Colonies to different Parts of the Body; and inflame, erode, and exulcerate the Parts they fix on; in short, which without any regard had to the particular Quality of any Humor, occasion all the Symptoms that occur in the Venereal Disease. . . ." A neat description of the *Spirochaeta pallida,* and Astruc immediately dismissed it as fantastic.

Concerning the mechanism of transmission, there were almost as many theories as doctors. Winds wafted the poison from person to person. The human breath was the medium. Cardinal Wolsey's enemies accused him of infecting Henry VIII by whispering in his ear. The Paris Parliament issued an edict making it a capital offense for a syphilitic to converse with others, and ordering infected nonresidents to return within twenty-four hours to "the Countries and Places where they were born, or where they had their Abode, or else where they please, under Pain of Death." A few who disobeyed were tossed into the Seine.

The Scots appear to have guessed earlier than any other people how syphilis was really communicated. By an ordinance of the town council of Aberdeen, enacted in 1497, "All light women must desist their vice and sin of venery and work for their support on pain, else, of being branded with a hot iron on their cheek and banished from town."

As the sexual character of syphilis became generally accepted, efforts to study and treat it were further obfuscated by a fog of moral and religious cant. Bigots proclaimed the disease to be a punishment inflicted by God upon sinners, who therefore merited no succor at the hands of man. This, however, did not deter Gabriel Fallopius, the anatomist after whom the Fallopian tubes were named, from devising a prophylactic linen sheath to be worn over the penis during copulation. Eleven hundred men, he reported, had used it and not one contracted syphilis. The invention of an improved sheath, in the seventeenth century, was popularly ascribed to an apocryphal Dr. Condom.

The sum total of knowledge about the pestilence gained during the two centuries after Fracastoro would not fill a big book. Paré gave syphilis as a cause of aneurysms. Paracelsus recorded cases of congenital syphilis. It was also surmised that the disease could be transmitted in more ways than one, such as through kisses and drinking vessels, from lying-in women to midwives and from the offspring to nurses, from cadavers to anatomists. The catalogue of known sequelae increased—chancre of the tonsils, lesions of the larynx, windpipe, lungs and heart, tumorlike growths on the brain, neuralgias and spinal deformities. But of the etiology of syphilis and its relation to other venereal diseases, the mystery remained.

John Hunter, whose patients probably numbered more sufferers from syphilis and gonorrhea than from any other ailments, inclined to the view that they were merely different manifestations of an identical infection. The former, he theorized, arose when the skin of the penis, the latter when the mucous membrane within the urethra, was the focus of attack. But how to prove it? From neither living victims nor dead had he been able to gather sufficient evidence, for the initial lesion of gonorrhea leaves no trace, and that of syphilis only a faint one. So John resolved to infect himself, to delay treatment, and to chart in his own body the day by day progress of the disease.

As impersonal, as detached as when he dissected insentient flesh, he picked up the pus-laden lancet, punctured his foreskin, then the head of his penis. The venom thus introduced he believed to be of gonorrheal origin. If his theory was valid, it should produce symptoms of syphilis. "This was on a Friday;" he noted, "on the Sunday following there was a teasing itching in those parts, which lasted till the Tuesday following."

He had meanwhile told Anne that their marriage must wait.

"Upon the Tuesday morning," the case history continued, "the parts of the prepuce where the puncture had been made were redder, thickened, and had formed a speck; by the Tuesday following the speck had increased. . . ."

It was the familiar primary lesion of syphilis—the hard ulcer since known as the Hunterian chancre. John's theory seemed to be confirmed.

To us who know so much more about venereal diseases than John Hunter, it is obvious that a mischance had befallen him. Syphilis is wholly distinct from gonorrhea and in severity as cancer to a wart.

Since John developed the syphilitic chancre, the patient from whose running sores he infected himself must have harbored both types of organism. Otherwise John would have soon seen his fallacy. Few accidents ever cost an experimenter so dearly. It not only vitiated a study that was to last a lifetime, it wrecked his health.

But, confident of being on the right track, indifferent to the pain and the danger, John pushed the experiment to its limits, now palliating the symptoms with silver nitrate and mercury, now giving them free rein. "The mercury was left off, not being intended to destroy the poison, but to observe what parts it would next affect." The chancre recurred. The lymphatic gland in his right groin swelled. "I had for some time conceived the idea that the most effectual way to put back a bubo was to rub in mercury on that leg and thigh; that thus a current of mercury would pass through the inflamed gland. Here was a good opportunity of making the experiment. A few days after beginning the mercury in this method the gland subsided considerably. It was then left off, for the intention was not to cure it completely at present. The gland some time after began to swell again." A tonsil ulcerated, "which was allowed to go on till the nature of it was ascertained." A coppery rash blotched his skin.

When finally satisfied that he had observed every symptom, he applied the optimum dosage of mercury. The external lesions vanished. He had endured them for three years.

"The above case," he concluded, "is only uncommon in the mode of contracting the disease, and the particular views with which some parts of the treatment were directed, but as it was meant to prove many things which, though not uncommon, are yet not attended to, attention was paid to all the circumstances. It proves many things, and opens a field for further conjecture. It proves, first, that matter from a gonorrhea will produce chancres."

During the springtime, two years after he infected himself, John had begun to suffer from pains in the joints of his feet. Now the right foot, now the left, and sometimes both together reddened and swelled. The pains beset him the next spring and the next, then troubled him no more. He believed the ailment to have been gout, with no relation to venereal disease.

Satisfied that he had rid himself of the last trace of that poison, he hurried to Anne Home.

V. JERMYN STREET
1771-1783

19. ". . . HAPPY IN A WIFE"

With a minimum of formality and few attendants, they were married in St. James's Church, Piccadilly, the Reverend William Parker officiating, at eight o'clock on the morning of Sunday, July 22, 1771, that being the only hour and day of the week John felt he could spare away from his work. The squat, homely groom was forty-three, his tall, fair bride twenty-nine. Anne's parents witnessed the signing of the register. The rest of the wedding party consisted of Robert and Mary Mylne, who had been married the year before, pigeon-plump little Everard Home, and half a dozen of John's pupils and friends, among them Captain Cook and Joseph Banks, lately returned from their voyage to the South Seas. The explorers gave the couple a set of Chippendale furniture carved out of black acacia, which they had taken aboard in New Holland (Australia). From Captain Cook John also received a quantity of antipodean animals and plants.

William Hunter was not present. The day before John had informed him in a curt note: "As this is a ceremony of which you are not particularly fond, I will not make a point of having your company there."

Before settling down in Jermyn Street, the newlyweds spent a two-day honeymoon at Earl's Court, where John was enlarging the main house, building cages for his menagerie, and laying out botanical gardens. It is impossible to read John's account of his self-inflicted disease without wondering whether Anne and her children shared the consequences. When he went to his wife's bed, had the infection entered the latent, noncommunicable stage, or did he transmit it to her? Inadequately treated, syphilis can remain infectious for many years, and in women the early symptoms may pass unnoticed. Though not inheritable from the father, if the mother has been infected before or during pregnancy, the disease is likely to invade the fetus. In the first five years of marriage Anne bore four children.

"As to myself, with respect to my family," John wrote to his brother-in-law, the Reverend James Baillie, shortly before Anne's last confinement, "I can only say yet, that I am happy in a wife, but my children are too young to form any judgment of. They consist of a stout red-headed boy, called Jock, three years and some months old, and a weak girl call'd Mary-Anne, near two. We lost a fine boy call'd Jemmy who would have been now about twelve months; and Anny is near her time of a fourth. I am not anxious about my children but in their doing well in this world. I would rather make them feel one moral virtue, than read librarys of all the dead and living languages."

Mary-Anne died the following year. Jock—John Banks Hunter, named after Joseph Banks—survived infancy, but in maturity showed signs of mental disturbance. Only the fourth child, Agnes Margaretta, reached an advanced age without any apparent infirmities, but she was then reduced to paralysis and semi-imbecility by a series of seizures, from what cause her doctors never determined.

"I am happy in a wife . . ." And Anne, much later, expressed her feelings for John in verse:

> In thee I bear so dear a part,
>   By love so firm am thine,
> That each affection of thy heart,
>   By sympathy is mine.
>
> When thou art grieved, I grieve no less;
>   My joys by thine are known;
> And every good thou woulds't possess
>   Becomes in wish my own.

As the wife of the world's most indefatigable anatomical collector and experimenter, Anne had a lot to put up with, and she put up with it cheerfully. No complaint escaped her as the house overflowed with mummified exotics, with pickled double-headed babies, with fossils, skeletons and cadavers, while students, draughtsmen and dissectors scurried from room to room, reeking of dye and decay, their arms bloodied to the elbows. The yard was a Golgotha of bones, animal and human. A stuffed giraffe too tall to fit under the ceilings John shortened by lopping off the legs at the knees and stationed in the entrance hall, a sight to stupefy Anne's tasteful callers.

She nevertheless managed to maintain, in the limited space available to her, one of the liveliest salons in London. Solely in the hopes of being invited, a lady unknown to the Hunters, of perfectly sound health, asked John to bleed her. At Anne's Thursday afternoon *conversaziones*, at her soirées, might be found Horace Walpole, Oliver Goldsmith, Archdeacon Robert Nares, the prestigious promoter of the *British Critic*, Elizabeth Carter, poet and authority on classical literature, Lady Byron, Hester Thrale, Elizabeth Montagu, and Mary Delany, the last three celebrated *salonières* themselves. They made repartee and music, recited their own poems and *belles lettres*, sang and sedately danced, while with the floral aroma of powder and perfume there mingled charnel stenches drifting from the nether regions of the house, where parts of carcasses—an elephant's viscera, a carp's spine, a murderer's brain—lay open to John's inquisitive knife. "The heart of a Frog," Mrs. Thrale wrote shudderingly in her notebook, "will not cease to beat *says John Hunter* for four hours after it has been torne from the Body of the Animal Poor Creature—*il a bu jusqu'au lies la coupe amère de la Sensibilité*, might Jean Jacques observe in this place."

It was a mark of Anne's finesse that her most redoubtable social rival, Mrs. Montagu, "Queen of the Bluestockings," whose *conversaziones* fell on Friday, bore her no rancor and became a devoted friend. Indeed, of all the bluestockings only the acidulous Fanny Burney withheld unqualified admiration of Anne. "Extremely pretty, and reckoned very ingenious," was the verdict she entered in her diary, "a fine woman and highly accomplished, but with rather too much glare, both without and within."

Tommy Shippen, during a visit to London in 1787, wrote home: "From [Mrs. Hunter's] appearance you would suppose her 23 or 30 years of age [she was then 45] and she is graceful, genteel and elegant beyond anything I have seen in England. . . . I am sure I do no injustice to Mr. Hunter in giving Mrs. Hunter the sole credit of the elegant arrangement of everything I saw at the house and I might also say that I had seen nothing so elegant as the entertainment this day since I have been here."

No injustice was done. Though John did not begrudge Anne her pleasures or deny her ample means to indulge them, he scorned all social events as fit only for idlers. Upon arriving home late one night, edgy after hours of consultation and surgery, and finding the house full of merrymakers, he announced from the doorway: "I knew nothing of this kick-up. I should have been informed beforehand. As I am now returned to study, I hope the company will retire." The festivities broke up in icy silence.

Such interest as John took in Anne's coterie was apt to be embarrassingly clinical. He repeatedly told General James Murray, a twice-wounded veteran of the French-Indian War, "I would like very much to peep into your chest."

Haydn, a prize lion of Anne's during the year he spent in London, fascinated John because of a polyp in his nose. "You should let me remove it," the surgeon told him. "It distorts your face and frightens the ladies."

In view of his amatory successes the composer felt he could ignore the advice. A few days later John decoyed him to his office with a trumped-up message. Two stalwarts grabbed him from behind and dragged him towards an operating chair, as John advanced, scalpel at the ready. Screaming and struggling, Haydn kicked himself free.

"Do you wish," John asked him reproachfully, "to take your foe to the grave?"

"Such is my intention," replied the Austrian, and bolted.

He lived to regret his trepidity. In his old age the polyp grew bigger, causing him great discomfort, but he was then too debilitated to bear surgery. "I shall have to take my foe to the grave with me," he said.

The lyrics Anne composed for one of Haydn's canzonets alone of all her literary efforts are still remembered:

> *My mother bids me bind my hair*
> * With bands of rosy hue,*
> *To tie up my sleeves with ribbons rare,*
> * And lace my bodice blue.*
>
> *For why, she cries, sit still and weep,*
> * While others dance and play?*
> *Alas! I scarce can go or creep,*
> * While Lubin is away.*

'Tis sad to think the days are gone,
When those we love were near;
I sit upon this mossy stone,
And sigh when none can hear.

And while I spin my flaxen thread,
And sing my simple lay,
The village seems asleep or dead,
Now Lubin is away.

"Madam," said Walpole, after hearing the canzonet, "Mr. Haydn is the greatest composer of the day and 'pon honour your verses are worthy of his music."

Anne also wrote a libretto for Haydn's *The Creation*, but it was rejected in favor of a version by one Lidley, translated into German for a performance in Vienna, and translated back into English for the Covent Garden Opera. Commiserating with Anne, the poet George Thomson said, "It is not the first time your muse and Haydn's have met, as we see from the beautiful canzonets. Would he had been directed by you about the words for *The Creation*. It is lamentable to see such divine music joined with such miserable broken English."

John placed an added strain upon his forbearing wife by expecting her to be agreeable to the human oddments he constantly brought into the house because he found them amusing or instructive. The egregious Van Butchell's purple-dyed pony was sometimes to be seen hitched to a post in front of No. 42 Jermyn Street. Another guest, as well as patient, was the one-eyed, octogenarian, satyromaniacal Duke of Queensberry, Marquis of Drumlanrig, Earl of March and Knight of the Thistle, who looked like Punchinello, thought and talked of little else but nubile girls, bathed in milk, and applied veal cutlets to his face to improve his complexion. The acquaintance ripened after John treated the Duke for a ruptured tendon.

From time to time the arch-charlatan and cancer-curer, John Taylor, would drop in. "The most ignorant man I ever knew, but sprightly," Johnson said of him. "He was an example of how far impudence could carry ignorance." But it was John's notion that even a quack might somehow stumble upon a medical truth, and was therefore worth cultivating.

Taylor specialized in eye diseases and rectal cancer. Styling himself "Chevalier of Whitworth, Oculist to the King of Britain, Ducal Oculist, and Count Oculist," he was the inventor of a language he called "the True Ciceronian, prodigiously difficult and never attempted before." An example: "Of the eye, on the wonders, lecture will I."

John first met him when they were both sent for by the Bishop of Durham, who had rectal cancer. Far from taking umbrage, John blandly declared, "I have no objection to meeting anybody."

Taylor was equally conciliatory. He held, he said, "no opinion of any but Jack Hunter," and had refused to examine the Bishop until the surgeon arrived. His customary method of treatment was to pass a bougie smeared with an ointment of secret ingredients up the anus.

"What's it made of?" John asked.

"That's not fair," Taylor protested. "No, no, Jack, I'll send you as much as you please, but I won't tell you what it's made of."

Neither consultant did the Bishop any good.

One of the severest challenges to Anne as a hostess arose when the explorer, George Cartwright, returned from Labrador in the fall of 1773, accompanied by a family of Eskimos, the first of their breed to set foot in England. John, beside himself with curiosity, insisted they all come to dinner. There were five Eskimos, whom Cartwright, a student of Eskimo dialects, introduced as Attiock, the head of the family; his youngest wife, Ickongoque; their infant daughter, Ickenna; the chieftain's brother, Tooklavinia; and Tooklavinia's wife, Caubrick. Panic seized the visitors almost immediately. Attiock, straying into the yard, emitted a howl of terror. His kinsfolk, followed by the entire Hunter household, rushed out to find him quaking before a mound of bones.

"Take us home," he entreated Cartwright, convinced that they had fallen among cannibals.

"Are we to be killed too?" asked Ickongoque, clutching little Ickenna to her breast.

"Will they eat us and put our bones there?" Tooklavinia asked.

Cartwright hastened to assure them that their hosts were no cannibals. "These are the bones of criminals," he said, "given to Mr. Hunter after they were hanged so that he might better learn how to set those of the living."

The explanation somewhat quieted the Eskimos, but they sat morose and irritable throughout the evening, and were clearly relieved when it ended.

20. "THE DEAR MAN"

Professionally and financially John's outlook had never been brighter. His *Natural History of the Teeth,* published at one guinea, sold one thousand copies. In 1767 the Royal Society had admitted him as a Fellow, a signal mark of recognition, for, with the exception of men of rank or title, the society honored only those who communicated to it a piece of original research, which John had yet to do. Although a paper by William Hunter had been published in the society's *Philosophical Transactions* as early as 1743, he was elected three months after John.

The paper John eventually submitted, in 1772—the first of twenty-one—describing the digestive action of gastric juices, and how after death they dissolve the stomach, typified his teleological philosophy. The phenomenon existed in nature, therefore it must reflect design and purpose.

When he first observed the erosion of a dead man's stomach, he supposed the process to have started during life as a result of disease. But he could not relate it to any of the patient's known disorders. Was it then a natural process? Feeding a variety of animals different foods and killing them at different periods, he opened the stomachs. In each instance he found both food and stomach partially digested. It struck him that the stomach, deprived of its "living principle," could no longer resist the residual flow of gastric juices. The organ, now inanimate matter, was thus digested like food.

Conversely, he reasoned, it was the living principle that enabled certain animals—a fish tapeworm would be an example—to grow inside the human organism, uninjured by the gastric juices. "If it were possible," he set forth, "for a man's hand to be introduced into the stomach of a living animal and kept there for a considerable time, it would be found that the dissolvent powers of the stomach could have no effect upon it [not strictly true: the skin would undergo changes]; but if the same hand were separated from the body, and introduced into the same stomach, we should then find that the stomach could immediately act upon it."

Soon after winning his Royal Society fellowship, John became a member of the Corporation of Surgeons, and the governors of St. George's Hospital at long last appointed him to the surgical staff. The latter position carried substantial emoluments. He was entitled to bind apprentices to him for five years, receiving from each of them £500, and to share equally with the three other staff surgeons in the pupils' annual fees. During his tenure those fees rose from £428 to £1,064. But John had to shoulder the heaviest burden of teaching, since more than half the pupils chose to walk the wards at his side, a preference that galled his colleagues no less because he frequently reminded them of it. In addition, the prestige of being associated with St. George's increased both his private practice and the number of his house pupils, who paid him £100 a year board plus four guineas per course.

Profit, however, was not John's paramount concern. As he told his fellow surgeons years after, during a bitter dispute over the division of pupils' fees: "When I solicited to be appointed, it was not with a view to augment my income, but to acquire opportunities of extending my knowledge that I might be more useful to mankind." At the time of the hospital appointment he wrote to James Baillie: "It is nearly all I want; beyond which I have no ambition. While all these concurring circumstances go on, I must continue to be one of the happiest men living."

He finally compelled himself to lecture when he realized that his ideas were being distorted in repetition at second and third hand, and his discoveries credited to others. He came to feel, too, that lecturing "resembles a tradesman taking stock; without which he never knows what he possesses or in what he is deficient." But although he regularly delivered fifty lectures a term, facing an audience lost none of its terrors for him. To steel himself to it, he would gulp down twenty drops of laudanum in a glass of port, and even with this bracer he would read the lecture from a manuscript, not daring to lift his eyes.

His maiden efforts, halting, cumbrous, often couched in the idiom of the streets, produced more laughter than enlightenment. What manner of clod was this, with his growling burr, his dye-stained hands and tangled thatch of carroty hair, who would say of his self-inflicted vene-real disease, "I knocked it down with mur-r-r-cur-r-ry and I killed it," and of a gunshot wound, "The ball having gone into the man's belly and hit his guts such a damn'd thump, they mor-r-r-tified?"

Attendance was meager at first, and at no time did it exceed thirty. John once found himself about to address an audience of one, whereupon he dragged a skeleton into the room, seated it, and with a pawky grin began: "Gentlemen. . . ."

But for those who could glimpse the gold beneath the dross no other teacher excelled John, and there gradually rallied around him, like the Athenian youths around Socrates, a small, ardent band, enkindled by a wholly new philosophy of healing. "The dear man," they called him. "I found him so far superior to anything that I had conceived or heard," said one of his earliest disciples, Henry Cline, who at twenty-four was already a ranking surgeon, "that there seemed no comparison between the great mind of the man . . . and all the individuals who had gone before, ancient or modern." When, twenty years later, in the fullness of his experience, Cline revisited the lecture room, he remarked to John's secretary with a sigh, "Ah, Mr. Clift, we must all go to school again."

Paradoxically, John prefaced his talks on surgery by deprecating the art. Eager neophytes, fairly itching to wield a scalpel, would be told that to operate was to concede inadequacy. Surgery, the armed savage . . . John contended: "No surgeon should approach the victim of his operation without a sacred dread and reluctance, and should be superior to that popular *éclat* generally attending painful operations, often only because they are so, or because they are expensive to the patient. . . . If the disease is already formed, we ought to know the modes of action in the *body* and the *parts*, in their endeavor to relieve themselves; the powers they have of restoring themselves, and the means of assisting those powers. Or, if these prove insufficient, we judge, by all the attending circumstances, how far excision may be necessary, and what condition is most favourable for an operation. To determine on this last point is exceedingly difficult, and in some instances, exceeds our present knowledge. Never perform an operation on another person which, under similar circumstances, you would not have performed upon yourself."

When surgery could not be avoided, the surgeon, before undertaking it, was to consider the whole man, his life history, habits, constitutional idiosyncrasies, and previous ailments; the structure and function of his organs in health; the systemic changes at the onset and during the course of the disease, and those likely to accompany the postoperative and convalescent stages; the interactions of his mind, emotions, and body.

John was aware of the psychic factors in disease and the power of autosuggestion. "The various effects of the mind upon the body are almost without end. . . . There is not a natural action in the body, whether voluntary or involuntary, that may not be influenced by the peculiar state of the mind at the time, and every particular mode of the mind has some parts that are more readily influenced by it than others. The skin is affected by the feeling of shame; the secretion or even the non-secretion of the testicles takes place under certain states of the mind. Palpitations of the heart and quick respirations are brought on by some states; purging and increased secretions of urine by others.

"[The mind] often produces actions independently of the will, especially when those actions are begun by the will, and when the mind is affected by a recollection of them; or even contrary to the will. Thus, fear produces a vibratory contraction of all the voluntary muscles, while the will is doing all it can to stop it. Since the mind has such power over the natural actions of the body, we might suppose it would have considerable effect in disease; and this we actually find it has, especially in those who have a strong susceptibility for such actions as the mind can most easily affect. We should naturally expect that it would be diseases principally connected with the nerves that the mind would most affect, though we do find that there are other diseases, with which they appear to have little connection, that are much affected by the state of the mind; and I believe that it is primarily those diseases in which the alteration is in the action of parts, not in their structure. . . . These diseases are called nervous."

He would cite the case of a middle-aged woman, normally of cheerful disposition, whose right sternomastoid muscle kept contracting under emotional stress, jerking her neck to that side. She could arrest the tic, if sufficiently collected, by contracting the left sternomastoid muscle. When pleasurably occupied, reading or chatting with friends, she was never troubled. But fear invariably started the contractions. In the presence of strangers, from whom she was anxious to conceal her defect, they were violent.

"This circumstance of the mind's continuing action when it has once taken it up," said John, "is remarkable in hiccup, which is often produced by laughing; thus hiccuping, which is an involuntary action, is produced by . . . a voluntary one. But as the state of mind is thus capable of producing a disease, another state of it may effect a cure: so the hiccup may be cured by producing fear."

Such psychological observations were interspersed throughout John's lectures and writings.

On deceit: "One of the imperfections of the human mind is the desire to be supposed what we are not, but what we should like to be. . . . No man is so fond of being thought a man of gallantry as he who has no passion for the female sex; yet would feel proud if it were conceived that he always had some intrigue on his hands, even at the expense of the innocent; while the man who is really passionately fond of the sex, and perhaps their dupe, would rather choose to hide that turn of mind, as if it were a defect."

On mental effects: "The mind, or sensitive principle, is affected by objects which make impressions, which impressions make an alteration in the parts of sensation, and according to the nature of the impression so is the mind affected. If we see a man dance, the variety of actions produces the same variety of impressions. . . . If it is a lively, quick dance . . . we feel lively; if it is grave, we feel grave. . . .

"The mind is not only affected according to the simple impression, as most probably is the case in brutes, but from experience and association of other impressions or ideas with the present; it arrives at the cause of the actions which produced these impressions, and this always produces a stronger effect than the simple impression. . . . Whatever actions affect the mind considerably, and more especially if the affection be joined with reflection, they make in some degree a lasting impression on it; or the mind more easily falls into the same state upon the simple recollection of the action and of its cause and effect. . . . For instance, a man shall be strongly affected by the death of a friend; and, more so, if there are at the time a great many relative affecting circumstances; such as the grief of other people, etc., to heighten the distress. But let some time elapse, and the true state of the mind will become really indifferent about the death and all its consequences; yet that man shall very readily fall into the same state of mind upon a relation of the circumstances, that made the first impressions, especially if in company with those friends.

"The mind is often in opposition to itself; one state of mind, if strong, shall get the better of another state which is weak, or the stronger state shall not allow the weaker to rise. . . ."

(John had confirmed this observation in himself when he went to the Drury Lane Theatre to see Sarah Siddons in a Shakespearian tragedy. An impassioned partisan of the Junoesque, fiery-eyed actress, he expected to be moved to tears, but forgot to bring a handkerchief. "The distress I was in for the want of that requisite when one is crying, and a kind of fear I should cry, stopped every tear, and I was even ashamed I did not, nor could not, cry.")

On anxiety: "A man who is condemned to die next morning may so far make up his mind as to get some rest that night; and this rest will be more or less in proportion to the state of his mind. But if that man is to have his life preserved on condition that he does sleep, he certainly cannot sleep; the very anxiety arising from desire and fear will prevent him. . . . Anxiety is expressive of the union of two passions, desire and fear. . . . The well performing of any action is in the inverse proportion to the anxiety."

On fear: "A brave man of good sense will endure any pain, or the chance of it, in a good cause; while the same pain, or chance of it in a bad or even indifferent cause will make him a coward or make him shudder. . . . Is fear a perfect and distinct state of mind? Does it ever exist but in a doubtful state of mind? Is it not a union of hope and despair? For whenever hope is gone, fear diminishes. Is it not an anticipation of evil, and the less an animal has the power of anticipation, the less fear he has?" (By this principle John explained the change in many condemned criminals from cowardice to courage when they had lost their last hope of reprieve.)

On sexual selection: "A man has an appetite to enjoy a woman; but if the mind has formed itself to any particular woman, the appetite or enjoyment can be suspended till that object is present; and the more the mind interferes, the greater stress will be laid upon this relation: the mere sexual enjoyment will be almost forgot, and the whole pursuit will be after the particular quality of the appetite. But perhaps it requires long habit to establish the influence of such a relative quality in the mind."

On pleasure and pain: "Everything that gives pleasure at first lessens by practice; and everything that gives pain becomes more easy."

John did not doubt that the panaceas peddled by quacks could sometimes help suggestible invalids. He had himself once demonstrated this through a patient suffering from an ague, who believed in the curative properties of spiders' webs. John brought a web into the sickroom, hiding it at first from the patient. The chills and fever continued. But as soon as he exhibited the web and performed the prescribed ritual, the symptoms abated.

In all branches of medicine and surgery John put principles before techniques. As Buckle observed, creative minds excel at one of two methods of ratiocination—the deductive, used by Plato, which calls for greater daring and imagination, interpreting phenomena in the light of assumed principles, or the cautious, inductive method, used by Bacon, arriving at principles from facts. Few thinkers ever successfully adopted both methods. Aristotle and Newton were exceptions, able with equal mastery to synthesize as well as to analyze, to marshal facts ahead of ideas or vice versa, almost infallibly choosing the line that promised the better result, and never allowing the one to encroach upon the other.

John inclined towards deductive reasoning, which Buckle considered characteristic of the Scottish mentality, as opposed to the inductive propensities of the English. He blundered most frequently, lapsed into his darkest obscurities, when he attempted to combine the Baconian and the Platonic methods.

"The principles of our art," he dinned into his pupils, "are not less necessary to be understood than the principles of other sciences; unless, indeed, the surgeon should wish to resemble the Chinese philosopher, whose knowledge consisted only in facts. In that case the science must remain unimproved until fresh facts arise. . . . Too much attention cannot be paid to facts; yet too many facts crowd the memory without advantage, any further than that they lead us to establish principles. By an acquaintance with principles we learn the *causes* of diseases. Without this knowledge a man cannot be a surgeon. Surgeons have been too much satisfied with considering effects only."

This struck John's contemporaries as heretical, and alienated the majority of them. His colleagues had no patience, moreover, with his search for a single unifying concept of the entire phenomenology of matter. They valued theory to the extent that it yielded tangible results, whereas John, closer to the spirit of pure science, would often pursue an idea without concerning himself about its practical potentialities. Nevertheless, there was hardly a major surgical development during the next two generations that had not germinated in the Hunterian seedbed.

John's theories of inflammation, how and why, in many morbid conditions, the blood vessels become congested and exude red corpuscles —theories dismissed as fantasies at the time he propounded them—were incorporated in the standard textbooks of the nineteenth century.

Joseph Lister read with wonder John's remarks on hectic fever, set down a century before Lister's own discoveries in antisepsis: "I believe the cure consists in the removal of the cause, viz., the local disease. . . . Strengtheners are proposed on account of the debility, which has evidently taken place; and antiseptics, from the idea of absorbed pus giving the blood a tendency to putrefaction." Equally impressive to Lister was John's proposal for treating compound fractures. "If," wrote the Victorian surgeon, "the coagulation at the orifice is allowed to dry and form a crust as was advised by John Hunter, all bad consequences are probably averted, and, the air being excluded, the blood beneath becomes organized and absorbed, exactly as in a simple fracture."

John was the first to recognize and explain inflammation of the veins, later termed phlebitis and shown to account for many hitherto unintelligible malignancies, such as a pulmonary embolism.

In expounding his precepts he was alternately proud and humble. "I have never met with impossibilities," he proclaimed. "If a thing be possible, why may I not do it as well as another man? If it will be impossible, I never think any more of it." He told a pupil: "I am but a pygmy in knowledge, yet I feel as a giant, when compared with those men [meaning most of the other St. George's surgeons]." And in a mood of humility: "The facility with which a man thinks gives him a superiority over others. Few have observed nature with more attention than myself, yet, even now, I think myself scarcely equal to the task I am undertaking—the elucidation of the economy of human life."

To the confusion of his pupils, he was continually amending his own views. When Astley Cooper pointed out to him that he was contradicting a statement he had made the year before, John retorted, "Vurra likely I did. I hope I grow wiser every year." He advised another puzzled pupil, "Never ask me what I have said, or what I have written, but if you will ask me what my present opinions are, I will tell you." He sometimes discouraged overzealous note-takers. "Better not write down that observation," he would say, "for vurra likely I shall think differently next year."

He mistrusted fast, glib thinkers, who published their papers prematurely. "It is surprising to see how a young man, if he catches an idea which has any novelty, will write away on it and tell you wonders." With excessively confident or lighthearted students he could be brutal. When a fledgling surgeon, having just completed a course, casually mentioned that he would now perhaps lecture on comparative anatomy himself, John remarked in chilling tones, "That is a bold undertaking. I had thoughts once myself of doing the same thing, but the difficulties and necessary qualifications were so great that I did not think myself competent to the task. But you, I dare say, may feel yourself quite equal to it."

Leigh Thomas, who was appointed surgeon to the British Embassy in China on John's recommendation, never forgot his initial encounter with the crusty Scot.

"Well, young gentleman," said John, when Thomas called at Jermyn Street, "so you are come to town to be a surgeon. And how long do you intend to stay?"

"One year, sir," replied Thomas.

"Then," said John, "I'll tell you what, that won't do. I've been here a great many years, and have worked hard too, and yet I don't know the principles of the art. Come to me tomorrow morning, young gentleman, and I will put you further in the way of things. Come early in the morning, as soon after four as you can."

Thomas appeared punctually at four. John had already been at work for some time, dissecting a beetle.

Before long John found himself teaching students from many lands, from Europe and the American colonies, and from every reach of society. George III, after appointing John Surgeon-Extraordinary, sent his licentious heir apparent, Prince George Augustus Frederick, to him, and later several of his eight other sons, for instruction in anatomy and medicine. John received them without enthusiasm. "Never take a gentleman as a pupil in physic," he used to say, "for, depend upon it, it is not simple curiosity, it is himself that is the object of his attention, and whatever knowledge he may acquire, it is only to employ upon himself, or tease others. He becomes his own patient ever after."

More to his liking was John Abernethy, a plain merchant's plain son, who worshipfully emulated "the dear man," his tartness as well as his methods. When, having himself achieved prominence as a surgeon, he was consulted by the Duke of York, he stood before His Grace whistling, hands in his pockets.

"I suppose you know who I am," said the Duke at length.

"Suppose I do," retorted Abernethy, "what of that?"

During the British invasion of France he kept pressing unsolicited military advice upon the Prince Regent. "Cut off their supplies," said he, "as the Duke of Wellington did in his campaigns, and the enemy will leave the citadel."

Abernethy became a first-rate diagnostician and a forceful lecturer, but so dogmatic, so intolerant of differing opinions, as to stifle individuality among his pupils. His *Surgical Observations on the Constitutional Origin and Treatment of Local Diseases*, his major published work and one of the earliest popular expositions of medicine, he quoted from so often that it became known in professional circles as "My Book."

His asperity in the consulting room was legendary, and had he not been exceptionally skillful, few patients would have crossed his threshold twice. Of a farmer who came to him complaining of a headache, he inquired flintily, "What quantity of ale do you take?"

"I takes my ale pretty well," the farmer allowed.

"Now, then, to begin the day. Breakfast—what time?"

"Oh, half-past seven."

"Ale then—how much?"

"I takes a quart."

"Luncheon?"

"At eleven o'clock I gets another smack."

"Ale then?"

"Oh, yes, my pint and a half."

"Dinner? Any ale then?"

"Yes, yes, another quart then."

"Tea—any ale to your tea?"

"Yes, yes."

"And supper?"

"I takes my fill and goes to sleep afterwards."

Abernethy chased him out of the house and down the street, bawling, "Go home, sir, and let me never see your face again! Go home, drink your ale, and be damned!"

Perhaps the greatest lesson John's students learned, what no other surgeon taught, was the application of principles derived from animal studies to the treatment of human disease, equipping them to operate on organs formerly considered inoperable. As Astley Cooper, the leading surgeon of the early nineteenth century, who earned £21,000 a year, recalled, "The surgeons of Hunter's day thought of him as a mere imaginative speculator, and any one who believed in him a blockhead and a black sheep in the profession."

But Cooper accomplished what Cheselden had been prevented from attempting: he relieved deafness by opening the eardrums, and thereby exploded the prevailing theory that destruction of those membranes inevitably destroys hearing. On the lower aorta, the great arterial tree, distributing blood through its branches to all the tissues, which no surgeon before had dared tamper with, he occasionally operated for an aneurysm.

Among other Hunterian "black sheep" were William Blizard, the first Professor of Comparative Surgery at the Royal College of Surgeons, whose private school became an adjunct to the London Hospital; Henry Cline, the master hand at St. Thomas's Hospital, and Anthony Carlisle, his equal at the Westminster Hospital; William Hey, who brought the cranial saw into general use, first described infantile hernia, and in Leeds established a Hunterian school of surgery.

Anne's brother, Everard, placed himself under John's wing, after his preparatory schooling. Him John judged more ambitious than apt, "all thumbs without the sense to tie down a bottle." But Everard recognized genius when he saw it, calculated the profit to be gained in its reflected light, and set about to make himself indispensable to his brother-in-law. A fellow student described him as "sly-eyed." He served John assiduously as secretary, emissary, greeter, and go-between. A quarrel interrupted the relationship when John delivered a particularly mordant reproof, and Everard, who had meanwhile obtained membership in the Corporation of Surgeons, joined the surgical staff of a naval expedition to Jamaica. He was back six years later, hat in hand, and he followed close thereafter, through marriage, fatherhood and a rich practice of his own, in John's wake. Ultimately he got control of the Hunter estate—with catastrophic result to John's lifework.

Of John's foreign pupils, a good many were already well along in their careers when they went to him. There was the Spaniard, Antonio de Gimbernat, who invented an operation for strangulated femoral hernia. One of the femoral ligaments, the lacunar, came to be known as Gimbernat's ligament. There was the mystical Pole, Samuel Joseph von Sommering, under whose leadership descriptive anatomists scaled new heights. His special field was teratology, the study of monstrosities. He could scarcely have found an authority more responsive than John. Von Sommering enumerated and named the cranial nerves, made important contributions to viniculture, to the study of fossils and sunspots. He also dabbled in Rosicrucianism, alchemy, and spiritualism. In a book on the soul, dedicated to Immanuel Kant, he tried to prove that consciousness resided in the cerebrospinal fluid. It led Goethe to chide him for tainting the waters of science with metaphysics. There was the Austrian, Johann Gottlieb Wolstein, who developed veterinary science in Austria and for twenty years directed the Vienna Veterinary Institute. By these pupils, and by many others, Hunterian doctrines were disseminated throughout the civilized world.

But it was a clergyman's son from Gloucestershire who outdistanced all the rest, and left a name to shine forever in the pantheon of man's deliverers from disease.

21. THE COUNTRY DOCTOR
"Don't think. Try it."

The clergyman's son enchanted Anne Hunter. He was witty without malice and erudite without pedantry. He could sing, play the flute and the violin, write music and verse. He expressed himself, even in casual conversation, with poetic imagery. At night, when he had laid aside his work, Anne would accompany him on the harpsichord in jaunty little airs of his own composition. It pleased John to learn that since early boyhood he had tramped the fields and woods of his native Berkeley, by the Severn River, collecting the nests of dormice, birds' eggs and fossils, and filling notebooks with his observations. The question once arose at a dinner party as to whether fire generated greater heat at its center or at its apex. The young poet-scientist drew up a lighted candle before his plate, thrust a finger into the flame, and held it there for several seconds. He then tried to hold his hand over the flame, but had to pull it back instantly. "There, gentlemen," said he, "the question is settled."

He was twenty-one when he journeyed to London in 1770, after studying pharmacology and surgery under a provincial surgeon, to become one of John's first house pupils. Broad and solid of build, with a round, open, cheerful face and short, curly hair, he dressed like a country squire in a sporting print—brass-buttoned blue coat, white buckskin breeches, silver-spurred jockey boots polished to the luster of black glass. John took to him at sight, and grew to prize him above all his pupils. He idolized John. "It was truly an interesting thing," his biographer wrote, "to hear him, in the evening of his days, descanting with

all the fervor of youthful friendship and attachment on the commanding and engaging peculiarities of Mr. Hunter's mind . . . when he
described the honesty and warmth of his heart, and his never ceasing
energy in the pursuit of knowledge, it was impossible not to be animated by the recital." His name was Edward Jenner.

John recognized in the newcomer a capacity for creative research, a
curiosity as omnivorous as his own, and he drove him relentlessly.
"Don't think," he would say, when Jenner stopped to weigh the feasibility of some thorny experiment. "Try it."

An enigma they often pondered together was natural immunity from
disease. Why did repeated exposure to certain diseases render the human organism less susceptible to them? How explain the antagonism
of diseases, whereby the system, while harboring one, was apparently
resistant to others? Why was it that those who survived smallpox were
seldom reinfected?

Those who survived . . .

"The most terrible of all the ministers of death," as Macaulay called
it, killed almost half of its victims, left others disfigured, crippled, blind.
It was a perpetual and universal scourge. Approximately a tenth of
the human race died of it. In the Russian Empire, in a single year,
it wiped out two million people; in Europe, every year, more than two
hundred thousand. The world-wide mortality since the beginning of
the century had exceeded forty million. According to an old saying, no
mother could count her children until they had come through smallpox.
So rare was a face free of pockmarks that a woman without them might
pass for a beauty.

The slow realization that people who survived smallpox almost never
contracted the disease again suggested a preventive. It was introduced
in England by the globe-trotting Lady Mary Wortley Montagu, whose
nephew and only brother both had died of smallpox, and whose splendid eyelashes had been destroyed by it. From Constantinople, where
she was living in 1717 as the wife of the British ambassador, she wrote
to a friend, Sarah Chiswell: "I am going to tell you a thing that I am
sure will make you wish yourself here. The smallpox, so fatal, and so
general amongst us, is here entirely harmless by the invention of in-
grafting, which is the term they give it. There is a set of old women
who make it their business to perform the operation every autumn, in
the month of September, when the great heat is abated. People send
to one another to know if any of their family has a mind to have the

smallpox; they make parties for this purpose, and when they are met (commonly fifteen or sixteen together), the old woman comes with a nut-shell full of the matter of the best sort of smallpox, and asks what veins you please to have opened. She immediately rips open that you offer to her with a large needle (which gives you no more pain than a common scratch), and puts into the vein as much venom as can lie upon the head of a needle, and after binds up the little wound with a hollow bit of shell; and in this manner opens four or five veins. The Grecians have commonly the superstition of opening one in the middle of the forehead, in each arm and on the breast, to mark the sign of the cross; but this has a very ill effect, all these wounds leaving little scars, and is not done by those that are not superstitious, who choose to have them in the legs, or that part of the arm that is concealed. The children or young patients play together all the rest of the day, and are in perfect health to the eighth. Then the fever begins to seize them, and they keep to their beds two days, very seldom three. Every year thousands undergo this operation; and the French ambassador says pleasantly, that they take the smallpox here by way of diversion, as they take the waters in other countries. There is no example of any one that has died of it; and you may believe I am very well satisfied of the safety of this experiment, since I intend to try it on my dear little son."

The son, Edward, was successfully inoculated, and so, when the Montagus returned to England, was their daughter, the future Countess of Bute. Lady Mary tirelessly strove to interest English physicians, but she could find none, as she bitingly commented, with "virtue enough to destroy such a considerable branch of their revenue for the good of mankind." Eventually, a Dr. Keith submitted his own daughter to the test and when she recovered, he supported Lady Mary's campaign. Inoculation achieved a moderate vogue. In 1754 the College of Physicians endorsed it.

The hopes thus raised, however, proved to be false. True, smallpox induced by inoculation was comparatively mild, with a mortality of one to three per cent, and it did confer immunity. But it was contagious and communicated the disease in its virulent form, so that those inoculated imperiled the entire community.

Discussing smallpox with John, Jenner continually referred to vaccinia, or cowpox, a minor affliction of cattle, characterized by pustular eruptions, and transmissible to man through contact. Jenner's birthplace was a market town in rich dairy country, renowned for its "double

Gloucester" cheese, and he told John of the dairymen's belief that a touch of cowpox gave lifetime protection against smallpox. He showed him a sketch of the pustules on a milker's fingers, which John copied for his own records. Probably, John speculated, if cowpox and smallpox were to be transmitted simultaneously, only one disease would develop.

Vaccinia—could the dairymen be right? *Don't think. Try it.* But not for a long time would Jenner be able to experiment clinically with vaccinia because the disease was uncommon in his part of the world.

He spent two years with John. Joseph Banks needed a skilled hand to arrange and classify his South Seas specimens, and on John's recommendation he entrusted them to Jenner, who performed the task so ably that Banks and Captain Cook offered him a berth as official naturalist on their second voyage around the world. But Jenner was happiest in the country, and he returned to Berkeley, there to enter general surgical and medical practice, though he obtained no degree until his forty-third year, when St. Andrew's University awarded him a doctorate of medicine.

Engrossed, when not attending patients, in ornithology, geology, and immunology, in the organization of two local scientific clubs, which he named Convivio-Medical and Medical-Convivio, and in aeronautics (he constructed a hydrogen gas balloon), he seldom visited London. Since John seldom left it, they saw little of each other, but they corresponded regularly. Every line from "the dear man" Jenner preserved, forty-eight letters in all, bristling with advice and dictates as perky, tart, provocative and affectionate as they were roughly phrased.

Jenner had hardly settled down in Berkeley before John was badgering him for regional specimens of everything that swam, crawled, or flew. "I shall be glad of your observations on the cuckoo, and upon the breeding of toads: be as particular as you possibly can. If you can pick up anything that is curious and prepare it for me, either in the fish or flesh way, do it." A few weeks later, after acknowledging the receipt of a cuckoo's stomach: "I should like to have a few more, for they do not all show the same thing. If possible, I wish you could remove the cuckoo's egg into another bird's nest, and tame the young, to see what note it has. There is employment for you, young man!" He also wanted the nests of a crow and a magpie, together with the branches of the trees they were built in. Also a young cuckoo. Also an old cuckoo. "I hear you saying, there is no end of your wants."

Jenner tried not to disappoint him and dutifully tracked the desired quarry through miles of brush. In return John kept his eyes open for bargains in paintings and bric-a-brac, what he banteringly called "Don Saltero's" after a Chelsea coffee-house founded by a barber named James Salter, who had cluttered the premises with gimcrackery. "Pictures have been very cheap, but the season is now over. . . . I purchased up a small landscape of Barrett's, of cattle and herd: I gave five pounds seven shillings and sixpence: it is one of his eight-guinea pictures. You shall have it or not as you please."

Jenner could also count on John for advice when confronted with surgical problems. It was usually succinct. "I would have you do nothing with the boy but dress him superficially: these funguses [on the boy's head] will die, and be damned to them, and drop off."

Were there any bats under Jenner's eaves? If so, John had a pretty experiment in mind. "Anny sends her compliments."

"I have but one order to send you, which is to send everything you can get, either animal, vegetable, or mineral, and the compound of the two, either animal or vegetable, mineralized." The boy with the funguses was not improving. Jenner feared the brain might be involved. "I would advise you not to meddle with it; if it is the brain, let it drop off; if it is fungus, let it either drop off or waste off: therefore be quiet, and think yourself well off that the boy is not dead. . . . You do not mention any bats."

Could he procure the bones of a large porpoise? Some salmon spawn? How would he like to examine eels? "Their sexes have not yet been found out, nor their mode of propagation; it is a thing of consequence in natural history." About those bats, Jenner should take their temperature. "Open a hole in the belly, just large enough to admit the ball [of a thermometer]; put the ball down towards the pelvis, and observe the heat there; observe the fluidity of the blood. Do all this in a cold place. . . . See if you can catch the number of pulsations and breathings in a bat without torture. . . . Cannot you get me a large porpoise for love or money?" And while he was on the subject of temperatures, let him, some frosty morning, see which vegetables froze. Let him bore holes in trees and see whether the sap flowed. Lest Jenner's thermometers be inadequate, John would forward one of his own making. ". . . but take care those damned clumsy fingers do not break it."

Of a marine mammal received he complained, "The bubbies are as flat as pancakes. . . . Was the milk sweet? Could you save some of it? if but two drops, to see if it grows sour. Try it with syrup of violets." Did he have another specimen? Were the breasts intact? The kidneys? Then please to send them. He could suit himself about treating the bones, either sending them as they were, or first steeping the flesh off in water. But he must include the stomach and a bit of intestine.

"Have you begun the eels? No porpoises. No salmon spawn. You see I am very greedy. . . . What the devil becomes of your eels in winter?"

Stirring news! Human skeletons had been unearthed near Berkeley. Of what period, was there any means of judging? In any event, John must have a share, especially of the skulls. "I have sent you the candlesticks as you desired. They cost five pounds and a shilling: so I owe you four shillings. . . ."

His requirements mounted steadily in quantity and complexity. "You are the only man I can apply to." He had been having a terrible time with hedgehogs. To observe their seasonal habits he had turned three of them loose during the late fall in the gardens of Earl's Court, leaving food for them at various spots. All three perished, presumably from exposure. Were they then hibernators? Jenner should follow some hedgehogs wherever they went. How did they behave? Did they burrow for warmth? Did they store food? Were they fat? He should look again in the spring to see if they were leaner. He should kill one and inspect the contents of its stomach. Was the blood as fluid as usual? And write, "dear Jenner, when you have nothing else to do."

The "Don Saltero's" piled up. "I have a picture of Bassan's that I lent a poor devil three guineas upon: he died and never redeemed the picture. I intend sending it to you. . . . I have a picture by Barrett and Stubbs. The landscape by Barrett; a horse frightened at the first seeing of a lion, by Stubbs. I got it for five guineas: will you have it?"

A rumor reaching him that Jenner had married a rich lady, he hastened to inquire was it true, trusting so, "for I do not know anybody more deserving of one." It was not true. Jenner, in fact, had been jilted, and he was feeling sorry for himself. John wasted few words in commiseration. "I can easily conceive how you must feel, for you have two passions to cope with, viz., that of being disappointed in love, and that of being defeated; but both will wear out, perhaps the first soonest . . . 'let her go, never mind her.' I shall employ you with hedgehogs."

John himself was "hedgehogless," an eagle having carried off one of his last two specimens, and a ferret having demolished the other. The misfortunes these creatures suffered at Earl's Court reminded an early Hunterian biographer of a remark the French physiologist, Magendie, made to his students: *"Vous savez, messieurs, que les chiens ne s'amusent pas içi."* John turned his attention instead to a consignment of bustards, peafowls, lizards, and birds' legs. "Are there no bats in the old castle at Berkeley?"

An improved tartar emetic Jenner compounded drew warm praise from John, and in his desire that his pupil should profit from it, he advised him, with a fine disregard for professional ethics, to keep the formula secret. Jenner not only declined to patent it, but published the formula in the *Transactions* of the Society for the Improvement of Medical and Chirurgical Knowledge, of which John was a founder.

Within seven years of leaving John's tutelage Jenner had arrived at a theory about cowpox and smallpox. He conceived them to be different forms of the same disease, the first modified by the bovine organism in which it developed. Cowpox, he concluded, did indeed seem to protect humans against smallpox, though not infallibly, probably because it had to be transmitted at a particular stage of its development. But the incidence of cowpox in Gloucestershire was still too low for conclusive proof.

John paused in his dissection of a Severn heron to consider the case of one of Jenner's patients who could not differentiate between certain colors. Did this signify a general defect of perception, or was the patient blind to some primary color? John improvised a test. "I will first premise that there are in nature but three colours, viz., *red, blue* and *yellow*, all the others being a combination of these three. First, present him with these three colours singly, and see what he calls them; then altogether (not mixed), and see how far they correspond with his first ideas of them: when that is ascertained, then begin to mix them; for instance, blue and yellow (which makes a green), see what he calls them; then a yellow and red (which makes a scarlet); next a blue and red (which makes a purple). Now to explain the intention of these experiments. Suppose he has a perfect idea of only one colour; and although you mix that colour ever so much, yet he sees none of the other, but only that colour in the mixture. Suppose all the three colours, when seen singly, or unmixed, with him are blue; mix red and blue (making a purple), he will only see the blue, the red not being visible to him; and so on of the others, according as he sees them. Suppose that a simple colour makes no impression, but a compound does, viz., green (which is composed of blue and yellow); then mix yellow and blue in all proportions, to see what colour these are: if he sees no green in any of them, then mix all the three colours in various proportions, and see what colours those make. When all the colours are mixed in various proportions, and the whole is green, perhaps of different shades, according to the quantity of blue and yellow, then you may fairly conclude that it is a mixture of the blue and yellow which produces it, the red never making any impression.

"If there is any other simple compound that he sees, as scarlet, which is the yellow and the Modena red; or a purple, which is blue and red; see if, when those two are predominant in the mixture (although there are all three colours in the mixture), that the compound becomes the visible colour."

The ways of that entertaining but unmaternal creature, the female cuckoo, loomed large in John's ruminations at this period. Could there be any doubt that she laid her eggs in the nests of less indolent birds for them to hatch and rear her young? If Jenner would once again, "to put all matters out of dispute," transfer a cuckoo's eggs from their original repository to another, then "there could be no supposition that the parent cuckoo would feed or take care of them." Would he also dispatch a new series of stuffed young cuckoos? Moths had got at the last lot. To the preparations Jenner eventually sent, John assigned a prominent place in his museum.

What was this tantalizing talk about the skin of a toad, prodigious in size, on display at Berkeley Castle? It gave John no rest. How could Jenner have failed to report such a wonder? "Let me know the truth of it, its dimensions, what bones are still in it, and if it can be stolen by some invisible being. . . . Have you any queer fish? . . . Anne sends, with little John, their compliments."

At the age of thirty-nine Jenner fell in love again, and this time the lady, Catherine Kingscote, reciprocated his devotion. They were married in 1788. A year later Jenner informed John that his wife had been delivered of a son, Edward, and asked him to be the godfather. "I wish you joy;" John wrote, "it never rains but it pours. Rather than the brat should not be a Christian I will stand godfather, for I should be unhappy if the poor little thing should go to the devil. . . . I hope Mrs. Jenner is well, and that you begin to look grave now that you are a father."

No prospect of glory or wealth could tempt Jenner to move to London, neither John's plans for a school of natural history with Jenner as chief assistant, nor Henry Cline's assurance that in London he might

earn £10,000 a year. A country doctor he would live and die.
To Cline he replied in lyrical vein, "Shall I, who even in the morning
of my days sought the lowly and sequestered paths of life, the valley
and not the mountains; shall I, now that my evening is fast approaching, hold myself up as an object for fortune and fame? Admitting it as
a certainty that I obtain both, what stock should I add to my little fund
of happiness? My fortune, with what flows in from my profession, is
sufficient to gratify my wishes; indeed so limited is my ambition and
that of my dearest connexions, that were I precluded from further
practice, I should be enabled to obtain all I want. As for fame, what is
it? A gilded butt, for ever pierced with the arrows of malignancy."

But fame came to him in overflowing measure. *Don't think. Try it.*
The name of the milkmaid, who had milked a poxy cow after scratching
her right hand on a thorn, was Sarah Nelmes. The plucky farmer's
son, eight years of age, was James Phipps. On May 14, 1796, Jenner
made two incisions in the boy's arms and inserted lymph from Sarah's
infected hand. Pustules, accompanied by a mild fever, appeared at the
site of the incisions. Within two weeks the symptoms subsided. The
crucial experiment followed on July 1. Through a fresh incision Jenner
introduced smallpox matter. Then, prayerfully, doctor and patient
waited—a week, two weeks . . .

On July 19 Jenner notified a friend, ". . . you will be gratified in
hearing that I have at length accomplished what I have been so long
waiting for, the passing of the Vaccine Virus from one human being
to another by the ordinary mode of inoculation."

After further tests, Jenner published, in 1798, his *Inquiry into the
Cause and Effect of the Variolae Vaccinae.* He lived to see smallpox
on the wane throughout the world.

Thomas Jefferson wrote him: "You have erased from the calendar of
human afflictions one of its greatest. Yours is the comfortable reflection
that mankind can never forget that you have lived; future nations will
know by history only that the loathesome small-pox has existed, and by
you has been extirpated."

During the war with France Jenner petitioned Napoleon for the re-
lease of some British prisoners. The Emperor was not disposed to grant
it until Josephine called his attention to the identity of the petitioner.
"Ah," said Napoleon, "we can refuse nothing to that man."

In Canada the chieftains of the Five Indian Nations convened to
draft a tribute to Jenner. "Brother! [it read] Our Father has delivered

to us the book you sent to instruct us how to use the discovery which the Great Spirit made to you, whereby the small-pox, that fatal enemy of our tribes, may be driven from the earth. We have deposited your book in the hands of the man of skill whom our great Father employs to attend us when sick or wounded.

"We shall not fail to teach our children to speak the name of Jenner; and to thank the Great Spirit for bestowing upon him so much wisdom and so much benevolence.

"We send with this a belt and a string of Wampum, in token of your precious gift; and we beseech the Great Spirit to take care of you in this world and in the land of spirits."

The belt remained among Jenner's most treasured possessions, together with the hide of the cow that infected Sarah Nelmes, and John Hunter's letters.

22. THE AMERICANS

Upon American medicine especially the influence of John, and to a considerable extent of William Hunter, was important. Nearly the whole of colonial physic, surgery, and obstetrics, as they began to move away from empiricism, reflected Hunterian doctrines, for starting with William Shippen, some of the foremost of the colonies' medical pioneers crossed the Atlantic during their formative years to study under one or both brothers.

From New York City in 1769 sailed Richard Bayley, aged twenty-four, leaving behind his wife of a few months, the daughter of Dr. John Charlton, to whom he had been apprenticed. He was home a year later, bursting with ideas absorbed from William Hunter, when an epidemic of what was probably diphtheria broke out, killing hundreds of children. Called by various symptomatic names—Angina trachealis, Suffocatio stridula, the Croup—it was so virulent that in one Long Island town it carried off all but two children.

Bayley made pathological examinations of the first victims in order to determine the nature and area of injury. What he observed, namely gross inflammation of the membranes of the trachea and larynx, enabled him to apply remedies that sharply reduced mortality. "The author," he wrote to William Hunter, elaborating his diagnoses and treatment, "is conscious that this letter will prove the most acceptable acknowledgment he can offer for the instructions you so generously bestowed upon him while a pupil at your theater."

Bayley thrived. He and Charlton were the first colonial practitioners to make their rounds in a carriage instead of on horseback. Not long after the birth of a daughter, he journeyed again to London for a refresher course in William's school, and he was still there at the outset of the Revolution. A confirmed royalist, he obtained a commission as surgeon to one of His Majesty's regiments, and with it returned to America aboard a man-o'-war. While stationed in Rhode Island, he got word that his wife was dying in New York. To go to her, he had to resign his commission. He arrived too late to see her alive.

The hostilities ended, Bayley began lecturing on pathology, his paramount interest, in the New York Hospital, illustrating his theories with his own collection of morbid specimens. Anatomy was taught under the same roof by a pupil of John Hunter's, handsome, stylish Philip Wright Post, who later married Bayley's daughter. By his contempt for prevalent therapeutic methods, which he voiced with Hunter-like bluntness, Bayley did not endear himself to his colleagues. They retaliated with slander, accusing him of putting scientific curiosity before humanity, of having callously experimented on sick British soldiers.

During the Doctors' Riot of 1788 the pathologist was besieged by a murderous rabble that had been stirred up by tales of body snatching and dissection. Swinging brickbats, they broke into the hospital and as Bayley, Post and their pupils took refuge in a nearby jail, they demolished the pathological exhibits. Other doctors soon filled the jail. When the mob tried to force it, Mayor James Duane called out the militia. Baron von Steuben, the hot-tempered Revolutionary hero, hastened to the scene and was promptly knocked down. "Fire, Duane, fire," he bellowed in his fury. The militia discharged a volley that killed seven rioters.

"It is sincerely wished," the New York *Packet* commented, "that our fellow citizens would manifest their zeal against vice and wickedness (as it abounds in the city) which kill men's souls and be less zealous for the preservation of the duller part. However we would not wish to be understood by this hint, to apologize for those who wantonly, and perhaps unnecessarily disturb the ashes of the dead."

The New York *Journal and Patriotic Daily Register* printed an ambiguous affidavit from Bayley denying that he had molested "the bodies of any person or persons interred in any churchyard or cemetery, belonging to any place of public worship," but not mentioning the anonymous corpses snatched from less respectable burial grounds like Potter's Field.

Bayley's renown as a surgeon was enhanced when he amputated a patient's gangrenous arm at the shoulder joint, employing a technique never before used in America. When Columbia College instituted a medical faculty in 1792, he was chosen to be Professor of Anatomy and Surgery, and upon that chair being divided the following year, his son-in-law succeeded to the professorship of surgery. The indifference of the city officials to social welfare disgusted Bayley, and with a few progressive doctors he promoted the New York Dispensary, where he tirelessly treated the poor.

At frequent intervals since the early eighteenth century the "Great Sickness"—yellow fever—had invaded the colonies. Characterized by jaundice, convulsions, and the vomiting of black blood, it wiped out, in 1793, a tenth of the population of Philadelphia, about five thousand people. Nobody dared shake hands; people wearing black crepe were assumed to be mourning for relatives killed by yellow fever, and were shunned. Two years later the pestilence ravaged New York, killing one out of four victims.

Bayley roamed the city day and night, combating what he proclaimed to be "a murderer of our own creating," nurtured by the filth of the harbor. His account of that epidemic, a milestone in the study of tropical diseases, described it as shipborne, a result of commercial intercourse with the West Indies. It was, he rightly surmised, infectious rather than contagious, its incidence highest in summer when the trading vessels put in. He demanded better sanitation on the waterfront and medical inspection of all craft from foreign ports.

Preventive medicine occupied Bayley almost exclusively after that. As health officer of the Port of New York, he promulgated State and Federal quarantine laws.

In 1801 an Irish immigrant ship docked with a number of fever-stricken passengers. Suspecting typhus, Bayley separated the sick from the hale, lodged them in separate tents, and ordered them all to leave their luggage aboard the ship. The following morning he found the whole lot in one tent, surrounded by their belongings. He stood there raging at them until his orders had been obeyed. In the afternoon he was attacked by stomach cramps. When he could hold up no longer, he dragged himself off to bed. Within a week he was dead.

Philip Wright Post, who survived his father-in-law by seventeen years, dominated post-Revolutionary surgery in New York. Tall and lean, his hair powdered and gathered at the back in a queue, grave of manner and concise of speech, he struck the cosmopolitan Dr. Valentine Mott, who had toured the medical world, as "one of the most luminous and perspicacious teachers I have ever listened to at home or abroad."

Post introduced to America John Hunter's operation for an aneurysm in the ham, at the time the most effective defense in the arsenal of surgery, whereby the diseased femoral artery was tied off and the tributary arteries left to perform the work of circulation. Post further applied the technique, for the first time successfully, to an artery underlying the clavicle, outside the neck muscles, an awkward spot.

Post's private anatomical museum, which Columbia inherited upon his death in 1828, remained to the end of the century the largest in America.

Among the passengers aboard the *Thomas*, the last Europe-bound American vessel to slip through the British blockade of Boston Harbor in 1775, was a twenty-one-year-old Rhode Island Quaker named Benjamin Waterhouse. Having begun the study of medicine at the age of sixteen as an apprentice to a Newport doctor, he meant to continue it under various European masters. "That prince of physiologists, John Hunter," he recalled years after, "once told me that he loved to be puzzled, for then he was sure he would learn something valuable."

In London Waterhouse lived with and assisted his cousin, Dr. John Fothergill. He went next to Edinburgh to hear lectures by the Monros, and thence to the University of Leyden for his doctorate of medicine, signing the register "a citizen of the free and United States of America," a title the monarchist faculty refused to have inscribed on his diploma. At Leyden he shared quarters with a precocious New Englander of thirteen, John Quincy Adams. Adams, Sr., the American Minister Plenipotentiary, joined them while awaiting the outcome of negotiations for a peace treaty with England.

When Waterhouse graduated, his cousin pressed him to settle permanently in London and take over part of his flourishing practice. It was a rosy prospect, but Waterhouse cared little about wealth and less about bedside therapy. Patients, he declared, bored him. He embarked for America full of missionary zeal to disseminate scientific rather than mechanical principles.

His reception was cool. Although the Harvard Medical School welcomed him as Professor of the Theory and Practice of Physic, when it opened in 1782, Waterhouse won practically nobody's admiration. He discovered, as Bayley did in New York, that nothing so disturbed the common run of practitioners as a new idea, and, like Bayley, he did not trouble to disguise his scorn for orthodoxy. In addition, he was a religious dissenter, professing Quaker ideals offensive to most Bostonians, a stinging critic of the autocracy that dictated university policy, and a Jeffersonian Democrat in a stronghold of Hamiltonian Federalists. He provoked the student body at Harvard when he circulated a diatribe against the heavy consumption of tobacco, "unruly wine and ardent spirits," to which he attributed an increase of delinquency and bad health among the undergraduates. He became so unpopular that the Boston Medical Society curtly rejected his petition to draw upon the almshouse infirmary for clinical subjects. Eventually Harvard sacked him.

Waterhouse was by then married for the second time, the father of seven children, and since he had never built up much of a private practice, in a poor way financially. Before the blow fell, however, he had brought a few thoughtful colleagues closer to the scientific spirit. He had established the first natural history course this side of the Atlantic, started a university museum of minerology, and founded the Cambridge Botanical Gardens. And he had introduced in America the most valuable prophylactic since America was colonized—smallpox vaccine.

Smallpox in the New World was pandemic. Transmitted to Mexico by the Spanish conquistadors, it killed three and a half million people there during the early decades of the sixteenth century. Spreading north, it eradicated half of the American Indians, then attacked the New England settlements. In Boston alone, during the next hundred years, there were six outbreaks. The prevalence of the plague was indicated by an announcement in the New York *Postboy* of October 16, 1752, intended to lull the fears of prospective visitors to the city: "We are assured that there are now very few families in this city but what either have or have had the smallpox; and that we have good reason to hope the City will soon be clear of that distemper."

An acquaintance of Waterhouse's student days in London had sent him, a year after its publication, Edward Jenner's paper on *Variolae Vaccinae*, the first copy to reach America. Waterhouse wrote Jenner for more information, and in the Boston *Columbian Sentinel* he gave a précis of the book, to which, knowing what to expect from the profession, he added, "This publication shared the fate of most others on new discoveries. A few received it as a very important discovery, highly interesting to humanity; some doubted it; others reserved that wise and prudent conduct which allows them to condemn or applaud, as the event might prove; while a greater number absolutely ridiculed it as one more of those medical whims which arise today and tomorrow are no more."

So it went in America. Waterhouse did win distinguished support when he advocated vaccination in an address before the American Academy of Arts and Sciences, then under the presidency of John Adams. Elsewhere progress was slow. To demonstrate his own confidence in the preventive, Waterhouse proposed to vaccinate his own children, then expose them to smallpox. But for a year he could find no trustworthy vaccine. He finally obtained some from Jenner's stock, and on July 8, 1800, he vaccinated his five-year-old son, Daniel. When the resulting pustule subsided, he took him to the private smallpox clinic of a Dr. Aspinwall. Under the father's directions Aspinwall punctured the boy's arm, inserted matter from a patient's pustules, and for good measure drew an infected thread through the broken skin. Neither Daniel nor his brothers and sisters, who were subjected to the same treatment, came to any harm, and public resistance faded to such a degree that the demand for vaccine far exceeded the supply.

But shortly Waterhouse's victory was reversed. Ignorant doctors used impure vaccine. Some even went back to inoculating with strains of smallpox instead of cowpox. Itinerant quacks cut the pus-impregnated shirts worn by smallpox victims into strips and hawked them as a source of vaccine. Catastrophe befell the citizens of Marblehead, Massachusetts, following the arrival of a merchant ship, a member of whose crew appeared to have cowpox. Several doctors drew matter from his sores with which to immunize their patients. But the sailor actually had smallpox, and the disease rapidly spread through the town.

As a result, by 1801 few Americans would risk vaccination. Waterhouse had to begin all over again converting both the profession and the public. "Could you believe," he complained in a letter to Jenner, "that not a single case of the cow-pox inoculation has yet occurred in Philadelphia?" Jenner sent a fresh batch of vaccine, most of which Waterhouse shrewdly transmitted to the new President of the United States, Thomas Jefferson, at his Monticello estate, with the plea that he vaccinate himself and his family. Jefferson complied, and he vaccinated some two hundred neighbors as well.

Waterhouse, meanwhile, after accumulating vaccine from his own herd of cowpox-infected cattle, persuaded reputable doctors in Boston and other cities to test it publicly on children. The uniformly good effects silenced opposition. Before he died in 1846, at the age of ninety-two, Waterhouse had the satisfaction of noting, "It [vaccination] is so universally adopted and has so completely put an end to the greatest pest that white society has ever had, that if you see a person who has pock marks you may be sure he is a foreigner."

When Dr. John Morgan walked the streets of his native Philadelphia, passers-by would stop and stare at the mushroom-like object he held over his head, the first of its kind ever seen thereabouts. It was, the doctor explained, a silk parasol. He had acquired it abroad, where he studied anatomy for a year under John Hunter, qualified for his M.D. degree at Edinburgh, and surveyed the leading medical schools and hospitals of France, Switzerland, and Italy. Another souvenir of his travels, amazing to Philadelphians, was a collection of glass eyes.

Morgan's place in the front rank of American physicians rests mainly upon a single achievement—the founding in 1765 at the College of Philadelphia (later the University of Pennsylvania) of the country's first medical school. An organizational genius, he outlined the plan for it while in London with the encouragement of the Hunters and some suggestions from Shippen, who later claimed the idea was his.

Morgan already had had a good deal of professional experience when he sailed for England at the age of twenty-five. Two years earlier, during the French-Indian War, he had acted as surgeon to General George Forbes's expedition against the French at Fort Duquesne. "So great," attested Benjamin Rush, himself one of the greatest of the colonial physicians, "was his diligence and humanity in attending the sick and wounded who were the subjects of his care that I well remember to have heard it said that if it were possible for any man to merit Heaven by his good works, Dr. Morgan would deserve it. . . ."

Abroad Morgan reaped honors normally reserved for older men. At Edinburgh he astounded the faculty by the originality of his graduation thesis. Antisepsis being then unknown, pus usually formed in wounds. But the nature of pus nobody understood. Morgan contended that it arose from the blood vessels, not, as many believed, from the solid tissues. He was proved right a hundred years later when the German pathologist, Julius Friedrich Cohnheim, using a microscope, saw that pus consists of white corpuscles that have broken through the walls of the blood vessels.

On the Continent Morgan not only learned but taught, demonstrating to his elders the Hunters' latest anatomical innovations. He returned home with a dazzling string of titles—Fellow of the Royal Society, Licentiate of the Royal College of Physicians at both Edinburgh and London, Associate of the Académie Royale de Chirurgie de Paris, member of Rome's Society of Belles Lettres. So impressed were the trustees of the College of Philadelphia that when Morgan submitted his long matured plan they adopted it without a dissenting vote and retained him to instruct physical theory and practice.

But no sooner invested than this first professor of America's first medical school exploded a bombshell. At the opening exercises he read a manifesto innocently entitled *A Discourse Upon the Institution of Medical Schools in America,* which challenged the profession's most cherished prerogatives and by implication insulted every practitioner present.

What scientific progress demanded, Morgan told his shocked audience, was specialization. The different branches of healing must be separated. It was impossible to practice, with equal efficiency, physic, surgery, obstetrics, pharmaceutics, and dentistry. For his part he would confine himself to internal medicine. He had, he disclosed, brought an apothecary from England, and he advised all doctors to let him, instead of their ill-trained apprentices, fill prescriptions. This was the crowning outrage, an attack upon their pocketbooks, for most doctors earned more money dispensing drugs than visiting sickbeds. So much the worse. A doctor should be a scientist, not a peddler of pills.

Ignoring the rumble of anger, Morgan went on to formulate standards of training for doctors such as hardly any man there could have met. In an era when the dimmest yokel could style himself a doctor on the strength of having passed a few months in a doctor's office, he called for a rigorous program of pre-medical studies. Applicants for admission to the new school should be versed in Latin, at least one other foreign language, mathematics, and natural history. If matriculated, they should be required to complete courses in anatomy, pharmacology, botany, chemistry, medical theory and practice, and clinical medicine. After a year's internship in the Pennsylvania Hospital, they might receive the degree of Bachelor of Medicine. But the M.D. degree should be withheld until they had practiced a specialty for three years and presented a thesis.

The iconoclast spoke for two days. He belabored the apprentice system that, providing no systematic training, turned loose upon the community droves of deadly blunderers. "Great is the havoc," Morgan stormed in a wildly emotional peroration, "which he spreads on every side, robbing the affectionate husband of his darling spouse or rendering the tender wife a helpless widow; increasing the number of orphans, mercilessly depriving them of their only comfort and hope by the untimely death of their beloved infants; and laying whole families desolate. Remorseless foe of mankind! actuated by more than savage cruelty! hold, hold thy exterminating hand!"

Later generations accepted Morgan's views as self-evident truths. The curriculum of the University of Pennsylvania Medical School and medical education in general developed along the lines he had laid down. But in his day such ideas were considered subversive, the ravings of an irresponsible visionary bent upon wrecking a system wiser men had spent their lives building. By the end of his discourse Morgan had made dangerous enemies, none more so than Shippen since the obstetrician felt he merited credit as the originator of the medical school plan. Although Shippen was elected Professor of Anatomy on Morgan's recommendation, he never stopped conspiring against him. He triumphed over him finally during the Revolution.

In 1775 the Continental Congress, to Shippen's boiling indignation, named Morgan Director-General of the Military Hospitals and Physician-in-Chief to the Continental Army. He had been married ten years to Mary Hopkinson, a Philadelphia belle, whose father, Thomas Hopkinson, sat on the Governor's Council. Too much in love to part even briefly, husband and wife rode north together to Washington's headquarters at Cambridge.

Conditions in the army hospitals and at the "flying camps" behind the lines horrified Morgan. Many of the doctors were unfit to tie a bandage, and often the competent ones could only stand by helplessly for lack of instruments to amputate, while wounded soldiers died in the agonies of gangrene. The surgical supplies of fifteen regiments included no more than three pairs of bullet forceps. Everything was lacking—drugs, shelter, food—and from the depleted treasury Congress would not allocate the funds to buy them. Neglect of the sick and wounded lost more battles than bad strategy.

Morgan dispatched letter after letter to the Medical Committee of Congress, imploring its approval for a plan he had drafted to reorganize the chaotic hospital service. He got no reply, and no disciplinary authority. As he struggled to bring about a semblance of order, he was defied at every turn by his subordinates in collusion with army officers who distrusted civilians. Washington supported him always, but Washington was having his own troubles with opponents in Congress.

While Morgan thus fought to save lives at the front, Shippen in Philadelphia was contriving his downfall. Into the ears of congressmen he poured calumnies: Morgan was inept; Morgan was vainglorious. After Shippen had been put in charge of a flying camp on Long Island, he boasted that every wounded man there had recovered. The congressmen believed him. Without specifying a single charge, they cashiered Morgan and gave Shippen his command.

Morgan demanded and eventually got a congressional hearing. He was vindicated. In fact, Congress had already enacted legislation proposed by him, requiring rigid examinations of candidates for army medical service, raising the pay of regimental doctors, and standardizing army medical regulations. But injustice had crushed Morgan's spirit. When Mary Morgan died childless, he lost all zest for life. Though only fifty, he taught no more at the school he had founded, abandoned his private practice, and sank listlessly into poverty. On October 15, 1789, Benjamin Rush wrote in his diary:

"This afternoon I was called to visit Dr. Morgan, but found him dead in a small hovel, surrounded by books and papers, and on a light, dirty bed. He was attended only by a washerwoman. . . . His disorder was influenza, but he had been previously debilitated by many other disorders. What a change from his former rank and prospects in life! The man who once filled half the world with his name, has now scarcely friends left enough to bury him."

The most inventive of John Hunter's American pupils, and the chief expositor of his theories in the New World, bore the implausible name of Physick—Philip Syng Physick. It afforded endless opportunities for chaff to those British who could not abide a native of the upstart nation that had humbled the monarchy in battle. One of them penned a ballad beginning

Sing Physic, sing physic: for Philip Syng Physick
Is dubbed Dr. Phil for his wonderful skill;
Each sick phiz he'll physic, he'll cure every phthisic,
Their lips fill with Philip with potion and pill.

No surgeon ever prepared for the profession with less enthusiasm. The idea was entirely his father's. Edmund Physick, an Englishman by birth, had emigrated to Philadelphia before the Revolution, amassed a fortune in real estate, and held the office of Keeper of the Great Seal of the Colony of Pennsylvania. Fiddling with a knife one day, he sliced a finger. Philip, then a schoolboy enrolled in the Academy of Friends, after watching a doctor bandage the wound, offered to change the dressing whenever necessary. This he did so deftly as to convince his sire that he was destined for surgery. The boy disclaimed any such ambition. He could not bear to see blood flow or to inflict pain. He was sickly, moreover, a prey to catarrh and nosebleeds, and debilitated by smallpox, which had pitted his pallid face. Towards the end of his laurel-crowned career he complained that he would have been a happier, healthier man if allowed to pursue the same trade as his maternal grandfather, Philip Syng, a silversmith, who fashioned the inkstand used by the signers of the Declaration of Independence. His father obliged him all the same to take pre-medical courses at the University of Pennsylvania, and to make sure that he got special attention, he paid his teachers extra.

During the first operation Philip watched, a leg amputation, he became so ill he had to be led out of the amphitheater. "I can never be a surgeon," he told his father. But that inexorable parent would not countenance such weakness, and from a sense of filial duty the wretched son resumed his studies. He applied himself heroically. Instructed to read a mammoth tome of suffocating tedium on medical practice, he committed every line to memory.

When he was twenty, a skinny, splayfooted, humorless youth, his father accompanied him to London and entered him in John Hunter's school. Upon presenting himself to the Scot, the senior Physick remarked: "Well, sir, I presume some books will be required for my son. I will thank you to mention them that I may get them."

"Here, sir," said John, "follow me. I will show you the books your son has to study," and ushering father and son into the dissecting room, he pointed to a row of cadavers. "These are the books. The others are fit for vurra little."

Once he hardened himself to the sight and stench of dissolution, Physick justified his father's fondest expectations. His classmates never warmed to him, finding him "dyspeptic, pessimistic and unsociable," though he was only diffident and self-conscious, but they marveled at his versatility. In John's revolutionary treatise on the blood he credited Physick ("whose accuracy I could depend on") for confirming by experiment many of the discoveries there set forth.

St. George's Hospital took him on as house surgeon. Among the first cases to confront him was a dislocated shoulder. The head of the humerus, the long bone running from shoulder to elbow, had been forced downward and lodged behind the armpit. The standard treatment called for an assistant and mechanical traction. Physick announced that he would dispense with both. Before a large class, which had assembled in the hopes of seeing the American make a fool of himself, he seated the patient on a high chair, and while diverting his attention with questions about the accident, placed his left hand under the armpit and in his right grasped the humerus. So swiftly that the sufferer felt no more than a single flash of pain, he pressed the elbow hard against the ribs. The bone snapped back into its proper cavity.

After the Royal College of Surgeons licensed Physick, John offered to employ him, but the Philadelphian chose to take an M.D. degree at Edinburgh, then practice in his birthplace. His doctoral thesis on apoplexy, presented in Latin, he dedicated to John.

When he came home in 1793, his father provided him with an office near the corner of Arch and Third streets. "My son," he admonished him, "you have cost me much money. You have now an outfit. Learn to take care of yourself."

At the outset Physick's cash assets totaled less than a dollar, and for three years he had a thin time of it. "I walked the pavements," he recollected long after, "without making as much by my practice as put soles on my shoes."

He was not idle, however. Yellow fever invaded Philadelphia. Physick devoted himself to the stricken with a courage Philadelphians never forgot, toiling incessantly in an emergency hospital set up at Bush Hill. Like Richard Bayley in New York, he tried to understand the nature of the disease by dissecting the dead. He concluded, correctly, that yellow fever was particularly destructive to the gastric tract.

Physick's economic distress was somewhat ameliorated when a number of families accepted his proposition that they each pay him an annual stipend of twenty dollars for full medical care—an early form of group health insurance. He later became Philadelphia's richest practitioner, not by charging a few patients big fees, but by charging many patients small ones. When a grateful husband, whose ailing wife was recuperating under the doctor's care, handed him two hundred dollars, Physick demanded: "Have you two ten dollar notes in your pocket?" The husband had. "Will you let me have them?" The husband complied. "Very well, here are your two hundred dollars; the two tens are quite enough."

His bedside manner was formidable. He would brook no resistance to his orders. To a patient who questioned the wisdom of being bled for pleurisy, he retorted: "Sir, I must have my own way, or none at all. I bid you good day." Another, wincing at the prospect of having his scrotum tapped for a hydrocele (an abnormal accumulation of water), was told: "Sir, I'll have none of this. Down with your pantaloons. I know perfectly what I am about."

He nearly met his match when, as White House physician, he attended Andrew Jackson. The old campaigner thought he knew as much about medicine as any M.D., and persistently doctored his own numerous ailments with massive doses of either sugar of lead or calomel. These ailments included chronic pleurisy, resulting from a lead bullet that had lodged in his chest during a duel, alternating bouts of diarrhea and constipation (possibly attributable to lead poisoning from the same source), skin eruptions, failing eyesight, and malaria. For internal symptoms he drank the sugar of lead, for external symptoms he rubbed the stuff into his pores. Only by exerting the full weight of his authority did Physick finally prevail upon the President to discontinue this dangerous self-treatment and submit to cupping. "I can do anything you think proper," said Jackson, "except give up coffee and tobacco." When Physick returned to Philadelphia, he attested to the "gentleness, the peculiar and indescribable charm" of his trying patient.

With all but the closest friends he remained taciturn and withdrawn. Small talk pained him. He attended few social gatherings and rarely entertained. He almost never laughed. The only recreation he permitted himself was brief visits during the summer to his brother's country estate. He was frugal, averse to reading, incurious about the stirring events in the burgeoning democracy around him. He married at thirty-two, Elizabeth Emlen, the daughter of an erudite and wealthy Quaker, who bore him four children. He was an austere but fond husband and father.

A forbidding man, yet one friend, who sensed the kindliness behind the frosty exterior, addressed these lines to Physick:

> They say thou'rt cold—unlike to other men;
> A snow-crowned peak of silence, towering high
> Above the heart's warm, soft, sequestered glen,
> As flashing sunset glories on the sky.
>
> Who say so, know thee not; nor can discern
> Beneath thy sage, professional disguise,
> How deep the feelings he whom they call stern,
> Hides from dull heads, hard hearts, or careless eyes.

Religious doubts troubled Physick. He found it difficult to reconcile the agonies he constantly witnessed with the existence of a benign Creator. "Death," he mused, "what can it be? With all our inquiry it is at last a fearful step in the dark." But evidently he resolved the conflict in the end, for he assured a relative, worried over his spiritual salvation, who asked him whether he had faith in the Christian religion, "Yes, indeed I have!"

A second attack of yellow fever, in 1797, nearly finished Physick. A few years later typhus infected him. This was followed by nephritis, kidney stones, dropsy, and arteriosclerosis, gradually reducing him to a skeletal ruin. He nevertheless carried on a huge private practice, lectured and served on the staffs of four hospitals, the most important being the Pennsylvania Hospital, the first general hospital in America, which Benjamin Franklin had founded in 1751.

During his tenure at the university and at the Pennsylvania Hospital Physick originated a profusion of surgical tools and techniques, a number of which are still used. He devised needle forceps for tying deep-lying blood vessels, the guillotine tonsillotome, a snare to extract diseased uvulas, improved dental forceps, new types of urethral catheter, bougies and gorgets, forceps for gripping and crushing stones inside the bladder, a cannula for insertion in the cranium to drain off water from hydrocephalic skulls, a double cannula with a wire loop for excising hemorrhoids, modified splints for fractures of the elbow, femur, and ankle. He was the first American to operate successfully for "artificial anus" (cloture of a fecal fistula). He introduced to American surgery the one valuable innovation of the French opthalmic quack, Baron Michel Jean-Baptiste Wenzel—a method of enucleating damaged lenses.

Hip-joint diseases he treated by immobilization instead of surgery, and dislocations, as he had in London, by manipulation instead of mechanical traction. He was the first to pump out the stomach in cases of poisoning, applying this method to a pair of Negro twins whose mother had accidentally fed them an overdose of laudanum, and using a rubber tube and pewter syringe of his own design. In sewing up an incision, the advantages of thread that the tissues can absorb, and which therefore need never be pulled out, are obvious. For more than a century catgut has been one of the commonest suturing materials, and it was Physick who first showed catgut to be absorbable.

He was also responsible for a national vogue in beverages when he advised patients with digestive impairments to drink carbonated water. At his suggestion the pharmacist who supplied it, one Townsend Speakman, added fruit juice for flavoring. The hale as well as the ailing came to relish the mixture, and so arose the great American soda-pop industry.

"Physick's Operation" was a new method of iridotomy. After the extraction of a cataract the iris may be so drawn that no pupil remains, and a "window," or new pupil, must be cut in the iris. Physick would snip out a tiny circular piece of tissue with an instrument he invented —a pair of punch forceps, both arms ending in a concave, sharp-rimmed disk. Modern opthalmic surgeons generally prefer scissors to Physick's forceps, but the object—to let in light through an artificially created window—is identical.

A grasp of physiology equaled by few of his contemporaries enabled Physick to develop an ingenious treatment for fractured humeri that failed to knit naturally. He would draw a seton, or skein of threads, through the gap, leaving it there to stimulate, as he knew a foreign body would, the formation of bony tissue and so facilitate union. That device has been superseded, but it was a major advance over the then prevalent agonizing and permanently crippling practice of sawing off the jagged bone ends.

Striking evidence of its success confronted Physick when a colleague summoned him for consultation to the bedside of a sailor dying of a mysterious fever. Physick recognized a former patient in whose humerus he had implanted a seton twenty-eight years earlier. The arm, the sailor told him, had not given a moment's trouble since. At this the scientist in Physick put the humanitarian to rout, and he talked the failing patient into willing him his body that he might make a post-mortem examination of the site of the fracture. Death soon followed, and upon receiving the body Physick dissected out the humerus. To his gratification, he found the break to be perfectly consolidated by an osseous band, with a minute hole through the center where the seton had passed.

Physick's contemporaries acclaimed him as "the Father of American Surgery." Yet, like John Hunter, who never picked up a scalpel without self-reproach, he considered surgery a surrender, an evil necessity imposed by inadequate knowledge of the human organism. It was said that "he never spilt a drop of blood uselessly, or, as a teacher, ever wasted a word."

In the fall of 1831 the Chief Justice of the United States, John Marshall, journeyed from his Richmond home to Philadelphia, seeking relief from the torture of bladder stones. He first consulted Dr. Jacob Randolph, Physick's son-in-law and protégé. By then illness had driven Physick, a magnificent lithotomist, into retirement, but Randolph entreated him to perform the operation upon the great jurist. He finally consented, with grave misgivings, for Marshall was seventy-five years old.

As in England, few men of means went to a hospital for surgery. No record indicates where the operation took place, but very likely Physick installed Marshall in his own house at 321 South Fourth Street.

No surgeon ever had a more valorous patient. Early in the morning of the appointed day Randolph preceded Physick to the sickroom. Marshall was seated before a table laden with food.

"Well, doctor," said the patient affably, "you find me taking breakfast, and I assure you it is a good one. I thought it very probable that this might be my last chance, and therefore I was determined to enjoy it and eat heartily."

"I am glad to see you so cheerful," said Randolph. "I hope all will soon be happily over."

Marshall betrayed no anxiety. He realized, he said, that the odds against him were heavy, but he would rather die under the knife than go on living in torment.

"What time will the operation be?" he asked when he had finished breakfast and taken the medicine Randolph brought.

"Eleven o'clock."

"Very well. Do you wish me now for any other purpose, or may I lie down and go to sleep?"

Astonished and moved by the old man's serenity, Randolph replied that nothing could be more desirable, whereupon Marshall fell at once into a deep sleep, from which Randolph had to arouse him when Physick appeared.

During the ordeal the Virginian uttered scarcely a sound. It lasted longer than most lithotomies, there being no less than a thousand calculi to extract, "varying in size from a partridge shot to a pea." But Marshall survived it and lived four more years.

Although his illustrious patient could readily afford to pay him, Physick declined to present a bill. Only after considerable persuasion would he accept a silver tankard, inscribed: "This tribute of gratitude for health restored offered by J. Marshall."

In the summer of 1837, at the age of sixty-nine, Physick was dying, and he knew it. "Ah, doctor," he greeted a young colleague, William Horner, who hailed him in the street, "how do you do? Do you see I am almost gone."

"I hope not, sir," said Horner. "I hope you will live to see many days of usefulness."

"Me," Physick scoffed, "me, useful with my frame? No, impossible, I must die soon."

Horner began to move away, when Physick called him back. "Doctor," said he in a rare outburst of emotion, "you are a friend of mine, I always esteemed you as such. I now take my last leave of you. I shall not see you again, I can't help it, I am sorry for it."

But a last delicate eye operation awaited him. A foreigner, his sight dimmed by glaucoma, had made his way to Philadelphia, sustained by his faith in Physick's power to cure him, and Physick was determined not to fail him. Randolph, who assisted the surgeon, recalled later: "I watched him with the most intense anxiety; notwithstanding at the time he was labouring under great mental and physical suffering."

The patient regained his sight, but never got a chance to thank his deliverer. From the operating room Physick went to his bed, not to leave it alive. He was buried in Christ Church cemetery.[e] In a memoir of his father-in-law, Randolph wrote, by way of an epitaph:

> *He gave his honours to the world again,*
> *His blessed part to Heaven, and slept in peace.*

Shippen, Bayley, Post, Waterhouse, Morgan, Physick . . . It was fitting that the American Philosophical Society, at the urging of its president, Benjamin Franklin, should have elected John Hunter an honorary member.

23. A SURGEON SCORNED

"O, sir," said John to one of his pupils, "we all have vermin that live on us." He was speaking of a man named Jessé Foot, who, according to rumor, had received £400 from a clique of anti-Hunterians to write a defamatory biography. Such a biography was indeed in progress, but it had probably been undertaken without pay. For this Jessé Foot, a surgeon of sorts and a literary hack, needed no monetary inducement to defame John. Like other venomous drippings from his pen, the biography, which would occupy him for some twenty years, was a pure labor of hate. To it can be traced the grossest of the slanders that continued to befoul John's memory long after his death.

Nothing so simple as pelf motivated Foot in what was possibly the most implacable persecution of one surgeon ever carried on by another. The driving force was compounded rather of sick vanity, of emotional hungers unappeased, of the compulsion to tear down what he could not rise up to. During his early, brief contacts with John, Foot seems to have prized him—even in the most abusive parts of the biography he failed to repress a grudging admiration—and he might perhaps, after the way of his kind, have become a Hunterian disciple as fanatic as later he was a reviler, had not John, recognizing a shoddy specimen, turned away. The wound of rejection festered, breeding maggots of hatred that gnawed at Foot to the end of his days. With frantic industry he scavenged for particulars he could twist to John's discredit, the flaws of character as well as the professional mistakes. There was no dearth of surgeons at St. George's and elsewhere happy to help him.

Foot may have been as demented as he looked, with his wild uprush of spiky hair, and big, protuberant eyeballs like overripe grapes bursting from their skins. Sixteen years younger than John, he came from Wiltshire. He studied medicine in London under George Fordyce, at twenty-two was admitted to the Corporation of Surgeons (Percivall Pott conducted the entrance examination), and went to the West Indies to practice for three years on the island of Nevis. The feudal life of the British planters appealed to Foot, and he later defended them against the abolitionists with an apologia for their barbarous treatment of slaves.

He traveled to Russia, and became, as he described it, "a privileged practitioner of the College of St. Petersbourg." Returning again to London, fortified by a sense of his own superior skill, he opened an office in the Strand, then moved to Soho, near the Spences' dental parlor, where he first caught sight of John Hunter. For eleven years he was house surgeon at Middlesex Hospital. His private practice grew lucrative enough to enable him to purchase a snug annuity.

An incessant, if turgid writer, Foot produced a spate of medical papers, bedizened with Latin quotations, in which he laid claim to signal achievements. Few were accepted by scientific publications. He also penned truckling biographies of Arthur Murphy, an actor, whose executor he was, and of his patients, Andrew Robinson Stoney, duelist, seducer, and fortune hunter, and his rich wife, the Countess of Strathmore.

At Middlesex Foot had invented a urethral bougie. John inspected it, saw no improvement over existing models, and said so. Foot's *bête noire* took shape in that moment. He aimed his first shafts at John's most vulnerable spot—his poor classical education—stinging him into one of the few rejoinders he ever deigned to make. "Jesse Foot," he told an anatomy class, "accuses me of not understanding the dead languages, but I could teach him that on the dead body which he never knew in any language, dead or living."

Immediately following the publication of John's treatise on venereal diseases, Foot rushed three treatises of his own into print, excoriating

John without contributing further to the subject. He now hoped to widen the rift between the pro- and anti-Hunter camps, and assume leadership of the latter. But though John's enemies were glad to use Foot as a cat's-paw, they were not complete fools; they looked to saner spokesmen. John kept silent, noting only in a memorandum to himself: "One may say of Jessé Foot as we sometimes say of young men, 'It was well their fathers were born before them.' It was well for Jessé Foot that I published my book before his."

By the candor with which he acknowledged his own errors, John himself furnished the ammunition for some of Foot's deadliest volleys. "Whenever I have seen the dura mater opened," he recalled in a lecture, "the brain has worked through the opening. This was the case with a Mr. Cooper, whose dura mater I opened with a crucial incision on account of the state of the parts beneath. He died, and I think it probable I killed him."

In December 1784, a rabid dog, prowling Jermyn Street, bit a woman and a small boy, the latter on the lip. The boy was taken where, as Foot put it, "reputation had directed he was to go." John tried to disinfect the wound with a caustic. The woman he treated at her home. Both victims died of hydrophobia.

Reviewing the boy's case in an open correspondence with a physician, John wrote: "I rubbed in mercury so that the mouth became sore. Twice I applied a caustic to the whole—but I am inclinable to believe that I did not touch every part where the teeth had been—from the termination of the case."

Pouncing upon this avowal, Foot dashed off an eighty-six-page pamphlet, *An Essay on the Bite of a Mad Dog, with John Hunter's Treatment of the Case of Master R—and also a Recital of the Successful Treatment of Two Cases by Jessé Foot, Surgeon.* "I do assert," he wrote, "that John Hunter did not do, for these patients, the best that could have been done, by the art of surgery—and that the miscarriage was not owing to the inevitable nature of the cases." Surgery, he held, not caustic was indicated. As to John's confession of error, "Unfeeling effrontery. . . . A modest man, a man of feeling would have blushed at such an apology."

This sniping was mere rehearsal for the grand onslaught Foot mounted under the guise of *The Life of John Hunter.* In a preface to the book, which was not finished until 1794, he piously reminded the reader that worthy men were not the only proper objects of historical inquiry. "The best and brightest examples of men should alone be the models for imitation; but yet it will ever be found necessary, for the purpose of inculcating their true value, to form a critical comparison with characters that have betrayed a contrary inclination." Of panegyrists ready to smooth and flatter, there would always be a plethora. "I write more to inform than to praise, more for example than glory." Thus wrapped in a mantle of moral grandeur, he proceeded to the indictment.

"John Hunter never was the author of any production which has appeared under his name. . . .

"He was never discovered in attempting to explore the occurrences most necessary to be accounted for, as the pride of his heart was only to select an obscure subject, which involved in it so much matter of wonder as to raise the public attention. . . .

"He cared not for truth, nor the use which might be made of any investigation in nature: and if he could give his subject the air of novelty, he cared neither from whom he took his information upon it. . . .

"Whenever he undertook to treat upon a subject already treated upon by another, his aim was either to pass the author over in silence, or in his way, to forestall the invention, by alluding to notes remotely said to be made upon the subject by himself. . . .

". . . he never made use of that art [surgery], but for the emoluments he derived from it; he considered solely the profits of surgery, as a means of carrying on the expenses of speculation. . . .

". . . [he] had no delight in comparative anatomy, when it was to be connected with comparative ingenuity; and the darker he made the room of information, the more he was at liberty to do within it whatever he chose without being detected. . . .

"This was his reasoning [when attempting a hazardous operation]— if I do not succeed, I cannot be blamed, as opinion was,—that the case would not admit of success;—but if I should succeed, I snatch a leaf of laurel. . . ."

Here Foot likened John to Richard III.

24. "BROTHER ASS, THE BODY"

No serious pain had afflicted John since his last bout of gout. But at ten o'clock one morning, in the spring of 1772, he was attacked by an internal spasm of such violence that he could neither stand nor lie down. A dose of laudanum mixed with tincture of rhubarb brought no relief. The pain increased, radiating through his chest.

As he thrashed about in torment, his eyes fell upon a looking glass. It showed him an ashen face, the lips white—the face of a corpse, he recalled afterwards—and there swept over him a sense of imminent death. He felt his pulse, but detected no beat. His breathing stopped. By an effort of will he got his lungs to pumping feebly.

Even as he fought for air a part of John's mind remained watchful, curious, registering his reactions as detachedly as though they were occurring in a clinical patient. (Later, recounting the seizure for the instruction of his pupils, he speculated: "Quaere, What would have been the consequence if I had not breathed? At the time, it struck me that I should have died; but that most probably would not have been the consequence, because, most probably, breathing is only necessary for the blood when it is circulating; but as there was no circulation going on, so no good could have arisen from breathing.")

Forty-five minutes passed by John's watch before the pain subsided and his pulse and respiration improved. He drank some Madeira wine, brandy and ginger. In the afternoon he recovered a little strength. "About two o'clock I was able to go about my business."

No other illness troubled him for three years. Then he collapsed under a second attack. He himself believed it to have been precipitated by worry over a debt. To oblige a young Scottish friend, Captain Lockhard Gordon of the Royal Sussex Regiment, he had stood security for a bank loan of £1,700. The captain defaulted and sailed with his regiment to America, leaving John to repay the money.

A complex syndrome accompanied John's ensuing malady, and at each stage he would jot down a minute description, provided he could hold pen to paper, or, when too enfeebled, dictate to Everard Home. In addition to stabbing chest pains, he was overcome by dizziness whenever he raised his head from his pillow. His sensory organs became abnormally acute. He could not tolerate light even with his eyes closed.

Faint sounds were like gunfire in his ears. He had hallucinations. He imagined himself to be only two feet tall and floating in midair. The slightest motion of his head or limbs produced the sensation of ranging immense distances at great speed. He was variously attended by his brother, by Drs. Huck Saunders, George Baker, and George Fordyce, who bled, cupped, purged and fed him emetics.

John lay abed ten days and then with Anne went to Bath to convalesce. Jenner, who visited them there, was appalled by the change in his teacher. He looked much older than his forty-nine years, his face deeply seamed, his normally brisk gait faltering. What Jenner surmised, from John's dispassionate recital of events, to be the nature of his illness and its prognosis, he could not bear to tell him, and a paper he happened to have prepared on the subject he postponed publishing lest it come to John's attention. In a letter he addressed, but decided for the same reason not to forward, to a physician of John's acquaintance, William Heberden, Jenner wrote:

"I thought he was affected with many symptoms of the Angina Pectoris. The dissections (as far as I have seen) of those who have died of it, throw but little light upon the subject. Though in the course of my practice I have seen many fall victims to this dreadful disease, yet I have only had two opportunities of an examination after death. In the first of these I found no material disease of the heart, except that the coronary artery appeared thickened.

"As no notice had been taken of such a circumstance by any body who had written on the subject, I concluded that we must seek for other causes as productive of the disease: but about three weeks ago, Mr. Paytherus, a surgeon at Ross, Herefordshire, desired me to examine with him the heart of a person who had died of the Angina Pectoris a few days before. Here we found the same appearance of the coronary arteries as in the former case. But what I had taken to be an ossification of the vessel itself, Mr. P. discovered to be a kind of firm fleshy tube, formed within the vessel, with a considerable quantity of ossific matter dispersed irregularly through it. This tube did not appear to have any vascular connection with the coats of the artery, but seemed to lie merely in simple contact with it.

"As the heart, I believe, in every subject that has died of the Angina Pectoris, has been found extremely loaded with fat; and as these vessels lie quite concealed in that substance, is it possible this appearance may have been overlooked? The importance of the coronary arteries, and how much the heart must suffer from their not being able duly to perform their functions (we cannot be surprised at the painful spasms) is a subject I need not enlarge upon, therefore shall only just remark that it is possible that all the symptoms may arise from this one circumstance.

"As I frequently write to Mr. H. I have been some time in hesitation respecting the propriety of communicating the matter to him, and should be exceedingly thankful to you, Sir, for your advice upon the subject. Should it be admitted that this is the cause of the disease, I fear the medical world may seek in vain for a remedy, and I am fearful, (if Mr. H. should admit this to be the cause of the disease) that it may deprive him of the hopes of a recovery."

Jenner and his contemporaries considered angina pectoris to be a disease in itself, not, as we do today, a symptom common to various coronary lesions. Nor did any of them conceive that such lesions—an inflammation of the coronary vessels, for example—could result from syphilis.

If John himself did not suspect the pain to be anginal, if he really believed it to be symptomatic of gout, his delusion was ironical. For he might have been expected to recognize the clinical picture of angina pectoris, since he had performed the first post-mortem examination of a body in which that condition had been diagnosed during life.

The victim was an anonymous doctor, an admirer of Heberden, of whom the poet Cowper wrote:

> *Virtuous and faithful Heberden, whose skill*
> *Attempts no task it cannot well fulfill,*
> *Gives melancholy up to Nature's care*
> *And sends the patient into purer air.*

In 1768, after reading a lecture Heberden delivered before the College of Physicians, in which he coined the term angina pectoris, the ailing doctor bequeathed him his body.

"I found it [Heberden's account]," he wrote in a letter accompanying the bequest, "to correspond so exactly with what I have experienced of late years, that it determined me to give you such particulars, as I can recollect, at those times to have felt; more especially as some sensation has frequently led me to think, that I should meet with sudden death. I am now in the fifty-second year of my age, of a middling size, a strong constitution, a short neck, and rather inclining to be fat. My pulsations at a medium are about 80 in a minute; the extremes, when in a perfect state of health, beyond which I scarcely even knew them, 72 and 90. I have enjoyed from my childhood so happy a state of health as never to have wanted, nor taken, a dose of physic of any kind for more than twenty years. As well as I can recollect, it is about four or five years since, that I first felt the disorder you treat of; it always attacked me when walking, and always after dinner, or in the evening. I never once felt it in the morning, nor when sitting, nor in bed. I never ride, and seldom use a coach; but it never affected me in one. The first symptom is a pretty full pain in my left arm a little above the elbow; and in perhaps half a minute it spreads across the left side of my breast and produces either a little faintness, or a thickness in my breathing; at least I imagined so, but the pain generally obliges me to stop. At first, as you observe, it went off instantly, but of late by degrees; and if, through impatience to wait its leaving me entirely, I resumed my walk, the pain returned. I have frequently, when in company, born the pain and continued my pace without indulging it, at which time it has lasted from five to ten minutes, and then gone off. As well as I can recollect, rather suddenly, as it came on, lessening gradually. Sometimes I have felt it once a week; other times a fortnight, a month, or a longer time, may elapse without its once attacking me; but, I think, I am more subject to it in the winter, than in the summer months. As, when the pain left me, I had no traces of having the least disorder within me of any kind, either from spitting blood, or any corrupted matter, nor ever entertained the least thought of any abscess being formed, I never troubled myself much about the cause of it, but attributed it to an obstruction in the circulation, or a species of the rheumatism.

"I shall now proceed to acquaint you with those sensations, which to me seem to indicate a sudden death; but which, not being concomitant with the above-mentioned disorder, I am ignorant whether they are to be attributed or not. I have often felt, when sitting, standing, and at times in my bed, what I can best express by calling it an universal pause within me of the operations of nature for perhaps three or four seconds; and she has resumed her functions; I felt a shock at the heart, like that which one would feel from a small weight being fastened to a string to some part of the body, and falling from the table to within a few inches of the floor. At times it will return two or three times in half an hour; at other times not once a week; and sometimes I do not feel it for a long time: and I think I have been less subject to it for a year past, than for several former ones. As you have mentioned several, who within your knowledge have died suddenly, that were troubled with the *angina pectoris,* I suspect they were subject to what I have delineated, as I think that much more likely to occasion a sudden death, than either of the causes to which you attribute it. But, be the cause what it may, if it please God to take me away suddenly, I have left directions on my will to send an account of my death to you, with a permission for you to order such an examination of my body, as will shew the cause of it; and perhaps, tend at the same time to a discovery of the origin of that disorder, which is the subject of this letter, and be productive of means to counteract and remove it. . . ."

He died soon after. The autopsy, which John undertook at Heberden's request, revealed areas of ossification in the aorta.

Between John's first and second attacks Heberden published a paper, which John doubtless read, reviewing the case history of the anonymous doctor and drawing inferences from some fifty similar cases he had diagnosed. Thus, though John gave no such indication, he could scarcely have failed to note a parallel to his own state of health. Unconsciously, perhaps, he rejected the knowledge of an affliction for which there was no effective treatment; perhaps he hoped to spare Anne. Whether he knew or not, however, the record he kept of his own illness, often adding to it while still in the grip of a seizure, was one of the most complete inventories ever compiled of the symptoms associated with what we now term coronary thrombosis. Incorporated by Everard Home into a memoir of his brother-in-law, it included accurate descriptions—among the earliest—of the irregular breathing later called Cheyne-Stokes respiration, of aphasia or speech impairment, of the nervous and mental concomitants.

The Hunters lingered in Bath, after John's second attack, for three months. But as Jenner feared, John never entirely recuperated. For the rest of his life the least exertion, physical or emotional, was apt to induce spasms ending in unconsciousness. "I . . . never saw any thing to equal the agonies he suffered;" wrote Home, "and when he fainted away, I thought him dead, as the pain did not seem to abate, but to carry him off, having first completely exhausted him."

Frequently, the mere act of undressing at night sufficed to produce an attack. So did animated discussion (he learned to avoid large gatherings), drinking wine (he gave it up), a difficult operation, concern over an experiment in progress. ". . . the exercize that generally brought it on," Home wrote, "was walking, especially on the ascent, either of stairs or rising ground, but never on going down either the one or the other; the affections of the mind that brought it on were principally anxiety or anger: it was not the cause of the anxiety, but the quantity that most affected him; the anxiety about the hiving of a swarm of bees brought it on; the anxiety lest an animal should make its escape before he could get a gun to shoot it; even the hearing of a story, in which the mind became so much engaged as to be interested in the event, although the particulars were of no consequence to him, would bring it on. . . ."

Wrath, to which John was so prone, exposed him to the direst attacks. A tardy coachman, an inattentive secretary, would throw him into volcanic rages. He realized his danger, yet was powerless to control his temper. "My life," he said, "is at the mercy of any rogue who chooses to provoke me."

There were occasional signs of mental deterioration, suggesting a brain lesion such as advanced syphilis may produce. While visiting the home of a friend, his memory suddenly lapsed, and for half an hour he was totally disoriented. At times he confused dreams with reality. For weeks he could sleep no more than an hour or two out of twenty-four.

Many a patient bore the brunt of his irrational outbursts. When a young man consulted him about a running sore, John glared at him and, folding his arms, repeated: "And so, sir, you have an obstinate running sore?" "Yes, sir," replied the sufferer hopefully. "Why, sir," John shouted, "if I had your running sore, I should say, 'Mr. Sore, run and be damned!'"

John came to despise, to feel ashamed of his body for its failings, which alone were capable of disrupting his work. "Brother Ass, the body," he called it in angry despair. But though disease crippled him physically and mentally, it did not apparently injure the major area of the cerebral cortex—the seat of intellectual function—for he retained unimpaired to the end his powers of observation and reasoning. The periods of his greatest debility were among his most creative.

25. THE SMELL OF BITTER ALMONDS

In 1777 the high season at Bath was enlivened by the presence of Captain John Donellan, popularly known as "Ring" or "Diamond" Donellan after the large and brilliant gem that adorned his finger. The illegitimate son of an Irish lieutenant-colonel, he had been educated at the Royal Military Academy, appointed, when only sixteen, to a cadetship, dispatched to India, and there commissioned captain. Although in his reminiscences he pictured himself as a doughty warrior, he served in only one campaign, against the French at Golconda, without distinction or gallantry. After the fall of the capital of Golconda, he was cashiered for peculations involving the division of spoils. The diamond that later suggested his sobriquet he stole from an Indian merchant. These derelictions, however, had not blighted his rise as a fashionable young London profligate. Handsome, debonair and glib, though slim of purse, he enjoyed access to some of the city's choicest gaming rooms and boudoirs. He was Director of Entertainments at the Pantheon in Oxford Street, a vast public pleasure palace perpetually astir with balls, masques, and musicales.

Among the nobility who visited Bath that summer were Lady Anna Maria Boughton, the addlepated widow of Sir Edward Boughton, sixth Baronet of Little Lawford, and her daughter, Theodosia Anna Maria Ramsay Beauchamp Boughton. They had neglected to reserve accommodations, and not a bed was to be found. At the last inn where they applied the landlord could provide only chairs to sleep on. Captain Donellan happened to be comfortably installed there, and upon learning of their plight, he had himself introduced, made a fine leg, and with a courtliness impossible to resist, proffered his quarters. In the morning the grateful ladies invited him to breakfast. Before the season ended the captain had won Miss Boughton's heart.

The Boughtons' social and economic situation left little to be desired. Sir Edward, who had been carried off by apoplexy six years earlier, had bequeathed them extensive assets, which included Lawford Hall in Warwickshire, a sumptuous, many-chambered mansion dating from the sixteenth century, its antiquity certified by the frequent reappearances of a one-armed Elizabethan ancestor. The will named only one other legatee beside the dowager and her daughter—a son, Sir

Theodosius Edward Allesley Boughton, then a spindly Etonian of sixteen. Were he to die without issue, his portion, yielding £2,000 per annum, would accrue to his sister. The young baronet was somewhat precocious. When Donellan visited him at Eton, he found him under medical care for gonorrhea.

The captain gathered that Lady Boughton, while flattered by his attentions, would be unlikely to welcome him as a son-in-law, and so he persuaded Theodosia to elope. He was right. Her ladyship closed her doors to the newlyweds, and for a year they lived by themselves in Bath, subsisting on Theodosia's income. Donellan strove by exemplary behavior to placate Lady Boughton. Forswearing his libertine ways, he devoted himself tenderly to his bride. He publicly renounced all claims to her present fortune and to any property she might inherit in the future (though if he signed a formal statement to that effect, it was never recovered). Lady Boughton finally relented. She bade the couple reside at Lawford Hall, and they arrived in June of 1778.

Sir Theodosius had also returned to the parental hearth. He soon reinfected himself in the arms of a local Paphian. An apothecary in nearby Rugby, Thomas Powell, prescribed an assortment of salves, febrifuges, and purgatives, so potent that the patient was sometimes confined to his bed all day.

Lady Boughton being witless, and Sir Theodosius preoccupied by amorous pursuits, the management of the estate fell to the captain. He acquitted himself to the satisfaction of everybody except Sir Theodosius, who resented his authority. The brothers-in-law bickered continually. By way of recreation Donellan rode, fished and hunted on the well-stocked grounds. He fashioned a chemical retort ostensibly to distill attar from the garden flowers.

Both at home and abroad the captain expressed grave concern over the state of Sir Theodosius's health, which though not good was far from critical. He told the Reverend Piers Newsham, the family's pastor, "His blood is a mass of mercury and corruption and his intellects are so affected that nobody knows what it is to live with him."

"If such is the case," the minister remarked, "I don't think the baronet's life is worth two years' purchase."

"Not one," said Donellan.

When Lady Boughton proposed to revisit Bath, he advised her against it, saying: "Don't talk about leaving Lawford Hall. Something or other may happen."

She thought he was referring to the dangers of a mishap due to her son's general recklessness. In taproom brawls he had three times been challenged to pistol duels, from which Donellan extricated him. For a lark he once scaled a church steeple, slipped, and might have broken his neck had not the captain, chancing upon the scene, caught him in his arms.

Sir Theodosius kept his medicines in a dressing room adjoining his bedroom, which was usually locked. One day, when he forgot to dose himself, Donellan suggested, "Why don't you set it in your outer room? Then you will not so soon forget it." The youth complied, and thereafter the bottles were ranged on the mantelpiece facing his bed.

As Sir Theodosius grew increasingly restive under the captain's dominion, he decided to clear out, and in July 1780 he announced that he intended, at the end of the month, to visit a friend in Northamptonshire. On Tuesday, July 29, the eve of his prospective journey, Powell, the apothecary, concocted an explosive two-ounce mixture of rhubarb, jalap, spirits of lavender, nutmeg water, and syrup of saffron. The patient's valet, Samuel Frost, called for it, and at six o'clock in the evening delivered it to Sir Theodosius, who carried it uncorked to his bedroom. Master and servant then set forth on horseback for a fishing jaunt.

Lady Boughton and Theodosia were strolling in the garden where, towards seven o'clock, Donellan joined them. "Sir Theodosius should have his physic," he said. "I've been to see him fishing. His feet were wet. I would have persuaded him to come in lest he take cold, but I could not." Actually, Samuel Frost recalled later, Sir Theodosius had fished from horseback, as was his curious custom, and never dismounted. He came home about nine o'clock in high spirits, ate supper, and retired.

Lady Boughton planned to be up early next day. At Newnham Wells, three quarters of a mile away, there was a mineral spring, whose properties—so Donellan had convinced her before she went to bed— would benefit her, and she agreed to accompany him there at six o'clock. Had she been punctual, what occurred in her son's bedroom that morning would have passed unobserved. But she wished first to inquire after his health. From the courtyard, at the appointed hour, Donellan, astride his horse, called up: "Is your ladyship ready to ride out?" "I shall be in about a quarter of an hour," she replied. He said he would ride on ahead.

When she approached her son's bedside, he indicated a phial on the mantelpiece labeled "Purging draught for Sir T. Boughton," and asked her to pour it into a cup. As she did so, she noticed a powdery sediment. It emitted an unfamiliar offensive odor. In groping afterwards for an analogy to describe it, she hit upon a phrase that was to become a cliché of the detective story. It smelled, she said, "very strongly like bitter almonds." Upon draining the cup, Sir Theodosius complained of a nauseating taste. Within two minutes he fell violently ill. "He struggled very much, it appeared to me, as if it was to keep it down, and made a prodigious rattling in his stomach and guggling."

The symptoms lasted about ten minutes. He then seemed to doze off. Thinking his distress to have been caused by his efforts not to vomit, Lady Boughton withdrew to finish her toilette. When she returned, her son's eyes were straining from their sockets, his teeth were clenched, foam flecked his lips.

She ran from the room, shrieking to the servants to fetch the apothecary and her son-in-law. The captain was just then entering the gates. The coachman, Will Frost, told him Lady Boughton urgently needed him and, relieving him of the horse, galloped off after the apothecary.

"What do you want?" Donellan inquired, as he strode into the sickroom.

Sir Theodosius was alive, but incapable of speech.

"Want!" exclaimed Lady Boughton. "Here's a terrible affair! I've been giving my son something that was wrong, instead of what the apothecary should have sent. It's an unaccountable thing in the doctor to have sent such a medicine, for if a dog had taken it, it would have killed him."

"Where is the physic bottle?" Donellan asked.

When she pointed it out to him, he refilled it with water, shook it thoroughly, and emptied it into a washbasin partly full of dirty water.

"Good God!" Lady Boughton protested. "What are you about? You should not have meddled with the bottle."

He picked up a second phial, filled that, dipped in a finger and popped the finger into his mouth. "I did so," he explained, "to taste it." But Lady Boughton had not seen him sample any water from the first phial.

The cook, Catherine Amos, and a maid, Sarah Blundell, came in. Sir Theodosius's chest was heaving. Catherine wiped the froth from his mouth. Donellan commanded the servants to dispose of the phials, the washbasin, and the soiled linen. "No," Lady Boughton objected, "leave them." But the captain insisted, and he was obeyed. "Here, take his stockings," he instructed Sarah. "They've been wet. He's catched cold, to be sure, and that might occasion his death." Lady Boughton felt the stockings. They were bone-dry.

Meeting Catherine in the passage outside the bedroom a few minutes later, Donellan observed, "Sir Theodosius was out very late over night a-fishing. It was silly of him, as he's been taking physic."

He went below to find Catherine's husband, Francis Amos, the gardener, whom he directed to snare a pair of pigeons for application to the feet of the moribund youth, a common medical practice of that time. "Poor fellow!" said he. "He lies in a sad agony now with this damned nasty distemper, the pox. It will be the death of him."

When Powell arrived, Sir Theodosius had been dead an hour. Donellan met the apothecary at the gates and led him up to the bedroom. The captain asked no questions and made no allusion to the phials, stating merely that Sir Theodosius had perished in convulsions. From Lady Boughton the puzzled apothecary later learned that the violent symptoms followed hard upon the drinking of the malodorous draught. The purgative he prepared, he assured her, could neither offend the nostrils nor harm the system.

During the rest of that day the captain held a number of astonishingly indiscreet conversations. In Lady Boughton's hearing he told Theodosia: "Your mother has been pleased to take notice of my washing the bottles out. I don't know what I should have done if I hadn't thought of saying I'd put the water in to taste it." When her ladyship turned away without comment, he repeated the remark.

He then rang for the coachman. "Will," he asked him, "don't you remember that I set out from those iron gates about seven o'clock?"

"Yes, sir," said Will.

"Then you are my evidence."

He spoke further with Francis Amos. "Now, gardener, you shall live at your ease and work at your ease; it shall not be as it was in Sir Theodosius's days. I wanted before to be master, but I have got master now, and shall be master." He later brought Francis his retort to clean. It was full of wet lime. "I used it to kill fleas," he said. Limewater was an approved anti-flea agent, but could not possibly be manufactured in a retort. On the other hand, it would have been an efficient detergent for scouring the retort.

In view of Lady Boughton's suspicions her actions were decidedly erratic. She entrusted the funeral arrangements entirely to Donellan, indicating no desire for a post mortem. Feeble-mindedness seems to be the only explanation. On the Saturday following the calamity, Sir Theodosius reposed in a coffin, ready for burial.

But sinister rumors were agitating the county. Was the apothecary's drug to blame for the sudden death? Or had it been doctored? The talk reached the ears of Sir Theodosius's legal guardian, Sir William Wheeler of Leamington. He wrote Donellan a polite letter, urging him to silence gossip by ordering an autopsy. In his reply the captain warmly assented; he hoped Sir William would be present. This the guardian deemed improper, but he recommended two surgeons to inspect the remains, Messrs. Wilmer of Coventry and Snow of Southam, and a physician, Dr. Rattray of Coventry. They reached Lawford Hall on the evening of September 4, six days after Sir Theodosius died. Greeting them at the door, a lighted taper in hand, Donellan declared: "You have been called upon to open the body of the deceased for the satisfaction of us all." He did not mention poison, but it was improbable that the rumors could have bypassed any inhabitant of the region.

A more timorous lot never disgraced their calling. When they saw that the corpse was fast decomposing, the weather being warm, they refused to touch it for fear of infection. Donellan did not press them, and they left. The captain informed Sir William of their visit by a letter so worded as to imply that a satisfactory examination had been completed.

A less squeamish Rugby surgeon, Samuel Bucknill, having learned otherwise, offered to perform an autopsy, whatever the risk. "It would not be fair," Donellan told him, "to do anything after men so eminent in their profession declined it and said it was impossible."

When Sir William discovered that the captain had misinformed him, he prevailed upon both Snow and Bucknill to go back to Lawford Hall. Bucknill arrived first, but was immediately called away to attend a dying patient. Snow turned up in his absence, would not act alone, and departed. To Bucknill, when he came again, the captain said: "Mr. Snow has given orders what to do, and we are proceeding according to those orders." Snow rode away. Donellan delayed no longer. The same day Sir Theodosius was entombed.

Thus, incredibly, all of these abortive transactions were conducted by a person under suspicion, and with the knowledge and apparent sanction of Lady Boughton, who professed to have suspected him from the first. When it became generally known that Sir Theodosius had been buried without an autopsy, public indignation exploded. Such a clamor was raised that the county coroner ordered the body to be exhumed, Bucknill to dissect it, and a jury to be empaneled.

Ten days had now elapsed and putrefaction was far advanced. Bucknill, with the Messrs. Wilmer and Snow and Dr. Rattray looking on, found the stomach and bowels to be inflamed. He examined the intestines no further, and the brain not at all. "It is impossible," Wilmer later testified, "to tell what occasioned the deceased's death."

At the coroner's hearing Lady Boughton described her son's last moments. As she was telling how Donellan had rinsed the phials, he surreptitiously plucked her gown. A juror named Crofts caught the gesture. (At Lawford Hall, during an adjournment, Donellan furiously reprimanded his mother-in-law. "You're not bound to give the whole account of it," he told her. "You're to answer only such questions as are put to you.") From Lady Boughton's account of the symptoms the medical witnesses concluded that the potion Sir Theodosius drank, whatever it contained, caused his death.

When Donellan realized that the idea he had been at such pains to implant, that Sir Theodosius died of disease, was gaining no support, he propounded a new one. In a letter addressed to the jury before the resumption of the inquest, he wrote: "During the time Sir Theodosius was there, a great part of it was spent procuring things to kill rats, with which this house swarms remarkably, he used to have arsenic by the pound weight at a time, and laid the same in and about the house in various places, and in many forms; we often expostulated with him about the extreme careless manner in which he acted, respecting himself and the family in general, his answer to us was, that the men servants knew where he had laid the arsenic, and for us, we had no business with it; at table we have not knowingly eaten anything for many months past, which we perceived him to touch, as we well knew his extreme inattention to the bad effects of the various things he frequently used to send for. . . ."

In short, Sir Theodosius accidentally poisoned himself with arsenic —a feeble invention, quickly invalidated by the other members of the household, who remembered no plague of rats and no purchases of rat-killer. But it proved helpful to the fumbling medical witnesses. Although Sir Theodosius's symptoms did not correspond to the known effects of arsenic poisoning, Dr. Rattray leaped at the suggestion; in the indictment eventually handed down arsenic was named as the fatal instrument.

On the second and last day of the coroner's hearing Sarah Blundell corroborated her mistress's testimony as to the disposition of the phials. Lady Boughton deposed: "Captain Donellan's swilling the bottles led me to suppose that some unfair dealings had been carried on respecting my son."

The jury returned a verdict of willful murder against Captain Donellan, and he was remanded for trial at the Warwick Assizes to be held the following March.

His behavior in gaol scarcely helped his case. Eager to secure the services of a Mr. Dunning, a celebrated trial counsel, he appealed to his wife through a solicitor for the required fee. She considered it exorbitant. When the solicitor so informed the prisoner, he blurted out in a rage: "And who got the money for her?"

The captain's cellmate, one John Darbyshire, who was in prison for debt, reported this dialogue to the crown authorities:

Darbyshire—Was the body poisoned or no?

Donellan—There's not a doubt of it.

Darbyshire—For God's sake, captain, who could do it?

Donellan—It was done among themselves. I had no hand in it.

Darbyshire—Who were themselves?

Donellan—Himself, Lady Boughton, the footman or the apothecary.

Darbyshire—Who do you mean by himself?

Donellan—Sir Theodosius.

Darbyshire—Sir Theodosius could not do it himself.

Donellan—No, I don't think he did.

Darbyshire—The apothecary could hardly do it, for he had no interest in it, and it's very unnatural to suppose that Lady Boughton could do it.

Donellan—Her ladyship is very covetous. She received an anonymous letter the day after Sir Theodosius's death, charging her plump with the poisoning of Sir Theodosius. She called me, and told it to me, and trembled. She desired that I would not let my wife know of that letter, and asked me if I would give up the right to the personal estate, and some estate of about £200 a year belonging to the family.

In an unsealed note to his wife, which he intended to be intercepted, he reiterated the accusations and implied that Sir Edward Boughton, too, had been slain. "I . . . hope that by this time you have removed under the friendly roof I last recommended to you, and no longer remain where you are likely to undergo the fate of those, that have already gone by sudden means, which providence will bring to light by-and-by: in my first letter to you . . . I mentioned a removal: I had my reasons; which will appear in an honest light, in March next, to the eternal confusion of an unnatural being."

Meanwhile, the fainthearted medical men, who had shrunk from performing an autopsy straightaway, re-entered the case. Had they dreamed at the time, they shamefacedly contended, that poison was in issue, had Donellan uttered the word, they would have braved every hazard. By way of amends they undertook a further investigation. Rattray, studying the scanty toxicological literature available, revised his original diagnosis of arsenic poisoning. A far likelier agent, it occurred to him, was laurel water, a distillate of cherry laurel leaves, containing hydrocyanic acid, which smells like bitter almonds. The woods surrounding Lawford Hall abounded in cherry laurel trees. Donellan owned a retort. "Now I have the rope round his neck which will hang him!" the King's Counsel, Henry Howarth, exulted, when he learned of it. Rattray would have felt surer of his grounds had he known then what came out long after—that among Donellan's belongings at Lawford Hall was a volume of the *Philosophical Transactions* marked at a passage explaining a method for distilling laurel water.

How much of the drug, in what strength, constituted a lethal dose remained to be determined. The scientific papers Rattray and his colleagues read recorded few instances of humans killed by it. In diluted form it was variously prescribed as an antispasmodic, a remedy for bronchial ailments, and a cough-syrup flavoring. Assuming that Donellan replaced the entire contents of the phial of laxative with laurel water, Sir Theodosius would have drunk two ounces. The investigators fed that quantity to a greyhound. To an aged mare they gave a pint and a half, to a cat one ounce, and to another mare a pint. The greyhound died in convulsions in thirty seconds, the first mare in fifteen minutes, the cat in three minutes, and the second mare in twenty-eight minutes.

On the basis of those four tests and of the odor described by Lady Boughton, Rattray and Wilmer decided that laurel water, and only laurel water, could have killed Sir Theodosius. Two more physicians whom Howarth consulted, Dr. Ashe of Birmingham and Dr. Parsons, Professor of Anatomy at Oxford, agreed with them, and all five men were retained to testify for the crown. Against such a galaxy what experts could the defense oppose? Newnham managed to find just one—John Hunter.

Of all the dissenting views John ever held none provoked greater derision than those he expressed at the Warwick Assizes. In contrast to the voluble, positive statements of the crown medical witnesses, his sparse, qualified testimony struck the judge as willfully obtuse. The judge missed the point. John never seriously doubted either that Donellan murdered Sir Theodosius or that he committed the crime with laurel water, but he believed the scope for strict scientific evidence to be extremely narrow, far narrower than the judge believed, and he refused to venture a step beyond it.

If proof of poison were to depend solely upon the medical findings, John felt, there could be no fair conviction. The minimal condition for such proof would have been a prompt autopsy. That cowardice had prevented, and so no witness could truthfully swear that the stomach ever contained poison of any description. Even when the body was belatedly opened, the autopsists failed to make a thorough examination. Their later animal experiments were too few and too crude for a nice determination of how laurel water acted. John conducted many more, with somewhat different results. As to Sir Theodosius's deathbed symptoms, if befuddled Lady Boughton conveyed them accurately, John could name a dozen natural causes that produced the same external effects.

John's grasp of toxicology was admittedly meager, though no more so than the opposition's. The science itself was in its infancy. In his lectures long afterwards he often regretted that he had been unable to bring better equipment into the courtroom. But within those limitations his testimony was a model of how medical evidence should be given, and a prime instance of his meticulous reasoning.

The trial opened at 7:30 A.M. on March 30, 1781, a Friday, before Mr. Justice Francis Buller. Six advocates composed the prosecutor's staff, and four represented the defendant. At a private gathering of jurists Justice Buller had characterized Lady Boughton as "all but a fool," who might founder under cross-examination. But she repeated her account of Sir Theodosius's death without significant variations from her earlier depositions. Donellan's incriminating behavior was then reconstructed by the apothecary, the Boughton servants, Sir William Wheeler, the doctors, and the prisoner's cellmate.

The crown's four medical witnesses followed each other to the stand. "Did you ever in your life," Newnham asked Rattray, hoping to discredit him, "attend to see the dissection of a human person that was poisoned, or suspected to be poisoned before?"

"No, sir," said Rattray.

"If you were mistaken then [about arsenic], why may you not be mistaken now?"

"Because the sensible qualities of this medicine [laurel water] are so strong, I don't think any poison from metals will have such effect so instantaneous."

"Now pray tell me what was your reason for supposing at one time, that he died of arsenic, and disclosing your opinion to be so?"

"At some time every man is mistaken in his opinion, it was my case then, I am not ashamed of owning it."

As Newnham pressed his advantage, he unwittingly elicited a new observation damaging to his client. Referring again to the autopsy, he asked whether Rattray had smelled the remains. "I could not avoid smelling it. . . ." the physician replied. "I had a particular taste in my mouth at the time, a kind of biting acrimony upon my tongue. And I have in all my experiments with laurel water always had the same taste from breathing over the water."

"Did you impute it to that cause then?" asked Newnham.

"No, I imputed it to the volatile salts escaping the body."

"Were not the volatile salts likely to occasion that?"

"No, I think they would not, I said to Mr. Wilmer I had a very odd taste in my mouth, and my gums bled."

"Had he the same?"

"I don't recollect he said he had."

"You attributed it to the volatility of the salts?"

"No. I did not at that time know how to account for it. At that time I attributed it to the effluvia, but since I have made trials of laurel water . . . it had constantly and uniformly that effect; there is a very volatile oil in it, I am confident."

Rattray's memory must have been playing him tricks, for it is improbable that after ten days in a putrefying stomach laurel water could retain its odor. Moreover, arsenic, which Rattray first maintained had poisoned Sir Theodosius, smells nothing like bitter almonds.

Wilmer confirmed the physician's report in general, though without mentioning the odor of the remains. Dr. Ashe said, "I have not a doubt he died of poison, and nothing else," Dr. Parsons that "he died in consequence of taking that draught."

There were only two witnesses, besides the prisoner himself and John Hunter, to testify for the defense—Andrew Miller, the former proprietor of The Bear and the Ragged Staff tavern in Rugby, and George Loggins. They told of two quarrels involving Sir Theodosius, which Donellan had mediated. By their testimony Newnham hoped to show that far from desiring the baronet's death the captain had saved his life.

Donellan submitted a brief written plea, consisting of little more than a denial of the charge, and completely evading such crucial points as why he rinsed the phials.

The clerk of the arraigns called: "Mr. Hunter!" The court officials turned, the spectators in the gallery stretched their necks for a clearer look. The stubby, bull-necked Scot, who detested formalities, lumbered to the stand, glowering, his massive, square jaw set. With no wig covering his reddish hair, now thinning and streaked gray, with his dark, worn coat bare of ornament, he presented a lackluster contrast to the lacy dignitaries surrounding him. He took the oath and sat down with an air of girding himself for battle against fools.

In the course of John's testimony Justice Buller saw fit to interject: "You are to give your opinion upon the symptoms only, not upon any other evidence." The admonition was superfluous. John confined himself to an area so circumscribed that he exasperated judge, jury, prosecutor, and counsel for the prisoner.

"You have been long in the habit of dissecting human subjects," said Newnham. "I presume you have dissected more than any man in Europe?"

"I have dissected some thousands during these thirty-three years," John replied.

"Are those appearances you have heard described such, in your judgment, as are the result of putrefaction in dead subjects?"

"Entirely."

"Are the symptoms that appeared after the medicine was given such as necessarily conclude that the person had taken poison?"

"Certainly not."

"If an apoplexy had come on, would not the symptoms have been nearly or somewhat similar?"

"Very much the same."

Newnham stressed the point. Had the witness ever known of a young man dying of an apoplectic or, say, an epileptic seizure? John had indeed, but, to Newnham's distress, he felt compelled to qualify the statement. "With regard to apoplexy, not so frequent: young subjects will perhaps die more frequently of epilepsies than old ones."

Newnham sought next to discredit the experimental methods of the crown experts. "Is there any analogy to be drawn from the effects of any given species of poison upon any animal of the brute creation, to that it may have upon a human subject?"

But John could not attack the prosecution on that ground. "As far as my experience goes," he said, "which is not a very confined one, because I have poisoned some thousands of animals, they are very nearly the same; opium, for instance, will poison a dog similar to a man: arsenic will have very near the same effect upon a dog as it would, I take for granted, upon a man. I know something of the effects of them, and I believe their operations will be nearly similar."

But were there no substances instantaneously fatal to animals, yet harmless to man? Spirits, for example, Newnham submitted hopefully.

"I apprehend a great deal depends upon the mode of experiment: no man is fit to make one but those who have made many, and paid considerable attention to all the circumstances. . . . It is a common experiment, which I believe seldom fails, that a little brandy will kill a cat: I have made the experiment, and have killed several cats, but it is a false experiment; in all those cases . . . it kills the cat by getting into her lungs, not into her stomach; because if you convey the same quantity of brandy, or three times as much, into the stomach, in such a way as the lungs shall not be affected, the cat will not die."

Newnham tried another tack, with greater success. "If you had been called upon to dissect a body suspected to have died of poison, should you or not have thought it necessary to have pursued your search through the guts?"

"Certainly."

"You have heard of the froth issuing from Sir Theodosius's mouth a minute or two before he died; is that peculiar to a man dying of poison, or is it not very common in many other complaints?"

"I fancy it is a general effect of people dying in what you may call health, in an apoplexy or epilepsy, in all sudden deaths, where the person was a moment before in perfect health."

"Should you consider yourself bound, by such an appearance, to impute the death of a subject to poison?"

"No, certainly not," John snapped. "I should rather suspect an apoplexy: and I wish in this case the head had been opened to remove all doubts."

"If the head had been opened, do you apprehend all doubts would have been removed?"

John corrected himself. "It would have been still further removed, because, although the body was putrid, so that one could not tell whether it was a recent inflammation, yet an apoplexy arises from the extravasation of blood in the brain, which would have laid in a coagulum."

"Then, in your judgment, upon the appearances the gentlemen have described, no inference can be drawn from thence that Sir Theodosius Boughton died of poison?"

"Certainly not; it does not give the least suspicion."

Howarth opened his cross-examination on a note of scorn. "I ask you," he demanded, "whether any reasonable man can entertain a doubt that that draught, whatever it was, produced those appearances?"

"I don't well know what answer to make to that question," John rejoined imperturbably.

"Upon the symptoms produced after the swallowing of the draught," Howarth persisted, "I ask you whether, in your judgment and opinion, that draught did not occasion his death?"

"I can only say, that it is a circumstance in favor of such an opinion."

This was too much for Justice Buller, who interposed, "That the draught was the occasion for his death?"

"No: because the symptoms afterwards are those of a man dying, who was in perfect health; a man dying of epilepsy or apoplexy, the symptoms would give one of those general ideas."

"It is the general idea you are asked about now," the judge persisted, "from the symptoms which appeared upon Sir Theodosius Boughton immediately after he took the draught, followed by his death so very soon after; whether, upon that part of the case, you are of the opinion that the draught was the occasion of his death?"

"If I knew the draught was poison, I should say, most probably that the symptoms arose from that; but when I don't know that the draught was poison, when I consider that a number of other things might occasion his death, I cannot answer positively to it."

"You recollect," the maddened judge asked, "the circumstance that was mentioned of a violent heaving in the stomach?"

"All that is the effect of the voluntary action being lost, and nothing going on but the involuntary."

Justice Buller relapsed into smoldering silence, while the prosecutor resumed the assault.

"Then you decline giving any opinion upon the subject?"

"I don't form any opinion to myself; I cannot form an opinion because I can conceive if he had taken a draught of poison it arose from that; I can conceive it might arise from other causes."

"If you are at all acquainted with the effects and operations of distilled laurel water, whether the having swallowed a draught of that, would not have produced the symptoms described?"

"I should suppose it would; I can only say this of the experiments I have made of laurel water upon animals, it has not been near so quick; I have injected laurel water directly into the blood of dogs, and they have not died; I have thrown laurel water, with a precaution, into the stomach, and it never produced so quick an effect with me, as described by those gentlemen."

The prisoner's counsel, still arguing apoplexy as a possible cause of Sir Theodosius's death, opened up a new line. Under the misconception, shared by the medical men of the day, that apoplexy was a disease rather than the result of one, and recalling how Sir Edward Boughton died, he asked: "Where a father has died of apoplexy, is not that understood, in some measure, to be constitutional?"

John replied: "There is no disease whatever that becomes constitutional but what can be given to a child . . . whatever is constitutional in the father, the father has a power of giving that to the children; by which means it becomes what is called a hereditary disease. There is no such thing as a hereditary disease, but there is an hereditary disposition for a disease." (With a few exceptions, such as diabetes and epilepsy, which are now believed to be sometimes inheritable, modern geneticists would agree.)

Howarth asked: "Is apoplexy likely to attack a thin young man who has been in the course of taking cooling medicines before?"

"Not so likely, surely, as another man," John conceded, "but I have, in my account of dissections, two young women dying of apoplexies."

"But in such a habit of body, particularly attended with the circumstance of having taken cooling medicines, it was very unlikely to happen?"

"I do not know the nature of medicine so well as to know that it would hinder an apoplexy taking effect."

The judge broke in with a final, furious effort. "Give me your opinion," he thundered, "in the best manner you can, one way or the other, whether, upon the whole symptoms described, the death proceeded from that medicine or any other cause?"

"I do not mean to equivocate," said John, "but, when I tell the sentiments of my own mind, what I felt at the time, I can give nothing decisive."

In his charge to the jury Justice Buller virtually instructed them to disregard John's testimony. "I wished very much to have got a direct answer from Mr. Hunter, if I could," he observed petulantly. "You have the very positive opinion of four or five gentlemen of the faculty that the deceased did die of poison. On the other side, you have what I really cannot call more than the doubt of another. . . ."

The jury took only ten minutes to find the defendant guilty.

Donellan spent his final hours composing a protestation of innocence in the third person, the burden of which was that Lady Boughton murdered her son. In this document he admitted for the first time to being familiar with laurel water, "but then it was along with other ingredients for preparing an aromatic bath for his feet, which he constantly used after a fit of gout, and found it to be very strengthening and serviceable."

Early on the morning of April 1 the captain was driven to the gallows in an undertaker's carriage. He showed neither fear nor remorse, but, with the aplomb of a popular actor, sat bowing and smiling to the hordes that lined the streets. Before the noose was adjusted he proclaimed: "As I am about to appear before the judgment of Almighty God, to whom the secrets of all hearts are known, I solemnly declare that I am innocent of the crime for which I am now going to suffer. I have drawn up a vindication of my character, which, when it appears, I hope the world will believe as the last words of a dying man, who here falls sacrifice to the malice and black devices of a mother-in-law." Then, to the hangman: "Pray, do not let us have any bungling."

There was none. Cut down after an hour, the body was carted to the town hall for public dissection.

In London John Hunter interrupted a lecture to remark, "A poor devil was lately hanged upon no other testimony than that of physical men whose first experiments were made on this occasion."

It is not surprising that John's performance in the Donellan trial created no great demand among lawyers for his services. He testified in only one other criminal case. On September 4, 1782, two officers of the Foot Guards, Colonel Cosmo Gordon and Lieutenant-Colonel Frederic Thomas, fought a pistol duel in Hyde Park, exchanging three shots at eight paces. Thomas died with a bullet through his stomach. The victor was tried for murder three weeks later at the Old Bailey, John Hunter appearing for the crown.

"Was the wound mortal?" the prosecutor asked him, expecting perhaps a reply of one syllable.

John—one suspects him of self-satire—answered: "There was nothing necessarily mortal in the wound, but the general effects on the whole system were sufficient to show that the patient could not live."

"You have no doubt, sir," said the prosecutor, "that the ball was the occasion of Lieutenant-Colonel Thomas's death?"

"None whatever."

The prosecutor prudently inquired no further.

VI. THE GOLDEN CALF
OF LEICESTER SQUARE
1781-1783

෴

26. THE CITADEL

The lease on No. 24 Jermyn Street expired in 1783, and John did
not renew it, for by then the house could contain no more than a
fraction of his anatomical specimens, and he was accumulating new
ones almost every day. If wife and children were to have any space
left to themselves, premises apart must be found for the colossal collection. Towards the spring of the year there fell vacant at No. 28
Leicester Fields (shortly renamed Leicester Square) a property comprising two buildings, with a garden between them one hundred feet
long and thirty feet wide. The arrangement was ideal, though the
existing lease had only twenty-four years to run. John paid for it, together with alterations, £6,000 plus annual taxes of £140, a reckless
investment since, not owning the land, he could never hope to recoup
the money.

It was a neighborhood of piquant associations and vivid contrasts,
where lordly mansions jostled gaudy halls of entertainment, where
artists and scholars worked among charlatans and showmen. The most
famous of its homes, Leicester House, whither two heirs apparent,
George II and III, had fled when paternal ire drove them from St.
James's Palace, a regency wit dubbed "the pouting-place of princes."
The square enclosed a fenced and elm-lined park laid out around a
gilt equestrian statue of George I. On the cobbled pavement beyond,
tattered urchins played chuck, a pitchman with a telescope charged a

penny a peep at the stars. In nearby King's Mews there was a cistern for thirsty horses, and any pickpockets caught prowling the area were doused in it.

Diversions for every taste abounded. Half a crown was the entrance fee to Ashton Lever's "Holophusikon," sixteen rooms of South Sea weapons, antiquities, and taxidermy, with an annex full of stuffed zebras and elephants. When that palled, one could inspect Burford's Panorama, which through the years successively depicted on the wall of a vast, circular chamber, in bas-relief and dazzling hues, the major events of British military history.

From ten in the morning to nine at night "The Invisible Lady, or Delphic Oracle" performed at No. 1 Leicester Square, "Where [according to her handbills] in a small Temple, impossible for human being to enter, and unconnected with any surrounding object, will proceed a voice, supposed to be manner in which

The Ancients Communicated with their Gods.

"And which will even describe the dress, nation, or any particular, and so completely deceiving the senses as to appear the EFFECT OF MAGIC.

"And there will also be produced, as if by Enchantment,

MUSIC

"From the softest to the highest note, close to the Ear, in this philosophical and highly pleasing Exhibition. Admittance one shilling."

(Many years after the Oracle retired, a medical student boarding at No. 1 accidentally penetrated her secret. A rotten plank collapsed under his tread, and he beheld a speaking tube rising from the room below.)

Actors and playwrights patronized The Feathers pub in Leicester Place; painters and sculptors, Slaughter's Coffee-house in St. Martin's Lane, behind the square; men of science, New Slaughter's, a few doors above. At New Slaughter's the Society for the Improvement of Medical and Chirurgical Knowledge, organized by John Hunter and George Fordyce, Senior Physician to St. Thomas's Hospital, convened once a month to compare notes on prevalent diseases. Membership was confined to practitioners who lived near enough to ensure their regular attendance—a total of ten.

A cannon projected from the roof of No. 11 Green Street, near the square, and at frequent intervals the tenant, William Woollett, an engraver, would climb up to fire what he called a "patteraro." Such was his way of celebrating the completion of a new plate.

A charming, childlike, gifted man, Woollett had long been a friend of John's. He became a patient when he contracted cancer, then dismissed John in favor of a quack named Plunkett, who dosed him with an arsenical compound.

John asked the quack, "What do you intend to do with the medicine?"

"Why, to cure the patient," said Plunkett.

"Let me know what you mean by that? Do you mean to alter the diseased state of the parts? Or do you mean by your medicine to remove the parts diseased?"

"I mean to destroy them."

"Well, then," said John, "that is nothing more than I or any other surgeon can do, with less pain to the patient."

Though his professional services had been rejected, John continued to visit Woollett as a friend, and each time the invalid professed to be mending, thanks to Plunkett's compound. John asked him to convey a message to the quack. "If," said he, "he will give me leave to watch regularly, and see myself the good effects, I will exert all my power to make him the richest man in the kingdom."

But Plunkett would not enter the same room with John. "He tortured poor Woollett for some time," John declared afterwards, "till at length he died."

There were other Leicester Square inhabitants well known to John. Hogarth's widow lived on the same side, at No. 29, beneath the sign of the Golden Head, which her husband had fashioned out of cork and glue. Diagonally across the park lived Dr. Cruikshank, William Hunter's former pupil and now Johnson's physician, and near him, at No. 47, Sir Joshua Reynolds, who gave the gayest parties in London, and rode in a carriage with the panels painted by his own brush to represent the four seasons.

Under John's tenancy No. 12 gradually expanded into a small citadel, harboring a population of more than fifty, and it drew many a shaft from the anti-Hunterians. They called him "the Golden Calf of Leicester Square." There is a legend that Robert Louis Stevenson had No. 12 in mind when he described Dr. Jekyll's laboratory. ("It was late in the afternoon when Mr. Utterson found his way to Dr. Jekyll's door, where he was at once admitted by Poole, and carried down by the kitchen offices across a yard which had once been a garden to the building which was indifferently known as the laboratory or dissecting-rooms. The doctor had bought the house from the heirs of a celebrated surgeon; and his own tastes being rather chemical than anatomical, had changed the destination of the block at the bottom of the garden.")

The bigger of the two houses, a broad, white, stone structure, rising four stories to a peaked roof, John designated as the family's living quarters. It provided all the scope for social activity Anne could desire. The ground floor hallway was so commodious that she stored her sedan chair there beside an enormous grandfather clock. The main salon, its four tall windows facing west on the square, could seat a full orchestra and a hundred guests or more. Anne adorned it with silver candelabra and paintings by Reynolds, Hogarth, Zoffani, and Zucarelli. For his own rare leisure moments John reserved a modest parlor at the rear, where he occasionally cat-napped on a sofa. This adjoined his waiting room and surgery, which patients entered from the square by a separate entrance.

To run the establishment required a domestic staff of eleven, reinforced by outside help. William Clift, the faithful amanuensis of John's last years, listed them, with a pithy notation or two, as follows:

Robert Adcock, Butler (after Mr. Dewell).
Ann Martin, from Southampton, House Keeper.
Elizabeth Roby, from Rochester, Lady's Maid.
Mr. Hunter's Coachman, Joe.
Mr. Hunter's Footman, John.
Mrs. Hunter's Coachman, James Goodall.
Mrs. Hunter's Footman, George Smith.
Mary Edwards, from Llanbeder, cook (Ann Denny, do.).
Martha Jones, House-maid.
Little Peggy, do. (*A great laugher*).
Mrs. Long (Constant Needlewoman).

In addition, John employed nine servants at Earl's Court, where the family spent weekends and most of the summer and fall. Clift's list goes on:

Peter Shields, Gardener.
Mrs. Shields, House-keeper and Dairy Woman.
Betty, Laundry-maid. (*Butter would not melt in her mouth, but somehow she became enceinte by an equally bashful Kensington sweetheart.*)

Tom Barton, Carter.
Scotch Willie, Half-Witted, employed in the fields.
Old David, Head Under Gardener, Hot-houses, &c.
Alexander, Out-door Gardener and Spring-guns.
Woman to weed in Garden, and fetch the cows.
Tom Barton's Wife, Assistant-Laundress.

The part-time help included "Mrs. Hunter's Livery Stable Keeper, Mr. Rand, Golden Sq.; Cart, Harness, and Collar Maker, Earl's Court; Farrier, nearly Constant, from Under-ground Stables; Stewardson, an old Butler, a constant Visitor."

The garden behind No. 12 ran east to Castle Street and the second building. Here, under the supervision of another housekeeper, Mrs. Elizabeth Adam, were fed and lodged John's resident pupils—normally, half a dozen at a time—his assistants, draughtsmen, dissectors, and pre-parators. Here, too, were the dissecting rooms and a printing press. John had taken to printing and distributing his own books in order to foil pirates. Unprincipled London booksellers would post copies of im-portant manuscripts to Dublin, where a cheap edition would be printed and exported to England to be sold simultaneously with the genuine article. Later John abandoned his system when honest booksellers, among whom he counted some of his fondest friends, protested the in-justice to them.

Because the stables and coach house lay below street level, John built a ramp leading down from Castle Street, to which he whimsically attached a drawbridge. One of his equipages magnified his reputation for eccentricity and never failed to attract hilarious crowds. It con-sisted of a cart drawn by three zebus, or Asiatic water buffaloes. Every Wednesday, during the harvest seasons, Scotch Willie would drive it to town from Earl's Court with a load of fruits and vegetables, and re-turn with the offal of the dissecting rooms to fertilize the fields. He once left it unattended on the way back while he skipped off to an ale-house. Some nosy boys peered inside the cart. The sight of disjected members sent them shrieking through the streets. In the ensuing riot Scotch Willie and the zebus barely escaped intact.

Construction of a third building two stories high, in the middle of the garden, began soon after John signed the lease. His earnings now ap-proached £6,000 a year, but that was not enough. He mortgaged the Earl's Court estate to the hilt. Two years passed before the new building could be used, and for the rest of his life John kept making changes that engaged the continual services of sawyers, glaziers, plumbers, masons, cabinetmakers, joiners, and upholsterers.

The lower floor was divided into a lecture theater and a reception room. In the latter the Lyceum Medicum Londoninse, another society founded by John and Fordyce, held a meeting every Friday evening from 8:30 to 11, during which significant case histories were reported and prepared for publication. The best speaker of the year received a five-guinea gold medal. Membership rules were rigid. Nobody could walk out of a meeting, or leave the city without permission, on pain of fine. For new members regular attendance was obligatory until they had delivered their first dissertation. Only then might they be occasionally allowed to absent themselves.

In a long, lofty, galleried hall on the upper floor John installed his anatomical collection, known ever after as the Hunterian Museum. The total cost came to £70,000.[f]

27. "THE GREAT UNWRITTEN BOOK"

Had John created nothing else, his museum would have immortalized him. No scientific edifice of such originality, range and beauty had ever proceeded from the mind of one man, and none like it has arisen since. Anatomical collections there already existed in abundance, but these were either mere classifications of heterogeneous specimens, with no unifying concept behind them, or peep shows for the morbid and the prurient. John integrated within a single thematic frame the manifold aspects of comparative anatomy. He composed a mass of animal and vegetable preparations, thousands upon thousands, into an orderly cosmorama that expounded, more eloquently than words, the laws of life. And this, his "great unwritten book," as a latter-day curator of the museum called it, was free from those defects of communication that so often blurred the meaning of his papers and lectures. For here, through systematic juxtapositions of nature's works, nature was made to speak and unveil part of her mystery. Here, in luminous language, was elaborated the grand motif: what distinguishes life from non-life in both individual and species is an innate power of self-maintenance, and by it are produced the endless, adaptive mutations of structure.

The museum was open to visitors but two months out of twelve. In October the founder welcomed scientists, in May "the noblemen and gentlemen who are in town only during the spring"—a strange proviso coming from a man who customarily paid scant respect to rank.

Let us accompany one of these privileged groups, choosing an occasion when John himself is disposed to act as our guide.

We knock at the Castle Street door and are admitted by Mrs. Adam, who ushers us past vats where bones lie bleaching, past the busy printing press and the dissecting rooms crowded with learners, into the garden below. John sits fidgeting on a stone bench, hunched over a cane, dictating notes from scraps of paper to Everard Home, who transcribes them in a tall ledger. His health has steadily declined since the move to Leicester Square. Purplish shadows stain his cheeks; his breathing is jerky. From time to time he forces a cough, a mannerism adopted in his illness, as if to jolt the sluggish wheels of his machinery into faster action. His slate-blue eyes are sunken, the lashes of a yellowish tinge. His lusterless gray hair drops straight to his coat collar. He wears black broadcloth.

Seeing us, he waves Home aside, stands up, leaning hard on his cane, and beckons us towards the central building. We pass under a glass canopy, covering half the garden, that John built to shelter specimens too bulky for the museum itself. As he lumbers ahead on his short, thick legs, he proudly draws attention to the skull of a forty-foot bottlenose whale. It is one of several he has mounted. Inside the museum, suspended by wires from the ceiling, float whole skeletons of an eleven-foot baby bottlenose, which Jenner caught, a third bottlenose of twenty-two feet, two grampuses eighteen and twenty-one feet long, and a seventeen-foot *Baleana rostra,* or piked whale. John has cause for pride. They are the only whale skeletons in England, and not for many years will there be hands skilled and patient enough to attempt such Herculean labor. ("As the great John Hunter says," wrote Herman Melville in *Moby Dick,* "the mere skeleton of a whale bears the same relation to the fully invested and padded animal as the insect does to the chrysalis.") The biggest bottlenose, John tells us, drifted ashore dying at the mouth of the Thames, and for days he and his pupils slithered across the oily carcass, stripping the flesh away from the bones.

We follow him into the building, up steep stairs to the gallery. He bemoans the lack of a descriptive catalogue, but for that tremendous task he has not yet found time. The thought that he might die before he can undertake it continually frets him.

He pauses on the top landing, panting like a runner, and after one of his forced coughs, explains the arrangement of the exhibits stretching before us as far as our eyes can see. "My design, gentlemen, in the formation of this museum," he says, "was to display throughout the chain of organized beings the various structures in which the functions of life are carried on."

The normal physiological specimens, we learn, fall into two major categories—those illustrating structures evolved for the maintenance of the individual, and those for the perpetuation of the race. They are grouped not by species, but by function, the stomachs, for example, of many different species being displayed in the same series, and each series ranging the evolutionary scale from the simplest mechanisms to the most complex. Thus, an opossum and a toad appear side by side because the first carries its young in its abdominal pouch and the second on its back.

The first subdivision of Category I deals with the motor apparatus of plants and animals. "Motion in plants," says John, "I conceive to depend on a property analogous to irritability in animals." To illustrate, he lifts a mimosa plant and shakes it. The leaflets droop and close, then, after more agitation, reopen as though inured to the shock.

We move on to preparations of muscular fiber. "One of the simplest forms of active solids," John notes. He shows us, in a series of insects, worms, fish, birds, and mammals, how, as life ascended the scale, certain organs were adapted to produce motion—either active motion, as in muscles, or passive, as in the skin of worms and insect larvae. Next are exemplified two forms of elastic motive power, the hinge of an oyster, which acts in opposition to muscular force, and the ligament extending from the back of the human head to the neck, which acts in concert with it. And finally a series showing adaptations for progressive motion, for flying, creeping ("Serpents," John says, "progress by means of their ribs, which have strong muscles attached, and move much like centipedes' legs"), for burrowing, climbing, leaping, running, tearing prey.

Digestion is the theme of the second subdivision. It begins with types of teeth, 170 of them from as many assorted species. John enumerates the variations in quantity, shape, structure and location, according to the food the animal eats. He discourses on the mode of formation and growth, of shedding and replacement. "In crocodiles," he observes, "there's a constant succession of new teeth, which form the same conical projecting pulp. In many kinds of fish the new teeth form in rows of distinct pulp. They may be situated within or without the rows used, but in either case they're brought into action by the absorption of the opposite side of the jaw."

So, stressing similarities and differences, John leads us to his series of stomachs, which number those of tapeworm larvae, of mollusks, bees, the Gillaroo trout, the porcupine, the peccary, the camel, the llama; to intestines; to kidneys; to glands; to examples of absorption—simple tubes in vegetables, in man a maze of veins and lymphatics; to circulatory systems, John's most delicate preparations, each tiny branch being injected with a dye.

Sensory organs make up the fourth subdivision. Among these he has placed the right hand of Thomas Beaufort, John of Gaunt's son, and the tattooed arms of South Sea Islanders to show how slowly, under certain conditions, skin decays.

One hundred and eighty examples of structural peculiarities complete Category I. There are regenerated newt's tails, the ewer of the pitcher plant, the green bones of a gar pike, insect stingers and snake fangs, the battery of an electric eel.

The volume of material consumed in these preparations is staggering. A detail: about five thousand huge flint glass jars, filled with spirits, contain John's wet preparations; yet there exists as yet no commercial manufacture of such receptacles. We can only conjecture that John had them specially made for him by one of London's few glassworks.

Wet preparations, according to the technique developed by John, involved five main steps. When dissecting the specimen, he explains, care must be taken not to lose the blood for then all the parts turn white and cannot be readily distinguished. He steeps the specimen in one of various solutions, depending on the structure to be emphasized. "Supposing a tongue to be preserved for the interweaving of the muscles," he says, "which is best seen from color. The color should be heightened. Therefore, instead of being steeped in water, it ought to be steeped in a solution of nitre, which gives a brightness to the blood in the muscles, and makes the distinction between muscles and other parts more conspicuous."

An alternative is to steep away all color in water, then inject artificial colors. "In very vascular parts, where nothing is seen but vessels, as the inner surface of the stomach, one should choose colors that please the eye."

Before enclosing the specimen in its jar the parts must be positioned for maximum exposure. To point up small organs, such as ducts and glands, John marks them with bristles. Rectified spirit of wine, combined with acid, is the preservative he generally uses. He suspends the specimen inside the jar by silk thread. Finally, he seals the jar with two thicknesses of pig's bladder and an outer cover of fitted sheet lead.

Because of the cost and scarcity of jars, John prepares many specimens by the dry method. After cleaning, he paints them with an arsenic solution, hangs them until dry, varnishes and revarnishes them. Bones he macerates or boils.

A third, and the most laborious method of preparation is by corrosion. This John applies chiefly to sections of vascular systems that traverse organs difficult to dissect accurately. Only the vessels, injected with brilliant dyes, are retained; the surrounding flesh is corroded away. The injected substances, consisting of wax, resin, turpentine, and tallow, John treats as a cast, of which the vessels are the mold. He soaks the organ in acid until the superfluous tissues have dissolved. What remains is a solidified continuum, delineating the system in reds, blues, yellows, and whites.

The second major category of the physiological specimens, illustrating the maintenance of race, has been called "a Temple of Venus." Here the drama of generation, as enacted by different forms of life, unfolds from copulation to birth. First, the hermaphroditic, self-impregnating animals: the starfish, the barnacle, the snail, the slug. Then, the genitalia of heterosexual species: the milt, or testis, of fish, a scorpion's penis, mammalian uteri. Ten preparations show pairs of animals in coitus. Embryos by the score follow: a fetal kangaroo, an aardvark, an armadillo, a pangolin, a walrus; the eggs of silkmoths, caterpillars, crocodiles.

If fire should gut the museum and John could salvage only one series, he would probably choose his twenty preparations depicting "the generative oeconomy of the Hive Bee." It includes a brood comb, with nearly all of the worker cells occupied by pupae, those of the drones by larvae in early stages of metamorphosis, and some of the open cells by full-grown bees, their abdomens projecting from the entrance in the posture in which they feed their young.

We come now to the pathological department, elucidating John's theory of order in disorder. Almost a thousand diseased human organs are arranged under three headings: restoration after disease, effects of disease, and location of disease. In the first section we see how wounds heal by first intention, when the incised edges of skin are drawn together and so held by sutures until union occurs; how by second intention, when the edges remain separated until granulation tissue builds up naturally to skin level. We see instances of adhesive inflammation, of suppuration, of ulceration, of cicatrization, of knit fractured bones, and reduced dislocations.

Under the second heading are organs damaged by scrofula, cancer, smallpox, gout, venereal diseases, hydrophobia; under the third, diseases of the esophagus, stomach, intestine, anus, liver, gall bladder, urinary bladder, spleen, kidney, uterus and its appendages in both impregnated and unimpregnated states; the brain and its membranes, the spinal cord and nerves; the eyes, gums, teeth, air passages, and lungs.

There is a natural history department of some 3,000 stuffed, dried or skeletonized animals, and 1,215 fossils; a department of human and comparative osteology with 963 preparations; and a miscellany of curiosities. Each series is copiously supplemented by drawings and models.

Lastly, we view the congenital monstrosities. These John collects for the same reason he collects diseased organs. "We're obliged to disease," he tells us, "for many of our hints on animal oeconomy, for explaining the action of parts, since wrong action often points out what the natural action was, and itself gives an idea of life. Monstrosities contribute to rectify our opinions in the same, if not more intelligible manner. From wrong construction of parts arises unnatural action, which by studying we may discover the natural action."

He has distributed the monsters, some prepared wet, some dry, into four series according to the type of deviation. To the first, preternatural situation of parts, belongs an embryo encysted in the belly of a male human. The second series, surplus parts, includes a woman's generative system with two uteri, one of them carrying a seven-month fetus, and a double skull from a six-year-old child. "During life," John remarks, "the upper head seems to have experienced sensations and performed mental operations distinct from those of the lower." In the third series, deficiency of parts, we find a lamb born faceless, a one-eyed pig, a pig with a trunk like an elephant's; in the fourth, hermaphrodites, a hen pheasant that grew a cock's plumage.

The most spectacular oddity is the full skeleton of a human giant almost a third again as tall as John. As we ply him with questions about its identity, how he acquired it and where, he beams with an air of naughty triumph, but makes no reply.

28. A TALL MAN

At the age of twenty-one Charles Byrne, a native of Littlebridge, a hamlet near the Derry-Tyrone county border in Ireland, stood eight feet, two inches tall in his stocking feet. His shoes measured just under fifteen inches long, his hands fourteen inches from wrist to middle finger. The inhabitants of Littlebridge attributed his size to the influence of the place where his parents, both of normal dimensions, supposedly conceived him. This was atop a high haystack. Five miles away lived two giant brothers named Knipe, and they, too, were believed to have been conceived on a haystack by the same acrophilic lovers.

While sightseeing in Edinburgh, where he embarked upon his career as a professional freak under the management of one Joe Vance, he had to crawl on all fours to get through the vaulted closes. A night-watchman on the North Bridge was petrified by the sight of Byrne lighting a pipe from a street lamp. He swore later that the giant did not even have to stand on tiptoe. John Kay, a Scottish caricaturist, gave Byrne valuable publicity when he depicted him surrounded by a group of Edinburgh notables none of whom stood higher than his hip.

But the Goliath was sound in neither mind nor body. At school he drooled so copiously that no other student would sit near him. He started drinking early in life, and by the time he landed in Scotland he was a confirmed alcoholic. He was also suffering from tuberculosis.

Journeying south through England, Byrne never failed to attract large, enthusiastic audiences. Though not of amiable disposition, he formed a warm attachment to a Polish midget less than three feet high, Count Joseph Borulwaski, as witty and erudite as Byrne was dim. The midget evidently returned his affection for they shared digs and occasionally exhibited themselves on the same platform.

Byrne visited London for the first time on April 11, 1782, and eleven days later the following notice appeared in the *Morning Herald*:

"Irish Giant. To be seen this, and every day this week, in his large elegant room, at the cane-shop, next door to Cox's Museum, Spring Gardens, Mr. Byrne, the surprising Irish Giant, who is allowed to be the tallest man in the world . . . The nobility and gentry are requested to take notice . . . Hours of admittance every day, Sundays excepted, from 11 to 3 and from 5 to 8, at half a crown each person."

When he had been on display a month, the same newspaper reported, with an effusiveness suggesting that the advertising department may have taken a hand in the writing: "However striking a curiosity may be, there is generally some difficulty in engaging the attention of the public; but even this was not the case with the modern living Colossus, or wonderful Irish Giant; for no sooner was he arrived at an elegant apartment at the cane-shop . . . than the curious of all degrees resorted to see him, being sensible that a prodigy like this never made its appearance among us before; and the most penetrating have frankly declared, that neither the tongue of the most fluid orator, or pen of the most ingenious writer, can sufficiently describe the elegance, symmetry and proportion of this wonderful phenomenon in nature, and thus all description must fall infinitely short of giving that satisfaction which may be obtained on a judicious inspection."

In a later issue the panegyrist resumed: "His address is singular and pleasing, his person truly shaped and proportioned to his height and affords agreeable surprise . . . He is beyond what is set forth in ancient or modern history. The ingenious and judicious who have honoured him with their company have bestowed the greatest encomiums on him, and on their departure have expressed their approbation and satisfaction. In short, the sight of him is more than the mind can conceive, the tongue express or pencil delineate, and stands without parallel in this or any other country. 'Take him for all in all, we shall scarce look on his like again'—Shakespear."

Regarding the giant's personal charm, there was some dissent. Silas Neville, a man-about-town and diarist, conceded that "even the Patagonians are nothing to this—8 ft., 2 in. Tall men walk considerably under his arm," but he added, "he stoops, is not well-shaped, his flesh loose, and his appearance far from wholesome. His voice sounds like thunder, and he is an ill-bred beast though very young. . . ."

Nevertheless, Byrne's popularity did not wane. The room in the cane-shop, the establishment of a Mr. Wigley, was always crowded, and its occupant inspired a pantomime entitled *Harlequin Teague or the Giant's Causeway*, which ran for months at the Haymarket Theatre. He drew the attention of Dr. James Graham, London's most successful charlatan, who saw in the giant a chance to glorify his "Temple of Health and Hymen" in Pall Mall.

Equipped at a reputed cost of £10,000, this pleasance was open at all hours. Upon payment of six guineas to two porters, done up in chain mail and flowing robes, the visitor mounted a flight of stairs to the strains of wind instruments played by musicians concealed under the treads. Perfume saturated the air. At the top of the ascent gaped the portals of the Great Apollo Apartment where the doctor himself, a Scot of thirty-eight, with a melodious speech, taught what he described as "the art of preventing barrenness, and of propagating a much more strong, beautiful, active, healthy, wise and virtuous race of human beings, than the present puny, insignificant, foolish, peevish, vicious, nonsensical race of Christians who quarrel, fight, bite, devour, and cut one another's throats, about they know not what!!!"

The lesson started with an "Eccentric Lecture on Generation" by the doctor, studded with provocative imagery. In the course of it the listeners would receive, through wires attached to the underside of their chairs, frequent little electrical shocks. Dr. Graham had been interested in electrical effects for more than ten years, ever since, as an itinerant quack in America, he had witnessed some of Benjamin Franklin's early experiments. At the climax of the lecture "Hebe Vestina, the Rosy Goddess of Health and Hymen" would rise through a trap door to distribute bottles of Dr. Graham's "aethereal balm," a potion guaranteed to increase both the desire and the capacity for propagation. For a time Hebe was portrayed by a former servant girl named Emma Lyon, better known in history as Lady Hamilton.

A new feature of the temple was the "Celestial Bed," also called the "Royal Patagonian Bed." Upholstered in blue satin and supported by six Ionic columns, it commanded the center of a vast, sumptuous, richly scented chamber through which floated snatches of sweet, distant music. Never intended for repose, it would begin, at the slightest movement of an occupant, to oscillate in rhythm to the music and to radiate electrical current. "Sons springing from the bed," Dr. Graham promised, "like Mars shall prove and daughters beauteous as the Queen of Love." And in printed copies of his lecture on generation he set forth: "Superior ecstasy which the partners enjoy in the Celestial Bed is really astonishing and never before thought of in this world; the barren certainly must become fruitful when they are so powerfully agitated in the delights of love." The price for a night in this bower was one hundred guineas a couple, breakfast included.

To the Irish giant and any companion of his choice, Dr. Graham offered the privilege gratis of being the first to occupy the Celestial Bed. But Byrne, with what one newspaper described as "the utmost delicacy, modesty and politeness," declined on the grounds that he was "a perfect stranger to the rites and mysteries of the Goddess Venus."

The exchange did neither showman any harm. The doctor made £30,000 that year, and the giant drew bigger crowds than ever.

Of the thousands who paid their half-crown to view Charles Byrne nobody was more fascinated than John Hunter. In his studies of the principles underlying deviations from normality, his opportunities to observe, let alone to collect, human specimens had been slim. He had had to content himself with a few fetal and infantile anomalies and with paintings of famous freaks, such as Teresa Crachiami, known as the "Sicilian Fairy," who measured twenty-two inches from crown to sole and weighed six pounds at the age of nine, when she died, and Byrne's friend, the scholarly Polish mite. Now, almost at his doorstep, was a rare example of giantism, one, moreover, as John's practiced eye told him, whose days were numbered.

John had in his employ at this time a factotum of resourcefulness and tenacity named Howison, and to him he assigned the mission of making Byrne an offer for his body. The gin-sodden colossus rejected it with horror.

But John was not to be thwarted. If he could not have the skeleton with its owner's consent, then, stap his vitals! he would have it without. At John's instigation, Howison followed the giant's every move. He would drop in at the cane-shop to stand somberly apart from the crowd and fix him with a baleful glare that clearly said, "Sooner or later . . ."

The giant ordered a lead coffin to be built. The undertaker was also to hire, when the last hour struck, a team of stalwart Irish corpse-watchers, and to see to it that they conveyed the coffin to the mouth of the Thames, towed it offshore and sank it.

These melancholy arrangements completed, the doomed man turned to the bottle with deeper thirst than ever. And the implacable Howison came and watched and came again. To escape that awful gaze, Byrne moved to new rooms above the confectionery of a Mr.

Mittenius in Charing Cross, then to the Sign of the Hampshire Pig in Piccadilly, imagining in his befuddlement that John's man would not find him. But to continue enjoying fame and fortune he had to advertise his whereabouts ("Gentlemen & ladies, 2/6; children and servants in livery, 1 s"), and the advertisements inevitably brought Howison.

John, moreover, was not alone in his hankering for the giant's body. Concocting schemes to appropriate it became a professional sport, played with zest and cunning by all of London's anatomists. A group of medical students, hearing of Byrne's plan to be buried at sea, constructed a diving bell.

In his terror the giant closed his doors to the public. He took a job as a porter in St. James's Palace. But the craving for celebrity proved too strong, and he resumed regular seances at his original London address, in Spring Gardens. Howison was among the first to welcome him back. Byrne moved to the house of a Mr. Haynes at No. 12 Cockburn Street. Howison followed the crowd there.

In the spring of his twenty-second year, by which time he had grown another two inches, the Irish giant was living at No. 23 Cockspur Street, when a combination of circumstances conspired to crush his spirit entirely. For a man in the advanced stages of tuberculosis and alcoholism, Howison's presence alone would have had deleterious results. But in addition there arose a formidable threat to Byrne's professional standing. Touring the provinces and rapidly approaching the capital was another Irish giant, Patrick Cotter O'Brien by name, who at nineteen already measured eight feet, three and a half inches tall. He claimed, furthermore, to be a direct descendant of that ancient nine-foot king of Ireland, Brian Boru.

The crowning blow to Byrne was the loss of his total savings of £770. Two versions of this catastrophe appeared in the newspapers. According to the first, the money was stolen from him as he sprawled dead drunk in a gin cellar. The second version had him hiding the money, all of it in one-pound notes, inside the fireplace of his room and forgetting to warn the servants not to light a fire.

Byrne tried to drown his woe in gin. On sobering up, he took to his bed, a quivering wreck, never to rise again. The end followed fast. On the evening of May 30, Howison, who had been keeping vigil in front of No. 23 Cockspur Street, notified John that the giant was not expected to live till dawn. The corpse-watchers were already on hand. A heavily weighted casket had been procured, and the journey to the

Channel would begin the moment Byrne breathed his last. John's eagerness rose to fever pitch.

As the night advanced, Howison reported that the watchers were taking turns at refreshing themselves in an alehouse near Cockspur Street. The plan that this piece of intelligence suggested John decided to execute himself. Master and servant repaired to the alehouse together.

The surgeon did not have long to wait. Almost immediately Howison was able to point out one of the watchers. John promptly got him into conversation and, after plying him with drink, showed his hand. He would pay £50 for delivery of the giant's body. The Irishman was neither surprised nor offended. He said he must confer with his companions. He was back shortly to announce that John must double his offer. What anatomist would not gladly spare £100 for such a specimen? John instantly consented. But when the watchers saw how eager he was, they raised the price again. And so it went, back and forth between the alehouse and the deathroom, until John agreed to pay £500, probably the largest sum ever paid for a single cadaver. Despite the lateness of the hour, Howison managed to borrow the cash from a man named Pidcock.

When Byrne finally died, the watchers stripped the corpse, so that if caught, they could not be charged with stealing property—an offense carrying heavier penalties than the body snatching itself. They nailed shut the empty casket and lugged the body down the stairs. John was waiting in his coach, with Howison perched on the driver's seat. Money and corpse swiftly changed hands. Then clattering through the stilled streets the coach sped straight on under the lightening sky to Earl's Court, the tense, little surgeon and the huge, naked cadaver jouncing together in the cramped blackness of the rear seat.

John dared not leave the matter in hand until morning, less from fear of the law than of an aroused mob. Upon arrival at Earl's Court he wheeled the body through a subterranean passage into a chamber containing a big copper caldron. He filled the caldron with water, lit a fire under it, and cutting the body into manageable segments, popped them in to boil away the flesh. The hasty process turned the bones of the Irish giant brown, but in all other respects they formed, when fitted together again, a splendid skeleton.

From the press accounts of Byrne's death John learned that his secret was safe. The Edinburgh *Evening Courant* reported, for example:

"Yesterday morning the body of Byrne, the famous Irish Giant (who died a few days ago), was carried to Margate, in order to be thrown into the sea, agreeable to his own request, he having been apprehensive that the surgeons would anatomize him."

For two years John did not reveal the existence of the skeleton—and then only to close friends. The only written allusion he ever made to it was two years after that, in a letter to Sir Joseph Banks. "I lately got a *tall man*," he confided, "but at the time could make no particular observations. I hope next summer to be able to show him."

Next summer he did, installing the £500-skeleton in a glass case in his museum beneath the paintings of the giant's tiny friend, Count Borulwaski, and of the Sicilian Fairy.[g]

29. EARL'S COURT

A neat border of death's heads embellished the fishpond where John bred carp, tench, leeches and eels for his freezing experiments. Nearby rose two pyramids of fossils. A crocodile's head, the jaws agape, projected over the entrance to the main house. Four life-size stone lions, two rampant, two couchant, flanked a double flight of steps. The roar of real lions, of tigers and leopards, chained in subterranean dens, shook the earth. Above the dens towered a mound shaped like an Indian burial cumulus, with a castellated rampart of brick and tile on top, from which the spires of Westminster Abbey could be glimpsed. Spring guns were mounted in the crenels to discourage trespassers.

Around the barnyard strangely altered fowl, some with human teeth or their own spurs grafted to their combs, others with genitals transplanted from the opposite sex, tottered in bewilderment. A hen pheasant trailed cock's plumage. Ostriches roamed the lawns. In the pastures grazed buffalo and androgynous cows. Wolves, jackals and dogs had been penned together to see what manner of hybrid they might engender. One litter numbered nine nonesuches of vulpine mien out of a jackal bitch by a mastiff. From holes bored into elms, poplars and yews protruded peacock feathers attached to thermometers registering the temperature at the heartwood. There was no truth to the rumor that droves of human monsters lolled about the place in indolent luxury, subject to anatomization when they died, though could John have found any freaks agreeable to such a pact, he would no doubt have provided for them munificently.

He had enlarged his original ninety-year freehold of two acres by parcels of adjacent land totaling fifty-two acres. To the main house, a red-brick villa of two stories in the late Georgian style, he had added long wings, and around the foundations sunk a covered cloister six feet deep as a keep for his smaller laboratory animals, the dormice, hedgehogs, rabbits, bats, and snakes. Access to the cloister was through a tunnel entered from a ramp behind the villa, down which Scotch Willie could trundle baskets of the squealing victims without distressing Anne or her weekend guests. Experiments proceeded discreetly next to the cloister in a catacomb full of contraptions John had rigged up himself or bought at what he imagined to be bargain prices. There was an "electrifying apparatus," a turning lathe made to the specifications of the Duke of Portland, and parts of an air pump invented by the Earl of Bute. The copper boiler in which he reduced cadavers to skeletons filled almost an entire chamber. He had thoughtfully installed a chimney and tight-fitting doors lest the horripilating effluvia invade the drawing room overhead, which Anne had decorated no less opulently than her salon in town. When she arrived for the summer season, she always brought a set of water-color panels illustrating the story of Cupid and Psyche to be nailed to the walls, and the nailholes concealed by a gilt frieze; in the fall the rosy lovers would be dismounted and carted back to Leicester Square.

"The cunning man," John's somewhat disquieted neighbors called him, and they seldom passed his redoubt without peering through the high, spiked gates to spy out his latest doings. As Leicester Square was the show window, so Earl's Court was the proving ground of Hunterian concepts. Here John was perpetually framing stratagems to unriddle the riddles that seethed in his brain.

Where do swallows go in winter? Samuel Johnson, like the great Vesalius, clung to the notion that they hibernated beneath frozen rivers. John, who suspected that they migrated, converted one of his cellar rooms into a bird dormitory, with a tub of water, uprooted trees, twig-lined hideaways, lengths of wooden pipe, and food. Swallows congregated by the thousands among the reeds of the Thames just prior to their hibernal disappearance. He hired rivermen to trap a flock. But inside the room the swallows showed no disposition to slumber, never touched the food, and in their struggles to escape battered themselves to death. A lone survivor, freed, at once winged southward. So much for Vesalius and Johnson.

Does coloration play a part in the sexual excitation of zebras? John tethered a male zebra beside a female ass in heat. The zebra ignored her. He then painted the ass with black and white stripes. The zebra promptly mounted her.

Why is man taller in the morning than at night? Because, was John's conjecture after studying a dissected spinal column, when he stands, the elastic cartilage between the vertebrae tends to be slightly compressed; when he reclines, it springs back.

Why do plants grow upward? More for light than warmth, John reasoned, because earth is often warmer at a depth than at the surface. But for light, then the growing plant should turn toward the source of light wherever situated. In a tub eighteen inches deep, filled with fine soil, he sowed beans and peas, placing each eye differently. Over the soil he stretched close-meshed netting, suspended the tub upside down from posts, and covered the bottom with wet straw and mats to shut out the sun. He drilled a hole in the bottom, and inserted a tube through which to water the soil. Underneath he laid mirrors in such a way as to reflect light upward to the soil. In due time, no tendrils emerging, he dug up the seedlings. All were sprouting, heads up, toward the bottom of the tub, and those planted with their eyes down had turned around. Clearly, light alone did not explain plant movements.

Next, "as one experiment leads to another, I wished to see how a bean would grow if kept in a constant rotary motion." How to ensure such motion? He chose a cylindrical basket to contain the soil, in which he embedded a single bean, fastening a wooden lid to each end, and thrusting a spindle through the center. He laid the basket across a vat full of water, with the tips of the spindle balanced on the rim. Around the basket he tightly wound cord, and tied the free end to a weighted, hermetically sealed box. He floated the box in the water, and bored a minute hole in the vat so that as the water escaped the box would slowly sink, unwinding the cord, and rotating the basket. The vat emptied in about twelve hours, during which time the basket made one and a half turns. John refilled the vat daily until he estimated that the bean stalk should have grown several inches. Then he had a look. "I . . . found it had grown as much as if it had been planted in the common ground, but it had no particular direction but that of passing in a straight line from the bean, which was at first towards the circumference, the direction in which it was planted; but in its course it had met with a small stone, which had turned it into the direction of the axis, and it had gone on in a straight line in that direction. Here, as there was no fixed inducement to grow in any one direction, the bean grew in a straight line, in that direction given it by chance."

(What John surmised, and so ingeniously sought to prove with a few simple materials, chemistry and time-lapse photography have since confirmed: that a complex of phenomena—photic, thermal, hydrous, gravitational—influence the movement of plants.)

Can the formation of pearls be artificially stimulated? He injected irritants into Scotch river mussels, and left them to develop at the bottom of the fishpond. He obtained enough pearls to string a necklace for Lady Banks.

How do bones grow? According to the French botanist, Henri Duhamel du Monceau, by extension throughout their length, the new osseous particles being intercalated among the old. John doubted it. He laid open the leg bones of piglets, drilled holes two inches apart, inserted lead shot, and sewed up the incisions. Examining the growing bones a few weeks later, he noted that the intervals between the shot had not increased, and so concluded that growth occurs, not by extension, but by accretions at the extremities and the circumference, the middle span scarcely lengthening from birth to maturity.

In supplementary tests he raised two piglets on madder, a red dye that tinges only those parts of a bone growing while the animal is restricted to that diet. He dissected the first piglet in two weeks. The bone surface was red. He cut away a section of bone. The dye had deeply stained the exterior ring, the interior only faintly. He let the second piglet live another two weeks, but without madder. When he sectioned a bone, he noted an effect precisely the reverse of the first experiment: the coloring towards the outer area was almost natural, the inner area red. From this he deduced that as new deposits accumulated at the surface, a proportionate quantity of the old deposits underneath disappeared, and in that way the bone's shape and relative position were retained.

Studying the contours at successive stages of growth, he drew a third inference. He saw nature as a sculptor: bones were formed, each according to its function, by an absorbent process, the superfluous tissue being gradually smoothed away as if by a hand shaping clay.

John acquired a special fondness for pigs because they yielded up to him so many answers to physiological questions. "I . . . gave pigs," he said, "a preference to any other animal, as being easily managed, producing several at a litter, and breeding perfectly under the confinement necessary for experiments."

Are ovaries worn out by repeated propagation? Or does their power decline at the same rate even if without breeding? How does the loss of one ovary affect the number of young produced? "I selected two females, all of the same farrow; and, having removed an ovarium from one of the females, I cut a slit in one ear to distinguish her from the other. They were well fed and kept warm, that there might be no impediment to their breeding; and whenever they farrowed, their pigs were taken away at exactly the same age.

"About the beginning of 1779 they both took the boar; the one which had been spayed earlier than the perfect female. The distance of time, however, was not great, and they continued breeding at nearly the same time. The spayed animal continued to breed till September 1783, when she was six years old, which was a space of more than four years. In that time she had eight farrows; but did not take the boar afterwards, and had in all seventy-six pigs. The perfect one continued breeding till September 1785, when she was about eight years old, a period of almost six years, in which time she had thirteen farrows, and had in all one hundred and sixty-two pigs; after this time she did not breed."

John's tentative conclusions: ovarian productivity is constitutionally limited; the absence of one ovary may diminish, but does not necessarily terminate, fertility. Final proof, he estimated, would require at least a decade of constant inquiry, "but an annual expense of twenty pounds for ten years, and the necessary attention to make the experiment complete, will be sufficient for my not having done it."

Sacrificing some of the denizens of his aviary, John demonstrated a unique property of birds: they breathe partly through their wing bones, that is, the air sacs in the bone cavities communicate with those of the lungs.

He also clarified the phenomenon of "pigeon's milk." "The young pigeon, like the young quadruped, till it is capable of digesting the common food of its kind, is fed with a substance secreted for that purpose by the parent animal; not, as in the Mammalia, by the female alone, but also by the male, which, perhaps, furnishes this nutriment in a degree still more abundant. . . . During incubation the coats of the crop in the pigeon are gradually enlarged and thickened, like what happens to the udder of females of the class Mammalia in the term of uterine gestation. . . . It is likewise evidently more vascular than in its former state, that it may convey a quantity of blood sufficient for secretion of the substance which is to nourish the young brood. . . . The young pigeon is fed for a little time with this substance only, as about the third day some of the common food is found mingled with it: as the pigeon grows older the proportion of common food is increased; so that by the time it is seven, eight, or nine days old the secretion of the curd ceases in the old ones, and of course no more will be found in the crop of the young. It is a curious fact that the parent pigeon has at first a power to throw up this curd without any mixture of common food, although afterwards both are thrown up according to the proportion required for the young ones."

Not the least fruitful of John's inquiries at Earl's Court originated in self-observation, when accidents befell him or he was ill. However acute the pain, the watcher in his mind never relaxed. Thus, a leg injury led him to discoveries of muscular principles that were to form a scientific basis for orthopedic surgery. Some medical historians, in fact, have referred to John, perhaps overgenerously, as the founder of orthopedics.

Probably to please Anne at one of her "kickups," he joined the dancing, a diversion so unfamiliar to him that he ruptured an Achilles' tendon. He recalled in subsequent lectures, "When this tendon [the fibrous ends of the calf muscles, yoking them to the heel bone, and forming the main extensor of the foot] is broken, it is seldom attended with pain in the parts. It commonly gives a pain, which instantly seizes the calf of the leg. The noise or snap which it produces gives no idea of the mischief done; but being at the same time attended with pain in the calf, and the patient not being able to walk as usual, he conceives that some one has struck him a hard body on the calf, and if he is so situated as not to have been liable to a blow, he becomes puzzled to conceive what can have happened."

The standard treatment was immobilization, with the heel strapped back to pull the ruptured ends together. But John, once again, counted on the natural self-reparative properties of injured tissue. According to one of the most important principles he had ever enunciated, "there is a circumstance attending accidental injury which does not belong to disease—namely, that the injury done has in all cases a tendency to produce the disposition and the means of a cure." Why shouldn't a torn tendon unite in a natural position as readily as a fractured bone? Moreover, if the pain could be borne, might not healing be hastened by walking soon after the accident? The chief danger to guard against, John reasoned, was further damage by involuntary muscular motion, all voluntary control being suspended. So he bandaged his calf, kept his heel slightly elevated by adding an extra thickness to his boot, and, stepping off the inner side of his foot, continued to hobble about. When in bed, to steady the calf muscle he wore a leather sock with a strap stretched taut from the heel to a belt. Within a few weeks he had almost completely regained the normal use of the muscle.

What had been the mechanics of this union? He repaired to his kennels with a couching needle, and severed the leg tendons subcutaneously of several dogs. Autopsies performed at different stages showed the break to have been mended by osseous deposits.

Pushing the investigation further, he arrived at a series of orthopedic tenets that have never been invalidated, to wit:

No muscle can act efficiently by itself, but only in opposition to or concert with another muscle.

Muscles, after being contracted to the utmost by a fracture of the corresponding bone, may acquire a new sphere of contraction and adjust themselves to the lengthened bone.

An impaired muscle can be educated to function again by the patient's will.

An opportunity to translate principle into practice arose during a visit to friends in the country. The lady of the house had been confined to a wheel chair for years, ever since she fractured both knee-pans. The bones had healed, but she could not contract the extensor muscles, and so she sat with bent legs. John lay awake all night pondering the probable cause of paralysis. In the morning he perched the patient on the edge of a table and instructed her to let her legs swing to and fro, trying at each swing to retract them farther under the table than the momentum carried them. She could not so much as twitch the extensors. John told her to repeat the attempt every day for an hour. "If you will exert your will," he promised, "you will gain the power. If at the end of a month, you have recovered the least motion, I have no doubt you will walk again."

Before a month elapsed she could retract her legs almost an inch. Thus encouraged, she became more energetic and the muscles more obedient, until she could check receding motions and prolong advancing ones. John then had her continue the exercise with weights tied to her feet to intensify muscular effort. When he came again four months later, she walked across the room to greet him.

John disparaged the work of the seventeenth-century Dutch entomologist, Jan Swammerdam, on the grounds that he had been overly concerned with minutiae. It is inconceivable, however, that Swammerdam or any other investigator could have exceeded John's devotion to detail in *his* studies of bees. Summer after summer he followed the smallest actions of the insects, individually and collectively in the swarm, until he had recorded the entire apian life cycle. "My head," he exclaimed at the height of his labors, "is a beehive!"

He built compartments of plate glass, each large enough to accommodate a comb throughout a summer's operations, with the sides hinged so they could be opened and any bee removed at any stage for closer inspection. Much of what he observed was new to natural history, and all of it was expounded with immaculate exactitude. When a crucial event happened in the life of a particular bee, such as the first egg-laying or a hatching, he would paint a white dot and the date on the glass opposite its cell. To find out how many bees might inhabit a hive, he killed and counted three colonies, counted 3,338, 4,472, 2,332. . . . He established a convenient measurement of bulk by filling an ale-house pint mug level to the brim with dead bees. The mug held 2,160. He took still another census to corroborate his suspicion that a hive contained but one queen bee. He never found more than one, and in colonies that failed to swarm the queen was absent or dead.

He learned how worker bees, the tribal architects and builders, manufactured the building material of their strongholds. The way they clawed at their own underbellies gave him his lead. What they were after, he discovered, was a waxy substance excreted through slots between their belly scales, which they molded into building blocks with their mandibles and legs.

Nothing eluded his scrutiny, no movement, no sound. The eerie vibrato of the swarms as they streamed like black and gold lava out of congested hives towards new quarters—how describe the pitch? While Anne sat at a pianoforte by an open window, slowly striking each key, John stood among the wreathing, shimmering myriads, ears cocked, comparing. . . . There, that was it—treble A above middle C.

On a small, oval dissecting table, fitted with wheels the easier to move it where the light was strongest, he laid bare the structure of cocoon and larva, of drone, worker, and queen, of *Apis mellifica* and *Bombus terrestris*, a task for gimlet eyes and fingertips like antennae. "The tongue of the bee may be said to consist of three parts respecting its length, having three articulations. . . ." Every ramification of every tiny organ he traced out to the last convolution, the nerves, alimentary tract, honey-bag, oviducts. . . . Of the bee's temperament—"offensive and irritable"—he could speak with unshakable authority, having endured stings that puffed up his face beyond recognition. After the first onslaughts it occurred to him to wear protective gear, and, typically, he rejected the conventional netting in favor of a bizarre wooden visor of his own design.

But bee stings were only minor hazards of John's activities at Earl's Court. The wonder is that, with his weak heart, he got through so many summers alive. He once wrestled a young bull to verify its defense mechanisms. They proved to be in fine working order. The bull knocked him arsy-versy, and would have impaled him if a nimble farmhand, hearing his cries, hadn't driven off the victor.

No help was near the day a lion snapped his chains and broke out of the den. John whipped him back with a handkerchief. Another summer two leopards escaped. One wandered into a yard full of dogs and began chewing them up, the other tried to scramble up a wall to freedom. John grabbed them both by the scruff. Strangely, they showed no more fight, but meekly suffered themselves to be returned to captivity. Then, all danger past, John fainted.

Few of John's contemporaries ever fully grasped the drift of his incessant quest. Most other anatomists and naturalists viewed his experiments with little more than a mild, amused interest, most practical surgeons with derision. To laymen, they were meaningless, the vaporings of a cracked brain. But what fun it all provided for London's wags and wits—the porkers spayed and porkers dyed, the metamorphoses of barnyard genders, the hermaphroditic kine, the congealed fish, the swallows' dormitory, the glass hives, the master of the manor in his bee mask . . . John Wolcot, who composed rhyming satires under the pseudonym of "Peter Pindar," imagined this dialogue between himself and Sir Joseph Banks:

Sir Joseph
Hunter with fish our House regales—

> *Peter*
> *The tender history of cooing whales!*
> *Sir Joseph*
> *Great in the noble art of gelding sows!*
> *Peter*
> *And giving to the boar a barren spouse!*
> *Who proves, what many unbelievers shocks,*
> *That age converts hen partridges to cocks!*
> *And why not, since it is denied by no man*
> *That age has made John Hunter an* Old Woman.

William Blake lampooned John in his unfinished burlesque novel, *An Island in the Moon:* "I only wish Jack Tearguts had had the cutting of Plutarch," says Sipsop, the Pythagorean. "He understands Anatomy better than the Ancients. He'll plunge his knife up to the hilt in a single drive, and thrust his fist in, and all in the space of a Quarter of an hour. He does not mind their crying, tho' they cry ever so. He'll swear at them & keep them down with his fist, & tell them he'll scrape their bones if they don't lay still and be quiet. What the devil should the people in the hospital that have it done for nothing make such a piece of work for?"[h]

30. A PLEASANT DEATH

Resentments between the brothers mounted. John had been cut deep by William's coldness to Anne at the time of his marriage, and that coldness persisted, not only to Anne but to her children. Nor did William contemplate with any joy John's overshadowing renown, the magnitude of his establishments and the multiplicity of his works. One famous Hunter in London was enough. Outside of scientific circles they met less and less. In his *Anatomy of the Human Gravid Uterus* William neglected to specify the contributions John made to it during the period of their close association. The tone of John's now infrequent communications to William tended to be sardonic. "The bearer," he wrote, in a note referring a patient to him, "is very desirous of your opinion. I do not know his case. He has no money and you don't want any, so that you are well met."

Brotherly relations turned sourer still following a squabble over a pathological specimen. John let William inspect a diseased internal organ that he had removed from a sailor's corpse for his museum. William somehow got possession of it and would not give it up.

In 1780 the hostilities reached an ugly climax. The provocation was John's, and the issue he raised false. The most charitable extenuation his bewildered friends could offer was a lapse of sanity, the effect of his constant bodily torment. Certainly never before had John been known to fight meanly. What he did was to ascribe to himself an early discovery of William's, and by implication accuse his brother of theft.

The discovery was the structure of the placenta, which William had announced as far back as 1755, mentioned often in his lectures, and described in the *Anatomy*. Nobody had ever disputed his title to priority, least of all John, who helped him with the dissection. Now, twenty-six years later, in a paper on the placenta read to the Royal Society, he claimed full credit. He had, he deposed, immediately reported the discovery to William, "who at first treated it and me with good-humoured raillery; but . . . he was soon convinced of the fact. Some of the parts were given to him, which he afterwards showed at his lectures, and probably they still remain in his collection."

Why didn't John object at the time? Why did he wait so long? William sent the society a fuming letter of protest. Let the members judge the rights of the matter! "I hope," he raged, "I have not overlooked opportunities of doing justice to Mr. Hunter's great merits, and of acknowledging that he had been an excellent assistant to me in this and many other pursuits. By doing so I always felt an inward gratification, shall I call it, or pride? I have given him all the little anatomical knowledge that I could communicate, and put him into the very best situation that I could, for becoming what this Society has, for some time, known him to be. May it be presumed then that I stand possessed of the discovery in question, till proofs shall be brought to dispossess me?"

John, in a rebuttal addressed to the society, cavalierly suggested that perhaps credit should be apportioned among "the several ingenious young gentlemen" who were William's pupils or assistants at the time of discovery.

The society looked away in disgust and embarrassment, refusing to arbitrate the quarrel. The letters were omitted from its minutes, and John's paper on the placenta did not achieve print in its *Philosophical Transactions*.

"I have lived to have my affections much disturbed by ingratitude,"

William wrote to Dorothea. The brothers never spoke to each other again.

As William aged, his cynicism hardened, his tongue grew sharper. He bickered with everybody. "Most philosophers," he held, "most great men, most anatomists and most other eminent men lie like the devil." For years he had flattered his royal patients, truckled to Tory politicians, and departed from his lectures to heap praise on the party. Now disillusioned—was it because no knighthood had crowned his efforts?—he declared, "I have taken my leave of politics, and am sorry to say that as far as I am a judge this country deserves humiliation or rather a scourge."

Walpole, once partial to William, had been repelled by his time-serving shift from the Whig to the Tory camp. He referred to him in his journals as "Goody Hunter," and to a fellow Whig he wrote: "Dr. Hunter, that Scotch nightman, had the impudence t'other day to pour out at his anatomic lecture a more outrageous Smeltiad than Smelt himself [Leonard Smelt, a political diatribist of Johnson's circle], and imputed all our disgraces and ruin to the opposition. Burke was present, and said he had heard of political arithmetic, but never before of political anatomy, yet for a Scot to dare thus in the heart of London, and be borne is proof enough that the nation itself is lost beyond redemption."

William's hankering for social status led him to meddle in the private affairs of aristocratic families, and he was not above violating professional confidences. James, the Second Earl Waldegrave, had married Walpole's niece, Maria, accounted one of the handsomest women in England. He died of smallpox four years later. There being no son, his brother John stood to inherit the title and the bulk of the estate. But at the time of James's death Maria believed herself pregnant and she so informed Lady Elizabeth Waldegrave, her sister-in-law. Lady Elizabeth did not rejoice at the possibility of her husband losing the fortune after all.

Six months elapsing without progressive signs of pregnancy, Maria sent for Dr. Hunter. No, he told her, there appeared to be no heir in the offing. She then had the generous impulse to notify Lady Elizabeth at once and so end her suspense. But William persuaded her to wait; he might conceivably be mistaken. He knew, of course, he had made no mistake. What he hoped was to curry favor with Lady Elizabeth by reporting the good news himself, which he did the same day.

William wanted the fashionable world to know that he was privy to many a skeleton in the cupboards of the great. At dinner tables he would retell a scandalous anecdote about another patient of lofty station, divulging no names, but dropping such hints as to enable his listeners to guess at them. "During the American war," he would relate in his beautifully modulated voice, "I was consulted by the daughter of a peer, who confessed herself pregnant, and requested my assistance. I advised her to retire for a time to the house of some confidential friend. She said that was impossible, as her father would not suffer her to be absent from him a single day. Some of the servants were, therefore, let into the secret, and I made an arrangement with the treasurer of the Foundling Hospital to receive the child, for which I was to pay a hundred pounds. I desired the lady to weigh well if she could bear pain without alarming the family by her cries. She said, 'Yes,' and she kept her word.

"At the usual period I delivered her, not of one child only, but of twins. Taking the two children away, I was conducted by a French servant through the kitchen, and left to ascend the area steps into the street. Luckily the lady's maid recollected that the door of the area might perhaps be locked, and she followed me just in time to prevent my being detained at the gate. I deposited the children in the Foundling Hospital, and paid for each a hundred pounds. . . ."

Here William would pause and, gazing archly around the table, add, "The father of the children was a colonel of the army, who went with his regiment to America, and died there. The mother afterwards married a person of her own rank."

In his late years the arid little bachelor fluctuated between extremes of extravagance and parsimony. He would dip deep into his capital to augment his Gentleman's Cabinet, then fretfully scrimp on the creature comforts until he had put by an equivalent sum, a sacrifice that, according to a Dr. Richard Brocklesby, who treated him for gout, seriously weakened him. ". . . spent 100,000 on his collection," Brocklesby noted, "Nothing on himself."

With other collectors who owned some treasure he coveted he could be ruthless. He told Francis Carter, a numismatist, who had recently dropped a fortune in foreign investments, "I am glad to hear of your loss, as it may force you to sell me your Greek coins." "God grant,"

Carter wrote to Nichols, the printer, "I may be able to keep them from [such collectors'] clutches!"

As William's library attained stupendous proportions, he grew chary of lending books, and to the borrowers whom he still favored he would first display a ledger with the warning penned on the flyleaf: "From having lost *many* Books by lending them to my Acquaintances, I resolve from this time to enter all lent Books into this Volume; and to draw a line through every article as soon as the Book is returned to me. And this volume may be depended upon as evidence as I shall take care to be correct." He would then register the date, the name of the borrower, and the title of the book. Benjamin Franklin evidently passed muster, because the list shows that three books about Mary, Queen of Scots, were loaned to him.

Towards his sixty-first year a mellowing influence entered William's life, arousing paternal feelings in him. There came to London the fourth member of the Hunter line to choose a medical career. He was Dorothea's son, Matthew, aged eighteen. Though William had never set eyes on the boy before, he had, since the Reverend Baillie's death in 1778, financed his education at the University of Glasgow, and from afar imposed upon him a rigid discipline, compelling him to send, as proof of progress in the classical exercises, frequent lengthy essays in Latin of his own composition, and, by way of character building, keeping him "pinsh'd for money." "First deserve, then expect," was the avuncular injunction.

Meeting Matthew now for the first time, William did not regret his efforts. He found him eager, intelligent, and warmhearted. He was small like both of his uncles, with plain features, plain manners, and a thick burr, but he shared William's taste for the arts. William made a permanent place for him in his home, and sent him to Balliol College, Oxford. Between semesters he gave him the same intensive anatomical training he had given his long-dead brother James and his estranged brother John.

"Matthew," he would demand during supplementary lessons after the regular classwork, "do you know anything of today's lecture?"

"Yes, sir, I hope I do."

"Well, then, demonstrate to me."

"I will go and fetch the preparations, sir."

"Oh, no, Matthew, if you know the subject really, you will know it whether the preparation be absent or present." And he would stand stiffly facing him, arms akimbo, his foot tapping, while Matthew reconstructed the lecture from memory.

In later years Matthew panegyrized his uncle in these words: "He was probably the best teacher of anatomy that ever lived. No one possessed more enthusiasm for the art, more persevering industry, more acuteness of investigation, more perspicuity of expression, or indeed a greater share of natural eloquence. He was uncommonly ready in his apprehensions, and singularly happy in making others understand what he knew himself. His arrangement of any subject was clear and judicious; he knew how far the attention would reach, and when it was beginning to decline; and he had a most happy talent of introducing anecdotes which might excite, amuse and instruct."

The bad blood between his uncles put a severe strain on the nephew's loyalties. He loved Uncle Willie; he had come to love Uncle Jock as much. It took exceptional tact to go continually back and forth from one to the other without antagonizing either, but Matthew succeeded. In a codicil to his will William left him his house; his collections to enjoy for twenty years, after which he was to transfer them to the University of Glasgow; the Long Calderwood property; and £5,000. The rest of his fortune, totaling £14,000, he set aside for the maintenance of the collections, and annuities for Dorothea and her other children. The will did not mention John, an omission that struck Matthew as so unjust that when he came into his portion he ceded Long Calderwood to him.

After graduating from Balliol, Matthew began teaching anatomy at the Great Windmill Street School. He was appointed physician to St. George's Hospital, and later physician to George III. Eventually he built up the biggest practice in London since Mead and Cheselden. He had meanwhile been pursuing an original line of pathological research, and it culminated in a work worthy of his uncles.

In all three of her surviving children (two had died at birth) Dorothea Baillie proved fortunate. Matthew's older sisters, Agnes and Joanna, who never married, kept house together in London, conquered the *beau monde*, and lived to be almost a hundred. Of Joanna, poet and playwright, a slight, pretty, solemn girl with a heavy Scottish accent, William Wordsworth said, "If I had to present any one foreigner as a model of an English gentlewoman, it would be Joanna Baillie." Among her twenty-seven plays, seven poetic legends, fugitive poems and religious treatises was a long series of blank verse "Plays of Passion," each exemplifying a different human passion through a protagonist helpless in its grip. The first three, *Basil* (love), *The Trial* (love comically treated), and *de Montfort* (hatred), published anonymously, were attributed to Sir Walter Scott. When the real author revealed herself, Scott hailed her as "the Immortal Joanna," and her plays as the most powerful since the Elizabethans. Sir Walter notwithstanding, they were closet dramas, almost impossible to stage, though a few achieved production, but written in language of considerable vigor. Mary Berry, the moon of Walpole's delight, and a playwright herself, "kneeled on a chair at the table to see what the book was like and was found there—feathers and satin shoes and all—by the servant who came to let in the winter morning light." The loveliest of Joanna's fugitive poems was inspired by a memory of Long Calderwood:

> *The gowan glitters on the sward,*
> *The lavrock's in the sky;*
> *And collie on my plaid keeps ward,*
> *And time is passing by.*
> *Oh, no! sad and slow,*
> *And lengthen'd on the ground,*
> *The shadow of our trysting-bush,*
> *It wears so slowly round!*
>
> *I coft yestreen, frae Chapman Tam,*
> *A snood of bonnie blue,*
> *And promised when our trysting cam',*
> *To tie it round her brow.*
> *Oh, no! sad and slow,*
> *The mark it winna pass;*
> *The shadow of that weary thorn*
> *Is tether'd on the grass.*

William finished the last of his thirty-odd books and monographs in 1783, a scanty output compared to John's, but of high quality. His works of enduring value included, beside *The Anatomy of the Gravid Uterus*, a contribution to forensic medicine as remarkable for its compassion and eloquence as for its sagacity. Numbers of unmarried mothers had been hanged as infanticides on evidence that William, from his knowledge of obstetrics and feminine psychology, believed to be faulty. The mere act of attempting to conceal the body of an illegitimate child was often taken as a presumption of guilt. In anger and pity, William laid down a cautionary guide for jurists and juries, *On the Signs of Murder in the Case of Bastard Children,* showing the fallibility of the accepted tests for determining the cause of death.

"The world will give me credit surely," he wrote, "for having had sufficient opportunities of knowing a good deal of female characters. I have seen the private as well as the public virtues, the private as well as the more public frailties of women in all ranks of life. I have been in their secrets, their counsellor and adviser in the moments of their greatest distress in body and mind. I have been a witness to their private conduct, when they were preparing themselves to meet danger, and have heard their last and most serious reflections, when they were certain they had but a few hours to live.

"What is commonly understood to be the murder of a bastard child by the mother, if the real circumstances were fully known, would be allowed to be a very different crime in different circumstances. . . . The mother has an unconquerable sense of shame, and pants after the preservation of character: so far she is virtuous and amiable. She has not the resolution to meet and avow infamy. In proportion as she loses the hope either of having been mistaken with regard to pregnancy, of being relieved from her terrors by a fortunate miscarriage, she every day sees her danger greater and nearer, and her mind more over-whelmed with terror and despair. . . . In this perplexity . . . they are meditating different schemes for concealing the birth of the child; but are wavering between difficulties on all sides, putting the evil hour off, and trusting too much to chance and fortune. In that state often they are overtaken sooner than they expected; their schemes are frustrated; their distress of body and mind deprives them of all judgment, and rational conduct; they are delivered by themselves, wherever they happened to retire in their fright and confusion; sometimes dying in the agonies of childbirth, and sometimes being quite exhausted they faint away, and become insensible of what is passing; and when they recover a little strength, find that the child, whether still-born or not, is completely lifeless. In such a case, is it to be expected, when it could answer no purpose, that a woman should divulge the secret? Will not the best dispositions of mind urge her to preserve her character? She will therefore hide every appearance of what has happened as well as she can; though if the discovery be made, that conduct will be set down as a proof of her guilt . . . surely the only crime is the having been pregnant, which the law does not mean to punish by death; and the attempt to conceal it by fair means should not be punishable by death, as that attempt seems to arise from a principle of virtuous shame."

He proceeded to attack the errors commonly committed by inexperienced coroners. The fact of a dead infant's lungs being still inflated he considered no incontrovertible evidence that it had survived birth, for "if a child makes but one gasp, and instantly dies, the lungs will swim in water as readily as if it breathed longer, and had then been strangled." A baby a-borning, he pointed out, normally begins to breathe when its head protrudes, but even with the best obstetrical care may die within an hour or two from damage inflicted during labor. "And why may not that misfortune happen to a woman who is brought to bed by herself?"

When the child's face looked black and swollen, "the vulgar" were apt to conclude that it had been strangled, because of the similar appearance of hanged men. But as every obstetrician knew, nothing was commoner in natural birth, particularly if the umbilical cord girded the baby's neck before the full emergence of its body.

William stressed the likelihood of fatal accidents when the mother fainted. The infant might be suffocated by the bedclothes; it might drown in the discharges of parturition.

If the public would weigh these factors, he pleaded, if only physicians of extensive obstetrical experience were to qualify as professional witnesses, "they may be the means of saving some unhappy and innocent woman."

A forensic authority, summarizing William's paper half a century later, pronounced it "the most influential and popular tract on Child-murder hitherto produced in this country." "The judges," he reported, "quote it with implicit faith in its perfection: the bar study it, and cross-examine the crown witnesses on the difficulties which it suggests; and medical men will probably not find it safe to venture into the witness-box without being familiarly acquainted with its contents."

But the capstone of William's monument was the Great Windmill School, which under the joint direction of Matthew Baillie and William Cruikshank continued to turn out many of England's best medical men, and left an indelible stamp on medicine everywhere.

The introductory lecture of William's courses always drew the heaviest attendance, because he ornamented it with his shiniest gems of literary allusion, history, and philosophy. On March 20, 1783, the beginning of his spring term, hundreds were waiting in the lecture theater. All that winter William had suffered from gout, and the pain had prostrated him. But like an old actor loath to miss an opening performance he forced himself to his feet. Midway through the lecture he fainted, and was carried back to bed. During the night he had a stroke.

In response to a message from Baillie, John came at once. But there was no reconciliation.

Towards the end William murmured, "If I had the strength to hold a pen, I would write how pleasant and easy a thing it is to die."

Baillie repeated this to John, who remarked, "Ay, but 'tis a poor thing when it comes to that."

William died on Sunday, March 30, and was buried the next Saturday evening in the rector's vault beneath St. James's Church. John did not appear. The mourners were few, leading the *Morning Chronicle* to comment: "A Garrick was attended to his grave in a manner that will ever do honour to literary and theatrical characters. Shall a Hunter be deposited in the tomb privately?"

Not long after, John's pupils were filing out of his lecture room, when he called them back. "Ho, gentlemen," he said, "one thing more, I need not remind you of—you all know the loss anatomy has lately sustained—" He could not continue. He turned to the wall, choked with tears.

VII. PROTEUS
1783-1793

৩৩৩৩

31. THE FACE OF THOUGHT

"We* are enabled to refer to this year [1785] two of his very finest male portraits, those of Joseph Sharpe, the honest lawyer . . . and John Hunter, the great comparative anatomist. Both are very full half-lengths, seated . . . the anatomist's, with the head raised, and abstracted eyes, as if following out some train of thought, closely linked and reaching far, till it can be fixed by the pen held in the relaxed hand. The mood of keen, close, connecting induction has never been so perfectly personified as in this figure. It looks as if the painter had been allowed to watch Hunter at work, himself unseen. . . ."

To persuade John to pose for a portrait by Sir Joshua had exhausted the joint efforts of Anne Hunter, his friends, and students. Except for the two oils by Anne's brother, Robert Home, there existed no likeness of John, and Sir Joshua, whose most powerful portraits included those of such men of intellect as William Hunter, Percivall Pott, Sir Joseph Banks, Johnson, Gibbon, Sterne, and Burke, was, by unanimous choice, the artist to paint it. A group of John's friends had offered to share the cost (Reynolds commanded fees as high as £500), but this John would not hear of. Nor did he care to spend for his own glorification money that might otherwise procure him new specimens. It was

* Charles Robert Leslie and Tom Taylor in their *Life and Times of Sir Joshua Reynolds*.

chiefly as a favor to the engraver, William Sharp, that he finally consented.

Sharp belonged to that flamboyant company of London odd fish, combining talent with eccentricity, who so diverted John in his lighter moods. A prodigious gourmand, shaped like a hogshead, garrulous, quixotic, and excitable, Sharp was singularly susceptible to the influence of mystics. First Mesmer, then Swedenborg attracted him. He next joined the cult of Richard Brothers, "Nephew of the Almighty and Prince of Hebrews, appointed by God to lead them to Canaan," a former naval officer who had developed messianic delusions after returning home from the wars to find that his wife had borne several children by various lovers. Arming himself with a staff stripped from a wild-rose bush, as he claimed his Uncle Jehovah had directed him, he roamed the country, prophesying disasters and making thousands of converts. None was more ardent than Sharp, who, in one of his favorite engravings, portrayed the prophet with celestial fires flickering about his head. Some prankster—suspicion fell on John Hunter—stole into his studio, and cut an extra comma in the plate so that the title read: "Fully believing this to be the man appointed, by God, I engrave his likeness."

When the "nephew of the Almighty" was incarcerated as a criminal lunatic for prophesying the assassination of George III, Sharp shifted his allegiance to Joanna Southcott, "the Lamb's Wife." At his own expense he brought her from her native Devonshire, where she had been a scullery maid, to London, and supported her there in high style. Joanna sold seals to the "elect," almost 100,000 of them, certifying them as worthy of survival after Doomsday. The market in seals abruptly collapsed when an elect named Mary Bateman was hanged for murder. In her fifty-second year Joanna announced that she had immaculately conceived "Shiloh, a spiritual man, the second Christ." Six doctors pronounced her pregnant. The news electrified her followers. Spurred on by Sharp, they contributed £300 towards a crib and pap spoons, and leased a mansion for the miraculous accouchement. But Joanna died before the event. An autopsy revealed no signs of pregnancy.

Though a superlative craftsman, Sharp harbored notions about human physiognomy as bizarre as his theological beliefs. People, he held, bore a resemblance to that bird or beast most like them in character. Thus, a cunning man might resemble a serpent, a meek man a lamb, a fierce man a tiger. What fauna John's grave, granitic lineaments suggested, wise owl or noble lion, Sharp did not divulge, but he felt confident of reaping a fortune from an engraving, if England's greatest anatomist would sit to England's greatest portraitist. And so, in May 1785, John, yielding to his strange friend's entreaty, walked across the square to No. 47.

The studio was octagonal, about twenty feet long and sixteen feet wide. The light streamed through a window cut high in the wall. Reynolds seated John in a revolving chair on a dais raised eighteen inches above the floor, facing the light, and began sketching with a pencil the length of his forearm. Never was an artist plagued by a more intractable sitter. To begin with, John was wearing a weedy beard and mustache that hid the strong lines of his mouth and jaw. He had grown them during an outbreak of rash (possibly a renewed symptom of venereal infection) that prevented him from shaving, and was now attached to them, despite Anne's disapproval and Sir Joshua's frustration. Worse still, he fidgeted, chattered, and kept changing expression throughout the sittings, which dragged on in four two-hour afternoon sessions a week until the autumn. The finished portrait pleased Sir Joshua no more than it did Anne, who later gave it away, though it had cost £50, 10s.

In for a penny, in for a pound. John agreed to sit again. He refused, however, to part with his whiskers. So between them Anne and Sir Joshua hatched a stratagem. When John next went to the studio, in November, the painter piqued his curiosity with talk of life masks. Had he never submitted to the process? No, never, said John, snapping at the bait, what was involved? Perhaps it might be adapted to anatomical preparations. Sir Joshua said he could easily demonstrate, were it not for the obstruction of John's beard. John shaved.

As Sir Joshua moistened plaster of Paris, inserted breathing tubes in John's nostrils, and covered his face with the mixture, John watched and questioned, storing each detail in his mind, to the moment his mouth and eyes were stopped up. Afterwards he solemnly studied his face in a mirror, and, noting a discoloration, pondered what physiological inference might be drawn from it. "When I had plaster of Paris applied to my face to make a mould," he recalled later in his treatise on blood, "in the taking it off it produced a kind of suction on the fore part of the nose, which I felt; and when the plaster was removed, on observing the part, it was red, as if the cells of the skin were loaded with extravasated blood; this was then of a fluid red, but it soon became a dark purple, which showed that it was arterial blood, and that by stagnating in the cells it became the colour of venal blood."

The offending beard disposed of, and John clad in a suit of wine-red velvet, the artist set to work again. He posed him on the dais in a pensive attitude, seated beside a writing table, his right hand holding a quill, the knuckles of his left pressed against his cheek. But John was as restive as a schoolboy kept after class. Tentatively Sir Joshua roughed out the head and body, doubtfully began placing the features, when a startling change in the sitter riveted his eye. Suddenly, in spirit, John was no longer present. Head cocked as if hearkening to remote voices, his gaze fixed upon an inner image, he had sunk deep into reverie, into that anesthetic state when, as he himself once described it, "the body loses consciousness of its own existence." Certainly, a great deal had happened recently in his life and work to grip his mind. He had barely recovered from a near fatal heart attack, he was almost ready to publish his observations on venereal diseases, and he was about to attempt his first operation for an aneurysm.

Enthralled, Reynolds spun the canvas around, drew the head anew between the roughly sketched legs, and before John had stirred, captured the transfiguration.

He completed the portrait, measuring fifty by forty-five inches, that month, and exhibited it the following year, along with twelve others, at the Royal Academy of Arts. It was adjudged a masterpiece. But Reynolds, a man of such humility that he shrank from praise because he felt painting came too easily for him to merit it, protested, "As he was remarkably still, it became a matter of no more difficulty than copying a barn or any object of still-life."

During the next four months Reynolds kept adding background accessories suggested by John. On the table, by his elbow, he reproduced two folio volumes labeled *Natural History of Vegetables* and *Natural History of Fossils,* and a third standing open at two pages of plates, the right showing a graded series of skeletal forelimbs in an ascending scale from monkey to dog to pig to ox to man, the right showing a descending series of skulls from European man to Australian aborigine to chimpanzee to macaque to dog to crocodile; under a glass bell, a dry preparation of a cancerous lung; on a mantel behind the table, a wet preparation of a dorsal bone graft, and dangling above that, the legs of Charles O'Byrne's skeleton, an acquisition John no longer thought it necessary to conceal. In his account book for 1785 Reynolds noted: "John Hunter, second payment—£50-10-0."

Sharp made two engravings, of which he sold hundreds of prints at two guineas apiece. John himself bought fifty. But what gratified Sharp most was Sir Joshua's endorsement. Until then the artist had doubted that line engraving could justly render the masses of his compositions, and had preferred mezzotints. But in the reproduction of the Hunter portrait Sharp achieved a subtle shadowing and density that won Reynolds over.

Among the art lovers who saw the painting when it hung in the Royal Academy was the Swiss theologian, Johann Lavater. "That man," he exclaimed, "thinks for himself!" [1]

32. THE STAG

Serendipity (serendi. pity). *1754.* [F. Serendip (*-b*), *former name of Ceylon -ITY; coined by Horace Walpole upon the title of the fairytale* The Three Princes of Serendip, *the heroes of which 'were always making discoveries, by accidents and sagacity, of things they were not in quest of'.] The faculty of making happy and unexpected discoveries by accident.*

—THE OXFORD ENGLISH DICTIONARY ON
HISTORICAL PRINCIPLES

During the spring of 1785 John was felled by his worst heart attack in years. Dr. John Coakley Lettsom, who saw him shortly after, told a colleague, "Poor Hunter is going from this busy stage. He can scarce go upstairs, so much is he affected with dyspnoea. He declares he was dead the other day for four minutes, not having pulsation in the heart or arteries. . . ."

But the lamentation was premature. John had revived again, and was pursuing one of the most rigorous inquiries of his career.

Most varieties of stag shed their antlers and grow a new pair every year. Among the pending investigations on John's crowded agenda was the mode of this growth. Through what channels did the new cartilage derive its nutriment? Probably, John speculated, through the two carotid arteries running up the sides of the animal's neck.

Richmond Park, a crown property of almost twenty-five hundred acres lying on the south bank of the Thames, seven miles from the center of London, had originally been enclosed by Charles I as a deer-hunting preserve, and though it had since been opened to the public, deer by the hundreds still roamed its thick groves. One of the privileges George III had accorded John was that of drawing upon the deer herds for experimental material, and in July of that year the surgeon availed himself of it. He had park wardens snare a young stag. He then laid bare one of the carotid arteries and tied it with surgical thread.

When he returned to examine the stag a few days later, it was as he expected: the antler corresponding to the ligated artery had stopped growing and felt cold to the touch. Clearly, it was receiving no nutriment. Would it be shed sooner than usual? On re-examining it a week later, after the wound around the ligature had healed, he saw, to his astonishment, that the antler was warm again and had resumed growing.

Could he have failed to ligate it securely? Was blood somehow still passing through it? He ordered the stag killed and brought to Leicester Square, where he dissected the area at the base of the antlers. He satisfied himself that he had not bungled the ligature. Yet a curious change had taken place. Some of the smaller arterial branches, above and below the ligature, were enlarged. It was through this mysteriously arisen auxiliary system, John reasoned, that blood must have been supplied to the antlers.

His swift conclusion was, in the words of Sir James Paget, one of the great pathologists of the nineteenth century, "a signal instance of the living force there is in facts when they are stored in a thoughtful mind." From the single observation of the altered blood vessels John deduced the entire principle of collateral circulation. According to this principle, the smaller, tributary arteries will, under "the stimulus of necessity," to use John's typically vitalist phrase, assume the functions of the larger. To verify this, John had Everard Home ligate the femoral artery of a dog and, later, dissect the leg. Home reported the same findings. Here was further confirmation of John's belief in the body's ability to throw up its own defenses.

Four months after the discovery, a forty-five-year-old coachman—

identified in John's records as "A.B."—was admitted to St. George's in the late stages of a popliteal aneurysm. An aneurysm, whose commonest causes include syphilis, is a dilatation and progressive deterioration of the walls of an artery. As the heartbeats transmit their regular impulses along the weakened passage, the walls are pushed outward, forming a pulsating sac. Untreated, the sac will eventually burst and the patient bleed to death.

The type of aneurysm afflicting A.B.—an aneurysm of the popliteus, or ham—was one to which coachmen were prone because of the continually cramped position of their knee joints. His plight was drawn to John's attention shortly before Christmas, as the surgeon, himself still weak from his last heart attack, was walking the wards with a group of his pupils and stopped to question him. As nearly as the coachman, in the extremity of his agony, could recall, the first symptoms had developed three years before. John drew back the bedclothes to inspect the tortured leg. He saw that both hamstrings were grotesquely distended. Between them rose a bulbous swelling. The rest of the leg as well as the foot was also swollen and mottled. Placing his hands alongside the tumor, John could feel the strong pulsations, each bringing another stab of pain to the sufferer. The whole leg felt hot.

In such cases the choice of treatment was limited. The artery would sometimes be ligated above and below the seat of the aneurysm and the sac opened and emptied. But the accompanying destruction of blood vessels was so often fatal that when Percivall Pott had suggested, as an alternative, amputating the leg, the medical world acclaimed him for his wise conservatism. The possibility of ligating the artery without cutting into the sac, so that the blood would no longer pump through the diseased tissue and weaken it further, had occurred to many surgeons, but had been generally discarded on the ground that a discontinuance of the normal blood supply would cause the leg to mortify.

For the coachman amputation had already been prescribed, when John paused by his bedside. Was this, then, the best the "armed savage" could devise? With all the force of his revulsion against surgical mutilation, John rejected it. And as he talked to the patient in his blunt yet inspiriting way, as he gently fingered the throbbing leg, there flashed across his mind his experiment with the stag. Why could not collateral circulation be stimulated in a man as well as in an animal? Suppose the aneurysm were to be left alone and the artery ligated at a point above it. Would not the blood, deflected to the branch arteries, bypass the diseased area, rejoin the main artery below it, and so nourish the leg?

John put the facts to the coachman with candor. He warned him that what he contemplated was untried, an incalculable risk. But if successful, he might survive and keep his leg. The coachman decided to trust the plainspoken little Scot. Before leaving the ward to begin his preparations, John could not resist exacting a promise—come what might, the patient must bequeath him the leg.

After days of planning, John entered St. George's operating theater in his long surgical dress, attended by his pupils and with fellow surgeons, both British and foreign, filling the gallery. He first explained the procedure and the results he hoped for. A pupil raised the point: what of the sac and its noxious content of clotted blood and dead tissue? How would it be got rid of without opening the sac? For this John was relying on another physiological action, the subject of one of his earliest investigations—the absorptive power of the lymphatics.

The patient was near death when John's aides laid him upon the operating table and secured his arms and legs. John wound a tourniquet around the upper thigh, about a foot above the aneurysm, and made two incisions, one on the outer, the other on the inner surface. These he deepened and widened through successive layers of tissue until he came to the fibrous sheath enclosing the femoral artery (since known as Hunter's canal). He cut away about an inch of the sheath, exposing the artery itself. With a thin spatula he detached the artery from its moorings and freed it. An assistant handed him an eyed probe through which had been passed a loop of thread. John drew it under the artery. He cut the loop so as to form two separate ligatures, pulled the strands taut, and carried the ends outside the wound. Then he drew the edges of the incisions together, joining them with sticking plaster and a linen bandage, and left them to heal by primary union. He repeated the operation on the same artery below the ham.

The repetition was a blunder John committed from fear of secondary hemorrhages. By thus leaving a blood-filled space in order to accommodate four different ligatures he actually increased the danger. Luck favored him, however. No severe bleeding occurred. "Wrap the leg in flannel," he told his assistants as he laid down his instruments, "but do not apply any artificial heat."

The first results showed within twenty-four hours, and they were encouraging. The leg regained its normal temperature. In a few days the swollen sac began to diminish. Six weeks later A.B. was driving a coach again, living proof that a damming of the bloodstream could cure an aneurysm. "The operation," commented the Italian surgeon, Assalini, who had witnessed it, "excited the greatest wonder and awakened the attention of all the surgeons in Europe."

John's patient faithfully reported to him at St. George's once a week. No bad effects of the operation were recorded. But when he came the last week in May it was with a severe cold, caught while working in wet weather. It developed into a remittent fever and on April 1 he died.

Evidently A.B. had forgotten his pre-operation promise, for John noted, in words hinting at traffic with the resurrectionists, that he procured the leg only "with some trouble and expense." Dissected and mounted, it duly took its place in the museum.

In later operations for popliteal aneurysm John corrected his initial error of overexposing the artery and made one ligature only. The fourth patient, a man of thirty-seven, also a coachman, lived for fifty years more.

There is no indication that John ever performed a fifth operation of the kind. He had established the principle. With his distaste for cutting, the reluctant surgeon was content to leave it to his disciples to refine the method. This they did, adapting it, moreover, to other arteries and eliminating aneurysms in regions once thought inaccessible to the knife, such as the chest and the brain. It remained for Astley Cooper to ligate the aorta, near the heart itself.

John's operation, still performed much as he conceived it, continues to obviate amputations and to save lives.

33. *LUES VENERA*

"Read John Hunter on the venereal disease," noted that oft-infected amorist, James Boswell, in his journal of April 20, 1786.

It would be pleasant to report that after the dreadful penalties John had incurred he achieved a great discovery. But his initial mischance in inoculating himself with a mixed infection instead of a pure strain of either gonorrhea or syphilis was irreparable. The fallacy into which it led him, and in which the majority of his contemporaries concurred, retarded the investigation of venereal diseases for fifty years. Not until 1838, when the French dermatologist, Philippe Ricord, published his findings, were gonorrhea and syphilis shown to be separate diseases, and not until 1905, with the discovery of the syphilis-causing *Spirochaeta pallida* by the German bacteriologist, Fritz Richard Schaudinn, and his countryman, the pathologist Paul Erich Hoffmann, could all the pieces of the puzzle be fitted together.

Yet John's *Treatise on the Venereal Disease*, the product of eighteen years' study, was not valueless. If nothing more, it lifted the subject out of the murk of prurience, hypocrisy and superstition that had shrouded it for centuries. But there was a good deal more. Although John drew the wrong inferences, he observed the facts accurately, and his careful description cleared a path towards the eventual solution. While insisting that gonorrhea and syphilis proceeded from the same infection, he clearly differentiated between the ulcerations peculiar to each. The hard, or Hunterian chancre, which John was the first to identify, was taken by every investigator who followed him as a point of departure.

John further affirmed the all-important truth that the local effects of syphilis may be succeeded, long after their subsidence, by profound constitutional damage, though that this was the probable explanation of his own chronic illness never dawned upon him. "The venereal disease also becomes the immediate cause of other disorders. . . . If the venereal disease attacks the lungs, although that disposition may be corrected, consumption may ensue; and in like manner where the bones are affected, or the nose, scrofulous swellings or fistula lachrymalis may be the consequence. . . ."

John was right, too, about the medium of contagion. "That the venereal disease is to be propagated only by matter is proved every day by a thousand instances. Married men contract the disease and not suspecting that they have caught it, cohabit with their wives. Upon discovering the symptoms of the disease they of course desist; yet in all my practice I never once found that the complaint was communicated under such circumstances, except where they had not been very attentive to the symptoms, and therefore continued the connexion after the discharge had appeared. I have gone so far as to allow husbands while infected, but before the appearance of discharge, to cohabit with their wives in order to save appearances, and always with safety. I could carry this still further, and even allow a man who has a gonorrhea to have connexion with a sound woman, provided that great care be taken to clear all the parts of any matter, by first syringing the urethra, making water, and washing the glans.

". . . There is no instance where it has given infection in the form of vapour, as is the case in so many other poisons."

In a digression midway through the *Treatise*, John seems to have caught a glimmer of the psychogenic factors underlying sexuality. It starts off with a repudiation of the ancient notion that masturbation in adolescence causes impotence. "How far attributing to this practice such a consequence is of public utility, I am doubtful, particularly as it is followed most commonly at an age when consequences are not sufficiently attended to, even in things less gratifying to the senses; but this I can say with certainty, that many of those affected with the complaints in question [that is, impotence] are miserable from this idea; and it is some consolation for them to know that it is possible it may arise from other causes. I am clear in my own mind that the books on the subject have done more harm than good.

"In the cases of this kind that have come under my care, although the persons themselves have been very ready to suppose that the disease has arisen from the cause here alluded to, yet they did not appear to have given more into the practice than common; and in particular, the worst case I have ever seen was where but very little of this practice had ever been used, much less than is common among boys."

Nothing, John goes on to argue, so depresses a man as the fear that he cannot copulate. A requisite to the complete performance of the reproductive organs, he adds, is perfect harmony of mind and body, "for the mind is subject to a thousand caprices, which affect the action of those parts.

"Copulation is an act of the body, the spring of which is in the mind; but it is not volition; and according to the state of the mind so is the act performed. To perform this act well, the body should be in health, and the mind should be perfectly confident of the powers of the body; it should have no difficulties, no fears, no apprehensions; not even an anxiety to perform the act well. . . . Perhaps no function of the machine depends so much upon the state of mind as this.

"The will and reasoning faculty have nothing to do with this power; they are only employed in the act, so far as voluntary parts are made use of; and if they ever interfere, which they sometimes do, it often produces another state of mind, which destroys that which is proper for the performance of the act; it produces a desire, a wish, a hope, which are only diffidence and uncertainty, and create in the mind the idea of a possibility of the want of success, which destroys the proper state of mind, or necessary confidence.

"There is perhaps no act in which a man feels himself more interested, or is more anxious to perform well, his pride being engaged in some degree, which, if within certain bounds, would produce a degree of perfection in an act depending upon the will, or an act in voluntary parts; but when it produces a state of mind contrary to that state, on which the perfection of the act depends, a failure must be the consequence.

"The body is not only rendered incapable of performing this act, by the mind being under the above influence, but also by the mind being perfectly confident of its power, but conscious of an impropriety in performing it; this, in many cases, produces a state of mind which shall take away all power. The state of a man's mind, respecting his sister, takes away all power. A conscientious man has been known to lose his powers on finding a woman he was going to be connected with unexpectedly a virgin. . . .

"From this account of the necessity of having the mind independent respecting the act, we must see that it may very often happen that the state of mind will be such as not to allow the animal to exert its natural powers; and every failure increases the evil. We must also see from this state of the case, that this act must be often interrupted; and the true cause of this interruption not being known, it will be laid to the charge of the body, or want of powers. As these cases do not arise from real inability, they are to be carefully distinguished from such as do; and perhaps the only way to distinguish them is to examine the state of mind respecting this act. So trifling often is the circumstance which shall produce this inability depending on the mind, that the very desire to please shall have that effect, as in making the woman the sole object to be gratified."

Among the numerous cases of impotence John had treated was that of a man who, though deeply enamored of his mistress, responded to her with diminished virility. Questioning him for more than an hour, John gathered that in her absence he frequently experienced intense desire, accompanied by a full erection. There could therefore be no organic defect.

"Are all women alike to you?" John asked.

"No," said the frustrated lover. "With some women I can have connexion as well as ever."

He admitted, when pressed, that he found himself lacking only with his mistress, whom, above all other women, he longed to gratify.

At this John began to suspect the trouble to be fear of inadequacy. "You may be cured," he said finally, "if you can rely perfectly on your own power of self-denial."

The patient assuring him that his will was strong, John instructed him to share his mistress's bed for the next six nights, but without touching her, no matter how violent a passion might assail him. Let him then resume the normal relationship, and inform John of the result.

The patient was back two weeks later, overjoyed by the success of the stratagem. "He told me," wrote John, "that this resolution had produced such a total alteration in the state of his mind that the power soon took place; for instead of going to bed with the fear of inability, he went with fears that he should be possessed with too much desire, too much power, so as to become uneasy to him, which really happened; for he would have been happy to have shortened the time; and when he had once broken the spell, the mind and powers went on together, and his mind never returned to its former state."

34. THE ORPHAN

Tuesday, February 14, 1792. John's birthday. But there was no family celebration. He was too ill.

That evening a new apprentice timidly presented himself at No. 28 Leicester Square. He carried four changes of shirt and neckcloth, castoffs from an older brother, all he owned beside the patched clothes on his back. He was William Clift from Bodmin, in Cornwall, and it happened to be his birthday too, his seventeenth. By a further coincidence, being a shade under five feet tall, with the same square, heavy jaw and blunt nose, he bore a resemblance to John so striking as to give rise to gossip that John had begot him. No blood ties existed, yet few fathers ever received more selfless devotion from a son than this shy little tyro was to render John.

He was born, the youngest of seven children, to a journeyman miller, "a very honest man [William recollected]: one tolerable reason why he did not succeed better in the world." The miller died a pauper when William was nine. His widow worked in the hay fields during the summer, winters she carded wool, and starved herself to put aside the threepence a week needed for the boy's education. She died when he was eleven, and he saw no more of school, but earned his bread as a jack-of-all-trades—gardener, carter, plowman, groom. He taught himself penmanship and drawing, practicing with chalk on the kitchen floors of the Bodmin homes where he toiled for a pittance.

The most benevolent of his occasional employers were Colonel Walter Raleigh Gilbert, a Gentleman-of-the-Bedchamber to George III, and his wife Nancy. Mrs. Gilbert had been a close friend of Anne Hunter ever since they were at the same school, and they often visited each other. While staying at the Hunters, Mrs. Gilbert heard John bewailing the departure, for more lucrative employment in Sumatra, of his ablest anatomical assistant and draughtsman, William Bell. "He's been with me fourteen years," he said. "I'm having difficulty replacing him."

"I know a very clever boy," Mrs. Gilbert volunteered, "who with proper instruction will become an excellent draughtsman, and probably answer your purpose very well in other matters." She would, if John wished and the boy was amenable, have a lawyer draw up indentures of apprenticeship as soon as she returned to Bodmin. John agreed to take her protégé on trial.

The boy needed no persuasion, but eagerly accompanied Mrs. Gilbert to a lawyer named George Brown, a splenderous figure in a scarlet gown and cap of crimson velvet, and with his sister Elizabeth and the colonel acting as witnesses, signed papers binding him to John Hunter for six years. No pay was specified, only his wardrobe, bed and board, and training in the skills his master would require of him.

As the ink was drying on the contract, the lawyer remarked, "You are going to London. When you come back hereafter in your own carriage, you will hardly know us, but don't forget your old friends."

"For God's sake, Mr. Brown," exclaimed Mrs. Gilbert, "don't put such ideas in the poor boy's head!"

"The poor boy"—so most people tended to think of him, and in later years it would be "poor Clift."

John was slow to recover from his latest seizure, and almost a week went by before he could talk to Clift. His dissecting-room porter,

Robert Haynes, took charge of the apprentice meanwhile, setting him, as his first chore, to making paper containers for small specimens. A good-hearted man, he gave him a little pocket money, and showed him the sights of the city. Anne, too, was kind to the newcomer, putting him at his ease, and encouraging him in his artistic bent. But of his initial encounter with Everard Home, who lived with his wife at No. 45 Leicester Square, and, because of John's frequent incapacity, now handled all of his night calls, Clift retained a disagreeable impression. Home asked him fatuously, indicating a dissecting room Clift had to pass at night on his way to bed, "Are you afraid of ghosts?" "I don't know, sir," Clift replied, "I never saw one. I was never afraid of any of my school-fellows, though bigger boys than me." Home laughed uproariously.

When he had finally met John, Clift wrote in his first letter home, ". . . he is a verry curious man, and plain as well for he has hair as white as snow and had never got it drest. I believe there is not a bit of Pride in him and all his clothes so plain (but very rich) that I am sure you wou'd not think he was such a grand gentleman. For here Barbers and Taylors and their wifes are all dukes and dutchesses on Sundays."

John had scarcely regained his feet before his services were needed on the other side of the square. An old friend lay mortally sick of an undiagnosed disease. "I suppose [Clift's letter continued] you have heard tell of Sir Joshua Reynolds that fine painter, well he will never draw any more, for he is dead and buried at St. Paul's Church on Saturday last and I was put by Mr. Haynes to see the procession and first there went My Lord Mayor's coach, then the City Marshall all in red and blue lace, then went the Hearse and then 42 mourning coaches with lords, knights and dukes of all sorts and then follow'd all the gentlemen's coaches that rode in the mourning coaches which was upwards of 120 more—well, it was the finest sight I ever saw in my life at that time."

The day after Reynolds died, February 24, John, assisted by Sir George Baker and Home, opened the body. ". . . the only diseased part was the liver, which was of a magnitude very uncommon, and at least double of what is natural; it weighed eleven pounds and was of a consistence which is usually called scirrhous." But John did not join the mourners, much as he had cherished the dead man's friendship. He shunned all ceremony as a thief of his most precious resource, time. Though he would spend it prodigally to prolong a life, or determine the cause of death, he would not spare an instant in obsequies. When called upon to ride in the cortege, he flung out, with a crassness that concealed his affection for the artist, "Let Reynolds and his friends go to the devil!"

Clift's early life in London was a continual enchantment. John hired a drawing teacher for him, "a little old hump of a fellow," then, as he progressed, enrolled him in the art classes of a Mr. Martin in Great Marlborough Street, and finally engaged a French draughtsman, a refugee from the Terror. "I have last week," the pupil happily informed his relatives, "been drawing a bird from nature for Mr. Hunter has a great collection of stuffed birds and Mr. Home . . . came into the room where I was drawing and said he thought it was done very well and went through to the other house and told Mr. Hunter and in the evening he [John] told me he was in hopes I should do very well in a little time. . . . Today morning Mrs. Hunter sent for me to come to her drawing room and she said she thought I had done it exceedingly well."

Delighted by the first clothes John bought him, he wrote, "It is of dark brown and the coat, waistcoat and breeches are of one sort. I have three new shirts that cost seven shillings each, they buy them here at the shops ready made. I have three neckcloths of the same sort I had of brother John and I have 4 new pocket handkerchiefs at ⅙ a piece. I have four pairs of worsted stockings." The price of everything astounded him, especially servants' hire. "I saw a girl that came to see one of our maids, she was not 18 and she was complaining that she wou'd not stay till only she cou'd get another place because she had but 7 guineas a year." Clift had nothing beyond the shilling or two that John, and the Gilberts, during their visits to London, doled out to him. Most of the money he spent on novels, gradually acquiring *The History of Tom Jones*, *The Vicar of Wakefield*, *Joseph Andrews*, *Roderick Random*, *Tristram Shandy*, and *Robinson Crusoe*.

With John's approval Haynes continued to guide the novice around London. A day at Greenwich Fair left him pleasantly shocked. "In Greenwich Park is where the people all meet and go to the top of a very steep hill and run down for a quarter of a mile and sometimes the girls come down such a nice tumble t'would make you split your sides to see them come down with such a fall and running their full force downhill that as they fall their petticoats fly right over their heads before some thousands of both sexes. There is some very creditable looking girls run and tumble as well as the girls of the town. . . .

When all the people was very busy in looking at the girls running a pickpocket stole a pocket handkerchief out of a gentleman's pocket and some of the young men saw him do it and they took him and drag'd him to a large pond in the park and they sous'd him as it were into the belly of a tulip over head and years and battered him with mud till they half kill'd him and would not let him come out till he had swam across two or three times."

As Nancy Gilbert had predicted, Clift proved equal to whatever tasks John assigned him. By the end of his first year he could macerate and inject specimens, dissect them in water or spirits, "the better to distinguish or remove jagged shreds of cellular membrane," take dictation, and reduce John's findings to orderly reports and sketches. He was initiated into the work of the museum when Sir Joseph Banks, having decided to disperse his collection, gave the British Museum half of it and John the rest. Clift selected and remounted the exhibits worth keeping. A new variety of black swan had been discovered in Australia and a specimen sent to John. It was too dilapidated to warrant the expense of an expert taxidermist, but too rare to throw away, and John turned it over, "as a first essay in preserving," to Clift, who rehabilitated it so skillfully that it won a perch in the museum. Clift's estimable predecessor, Bell, was all but forgotten until the news came from Sumatra that a fever had killed him. "Ah, poor Bell, poor Bell," John grieved, "had he stayed with me, he would still be alive and well."

Clift's love for his master ruled him to the end of his days. He believed him "in everything next to the Almighty in knowledge," served him with joyous abnegation, and remained as blind to his flaws as Jessé Foot to his qualities. "Generally, though cheerfully taciturn—" was Clift's characterization, "many a morning's labour passing over with scarcely a word of discourse: but shrewd and witty in his remarks, when he condescended to unbend and let himself out, as he sometimes did when resting himself, and standing upright, from his dissection after stooping for hours, as if nailed to the object. He could relate a professional anecdote very humorously, concisely and with much point, but with never the slightest inclination to ill-natured remarks, swearing or obscenity for which many of his contemporaries were notorious [those same contemporaries could testify differently]. . . . He was mild and kind in his manner, sufficiently but not servilely, courteous to everybody, and made no distinction between high and low, great or small; spoke as kindly and familiarly to his gardener or myself as to his equals or superiors; easily pleased when any about him shewed an inclination to please; and I believe everyone always did their best to effect that. . . ."

When the gossip imputing his paternity to John was repeated to Clift, he drew himself up to his full four feet eleven and a fraction, and retorted: "If I thought what you insinuate were true, there's not a duke in London I'd touch my hat to."

35. DAILY LIFE

Work began in the dissecting room at 6 A.M., when John came rumpled from his bed, wearing a tan surgical gown that fell loosely to his ankles. He now allowed himself no more than four hours' sleep a night, and that sleep was often broken by anginal spasms and hallucinatory terrors. Clift lit an argand lamp, laid out scalpels, syringes, jars of colored wax, and wheeled the oval dissecting table, with the specimen to be prepared, into the pool of light. John slipped on a pair of protective linen cuffs, what he called "keep-cleans," and stooping over the table, squinting at the specimen through tinted spectacles, resumed the paring away of superfluous tissue, the macerating, and the injecting. He would stand thus two or three hours at a stretch, motionless except for his fleet fingers, until his sore back muscles forced him to rest. He was simultaneously pursuing more than a hundred lines of inquiry, and Clift recorded the progress of each, supplemented by sketches, in a separate fascicle.

Before breakfast John might lecture to his house pupils in the Castle Street building, and give an anatomy lesson, though a good deal of the teaching was now done by Home and others.

He breakfasted at nine in his surgery, verifying the hour by the thick gold pocket watch his students at St. George's had given him, and if not served on the dot, he would fly into a rage. He ate sparingly, a restraint he urged upon his patients, especially the wealthy, who grew obese and dyspeptic from feasting, tippling, and lack of exercise. A prosperous Londoner's dinner might include several joints of red meat, game, fowl and fish pies, and puddings galore, all heaped upon the table together, and washed down with flagons of ale or wine. According to legend, the Duke of Grafton devoured an ox a day, and took the waters at Bath "to enable him to eat two." George III's favorite preacher, Samuel Ogden, used to complain that a roast goose was "not enough for two and just too much for one." Of every sixteen London shops one sold spirits. The annual per capita consumption of beer exceeded a hundred gallons. Topers with a fat purse, like William Pitt, Charles Fox, and Richard Sheridan, would down three to six bottles of port at a sitting. John Campbell, a political biographer, achieved a national record of thirteen bottles.

The breakfast dishes had to be cleared away by nine-thirty, when John received the first of his office patients. A more heterogeneous lot of invalids never rang a surgeon's doorbell. Out of cumbersome, gilt-paneled landaus tottered aged peers on gouty legs. Gonorrheal rakes drew up in racy phaetons; tradesmen, more thriftily, in public hackney-coaches that would carry them the length of London for half a crown. On foot from their airless cellar workshops trudged laborers and artisans, victims of occupational diseases—coppersmiths tuberculous from inspiring particles of the metal, paint-makers with lead poisoning, watch-gilders with skin cancers. . . . Every industry had its peculiar health hazards.

In John's waiting room the Duke of Richmond might find himself sitting between some grimy-handed coke heaver and his own haberdasher. John turned away nobody, and he adjusted his fees to the patient's pocketbook, one reason why his yearly income never rose above £6,000, whereas John Fothergill earned as much as £8,000, John Coakley Lettsom £12,000, and Astley Cooper £21,000. When asked how much he was owed, he would reply, "That you must determine yourself. You are the best judge of your own circumstances, and it is far from my wish to deprive you of the comforts of life." He would accept no payment from non-beneficed clergymen, from authors or artists. A merchant who retained him to operate upon his wife insisted that he name a fee in advance. John put it at twenty guineas. He did not see the couple again for two months. When, after a successful operation, he asked them why they had delayed, they explained that they had needed the time to raise the money. John refunded them nineteen guineas, keeping the twentieth "only that they might not be hurt with the idea of too great obligation."

Nor did he consider his responsibility to his patients ended with treatment and prescription. In behalf of a butcher too ill to tolerate the London air he pestered government officials until they found him a job at a seaport customs house. A visiting physician from Scotland, after spending a day with John, wrote home: "[He] was very busy in making up a runaway marriage between the son of a nobleman and the daughter of an Earl's brother. The whole is a secret yet. It is much against the will of the father of the young man, who knows, as yet, nothing of it. John sent them to Scotland last Saturday night, and as they had no money he had the dexterity to get hold of the money of the father of the young man and gave it to the son for a purpose of all others the most disagreeable to him. It will make a great noise tomorrow or next day and you will soon see their names in the newspapers."

Patients of rank and fortune might cool their heels in the waiting room half the morning, no matter how early they got there, for John treated the workingmen first, knowing that they toiled fourteen hours a day to earn a shilling or two. "You have no time to spare, as you live by it," he once told a zoo keeper, adding, with a scornful glance at a group of fidgeting noblemen, "Most of these can wait, as they have vurra little to do when they go home."

He was no comfort, however, to patients who expected to be cosseted. Trifling complaints infuriated him; self-indulgence drew his iciest contempt. When the Duke of Atholl brought his eldest boy down from Eton because of a scraped shin that seemed to be slow to heal, John informed him, "Had your Grace's son been the son of one of your Grace's servants, he would, at his age, have gone without stockings or shoes, and then he would have had no occasion to consult a surgeon concerning his leg, for the air would have been a sufficient stimulus to heal the wound. In England a young nobleman cannot be so unfashionable as to walk the streets bare-legged, but he may be allowed to walk with a hole cut in the leg of his stocking so as to expose the wound on the skin to the action of the air." And before the duke or his heir could object John took a pair of scissors and snipped away a piece of stocking.

A liverish farmer, fond of gin, for whom John prescribed total abstinence, protested, "Sir, that's impossible, for I cannot relinquish my employment, and you know, sir, it's impossible to work without some support."

So? How large a tract did the farmer cultivate? There were many acres. And how many horses to drag the plows? Two or three. So few for so much land?

"Pray, then, tell me, what do you give them to drink?"

"Enough and plenty," said the farmer, "because I work 'em hard."

George Nicol, the bookseller, got the rough side of John's tongue after Mrs. Nicol consulted the surgeon during her sixth pregnancy. Her first five children had all died in infancy. Her husband, she disclosed, a hardy North Countryman, believed in toughening the young by exposing them early to cold and hardship.

John furiously confronted the father. "Do you," he demanded, "intend to kill this child, as you have the others?"

"What the devil do you mean, sir?"

"Do you know the temperature of a hen with a callow brood? Because if you don't, I'll tell you."

When he had finished expounding a few elementary physiological truths, the bookseller promised to amend his system of child-rearing.

There being no tested therapy for numberless disorders, every practitioner had constantly to improvise. None did so more imaginatively nor upon a broader base of general principles than John. A linen draper, long married, came to him in despair over his failure to beget children. The cause was not hard to determine. Though neither impotent nor sterile, he suffered from a congenital anomaly termed hypospadias, in which the urethra opens upon the undersurface of the penis so that the sperm cannot pass to the glands. John conceived a unique remedy. Immediately after emission, he told the patient, let him suck up the sperm with a syringe, previously warmed, and inject it into his wife's vagina while that organ was still tumescent and in the ideal state to receive the seed.

The draper did so. Within the year his wife bore a healthy child—the first known product of human artificial insemination.[j]

At the age of fifty a man, identified in John's case book as John S —— L, fell prey to acute melancholia. He developed an aversion to his wife, to his children, to life itself. One night he awoke choking, and from that moment could no longer swallow. His physician sustained him with rectal feedings. The throat stricture persisting, he took him to John, who forthwith devised a novel stomach tube. Selecting a probang, or rod of whalebone, he sheathed it in an eel's skin to minimize irritation, padded one end with a sponge lest it scratch the esophagus, and to the other affixed a bladder and wooden pipe. Through this conduit easily digestible foods, such as jellies, beaten eggs, and sugared milk, were forced into the patient. At the same time laudanum was introduced rectally to alleviate the discomfort and valerian to calm the nerves. Gradually, John S —— L recovered his powers of ingestion.

At twelve-thirty sharp Goodall, the coachman, drove John's black carriage, drawn by a pair of baystone horses, around to the Leicester Square entrance. The remaining patients were dismissed with appointments for another morning, and John, leaning on an ivory-topped cane, set out on his round of house calls. "Well," he would mutter, loath to take more time away from his experimental work, "I must go and earn this damn'd guinea, or I shall be sure to want it tomorrow."

Clift, trotting after him to the carriage, would hand him a list of the addresses to be visited. On the seat he would range three small instrument cases, one made of tortoise shell, containing a phlebotomy lancet and a lithotomy knife designed by John; another of wood bound in sharkskin, containing a flexible silver catheter and tempered steel suturing needles; the third, a metal pocket case, containing a spatula fenestrated for lightness, sharp-pointed scissors, and a pair of X-shaped dressing forceps. John also carried a folding pocket scale to weigh money as a precaution against being cozened with clipped coins.

For a decade now the black carriage, with its black-garbed, brooding passenger, had been a familiar sight along the thoroughfares radiating from Leicester Square to the rim of the city. The Boswells knew it well. The first time it deposited John at their door in Great Portland Street, three members of the family awaited him. Drink and venery had greatly debilitated Boswell himself, Mrs. Boswell was tuberculous, and Alexander, the third of their five children, was suffering from an abdominal hernia.

"Sandie [Boswell wrote in his journal for that day, March 21, 1787] was ill again with his rupture. Mr. John Hunter visited him and found that Squires, the trussmaker, was right in his discovery that one of the testicles would not come down. This interrupted the cure of the Rupture, as no truss could be applied till the testicle should come down. This was hard, especially as he could not go to his Academy for fear of being hurt. I resolved to make him read, and to examine him myself till I could find one to come in and teach him. My Wife was a good deal better. Mr. Hunter thought she looked greatly better."

Of John's later ministrations he wrote:

"Saturday May 19 . . . went with my Wife and my two daughters to a concert at Mrs. Hunter's. . . . When we came home, my Wife was seised with another severe fit of spitting blood, so that Mr. John Hunter was called. She grew easier soon." (John himself had been bedridden for three weeks, but as he wrote to Jenner, "When two guineas rouse me, I cannot resist.")

"Friday 7 March 1788. I was sent for home, my Wife having become much more uneasy and being very frightened. I hastened to find her and found her in a complication of distress, with asthmatick and feverish complaints. I sent for John Hunter, who came and ordered something, and raised her Spirits somewhat. He told me she had only a bad cold, which produced all these symptoms. This relieved my anxiety."

"Sat. March 8. John Hunter called today on my wife of his own accord. She was considerably easier."

"Wednesday March 12. Had dismal apprehensions about my Wife. . . . She was bled by Mr. John Hunter and her blood was quite inflamed."

(Although John condemned many of the accepted medical practices, venesection was not one of them. He bled for all kinds of afflictions. When Philip Syng Physick asked him whether he should bleed a roofer who had fallen and got a brain concussion, John replied, "Bleed him? Bleed him, sir? No, sir; you would kill him outright. Wait, sir, until he reacts, and then bleed him—bleed him to death, sir!")

"Tuesday March 18. My Wife was rather easier, but I insisted that she should be bled again, which was accordingly done by Mr. John Hunter. Though she had a horror at that operation, she during this illness behaved wonderfully well and submitted to it twice."

The black carriage made several trips that winter to a shabby rooming house at No. 16 Holles Street, where Caroline Byron, having given birth to a son, George, was recuperating before going on to Aberdeen. She was in a pitiable state, abandoned by her debauched husband, penniless and without friends, and nursing a malformed infant. Some pre-natal condition had contracted both of the child's Achilles' tendons; the heel of the right foot was drawn up, the sole twisted inward.

John saw little probability of a cure, but he was confident that orthopedic boots of an improved design would enable the boy to walk efficiently, and he promised to forward the specifications to Mrs. Byron's physician in Aberdeen, a Dr. Livingston. John further noted in his case book: "On Monday [January 28], I inoculated [for smallpox] Master Byron in both arms. On the Tuesday the wounds were very much inflamed; also a space around them broader than a penny. This alarmed me as I suspected that it showed too great a disposition for the irritation. On the Wednesday, the surrounding inflammation was gone, and only that of the wounds; which was less than the preceding day."

Dr. Livingston evidently did not understand what sort of boot was wanted, because Mrs. Byron later wrote to her sister-in-law, Frances Leigh, in London, asking her to find "a proper shoe for George's foot, as I cannot get the right one made here." "Only the expense," she added, "prevents me from sending him up to London for Mr. Hunter to see his foot, as I am perfectly sure he would walk very well if he had a proper shoe and indeed Mr. Hunter said to me that his foot would be very well in time if he could have a proper shoe. . . ."

Mrs. Leigh called on John for more explicit instructions. He referred her to a bootmaker in the Strand, Timothy Sheldrake, and the boots were duly delivered. At school, according to his mother, George could walk and run as well as any boy.*

During the winter of 1788, too, the ubiquitous carriage might be seen in front of Schomberg House, No. 81 Pall Mall, the home of Thomas Gainsborough, as John conferred with William Heberden over the artist's declining health. While witnessing the trial of Warren Hastings, Gainsborough had felt a stabbing chill at the nape of his neck, and touching the spot, discovered a small lump. After their first examination the surgeon and the physician thought it to be an innocuous cyst, and they applied a salt-water poultice. But when they came again, the lump was greatly enlarged, suggesting to John a malignancy. Gainsborough, who had feared as much, cried, "I am a dead man!" He was buried six months later.

Though they had been able to do nothing for Gainsborough, Hunter and Heberden, who valued each other as friends as well as colleagues, and often stood together at the same sickbed, could take satisfaction in the survival of many another distinguished patient. Benjamin Franklin, for one, was still active in his eighties, despite gout and a bladder stone so painful that he could not bear the movement of a coach. He had a severe attack of gout in 1778 in London, when he was Minister Plenipotentiary there. The stone developed four years later in Paris during the peace negotiations between England and

* When Byron came to London, at the age of eleven, after John's death, his guardian, John Hanson, consulted Matthew Baillie, who first prescribed iron braces, then had Sheldrake make another pair of orthopedic boots. Eventually the poet got along with ordinary boots reinforced by corrective supports.

America. "I . . . now find at fourscore," he wrote, "that the three contraries have befallen me, being subject to the gout and the stone and not being master of all my passions. Like the proud girl in my country who wished and resolved not to marry a parson nor a Presbyterian nor an Irishman, and at length found herself married to an Irish Presbyterian parson."

To John Jay he wrote: "It is true, as you have heard, that I have the stone, but not that I had thoughts of being cut for it. It is as yet very tolerable. It gives me no pain but when in a Carriage on the Pavement, or when I make some sudden quick movement. If I can prevent its growing larger, which I hope to do by abstemious living and gentle exercize, I can go on pretty comfortably with it to the end of my Journey, which can now be at no great distance. I am chearful, enjoy the company of my Friends, sleep well, have sufficient appetite, and my Stomach performs well its Functions. The latter is very material to the preservation of Health. I therefore take no Drugs lest I should disorder it. You may judge that my Disease is not very grievous, since I am more afraid of the Medicines than of the Malady."

But it proved to be grievous enough. Had he made a wise decision? Could he survive surgery? Could he survive without it? He posted a history of his case to London, and shortly received a series of reports embodying the opinions of John Hunter, William Heberden, and three less known medical men.

Franklin, they agreed, was right to shun surgery, "taking into account the Time of Life of the Patient, and that the Symptoms are not so urgent as to render Life uncomfortable." He should regularly drink a lixivium, that is, water impregnated with alkaline salts, which "has some power as a Solvent, and if that should prove insufficient to prevent the further increase of the Stone without at all diminishing it, it may procure a great relief, for the painful effects of a stone in the Bladder do not depend so much upon the size, as the roughness of its surface, which arises from the constant secretion of new matter." If the lixivium upset him, he might try "fixed air" (carbonic acid) in the form of Seltzer water. They prescribed infusions of *ura ursi* (a diuretic), two "scruples" (40 grains), morning and evening in half a pint of water. They warned him to guard against constipation, which would aggravate his complaint, with "a teaspoonful of *Electuarium e Casia* [a senna compound], or a tablespoonful of Castor oil," or "any gentle laxative that he has found from experience to agree with him." Rough motion should be avoided, though he should continue walking about his room for exercise. When riding in a carriage, if he must ride in one, "it would be worth trying, how far his pain would be abated, by using the same precaution as in walking, that is, to go with his Bladder full." Before undertaking the journey he should administer to himself, by way of an anodyne, an enema consisting of warmed oil, water, and forty drops of laudanum, preceded by an enema of weak gruel or broth so that the anodyne might be retained longer. He should exclude from his diet salty meats, pepper, and strong spirits. As for wine, "We would advise him never to exceed that quantity that habit may have rendered necessary for the purposes of digestion."

Franklin lived, through intermittent attacks, another five years to the age of eighty-four, during which he served as President of the Council of Pennsylvania, attended the Constitutional Convention of 1787, supervised the construction of five buildings in Philadelphia, corresponded tirelessly with friends abroad, wrote numerous political and sociological papers, and continued his autobiography. "My Most Dear Old Friend," John wrote to him in 1786, "I take this opportunity of Enquiring after your health & to tell you that I am in the Land of the Living," and in 1787: "I feel myself obliged to you for your very polite letter, acquainting me that I am elected a member of the Philosophical Society in America. . . ."

In the early afternoon the black carriage, now gray with dust, the stallions' flanks steaming, racketed to a halt before St. George's, and John plodded up the long stone stairway to the surgical wards. When his pupils saw him, they crowded around him, eager to accompany him on his rounds. They outnumbered the pupils of all the other staff surgeons combined. But to John this tour of duty was an emotional as well as a physical ordeal, one he dreaded more each day, for as he walked the sand-strewn wards, examining his post-operative cases, preparing new arrivals for surgery, he could feel the oppressive weight of his colleagues' enmity.

He had earned it, of course. From the beginning he had opposed them, derided their empirical methods, and clamored for changes of hospital policy that would benefit the patients rather than enrich the surgeons. Tact and a soft tongue might have won him allies, but these graces never came easily to John, and in his sick old age he was ever tarter, ever more overbearing. He made loud, bad jokes at his adversaries' expense. He never let them forget that since 1770 two thirds of the students, whose tuition fees the entire staff shared, had chosen to enter under John Hunter. "I am a pygmy in knowledge, yet I feel as a giant compared to these men." Proud men, not all of them inept or mercenary, they had closed ranks against this dissenter who wore his laurels so aggressively. Though he had brought glory to St. George's, though none of them was likely to be remembered except as his associate, they would destroy him if they could.

The pack was led by John Gunning, still rancorous after thirty-five years, because, despite his seniority, the Scot had been promoted to house surgeon before him. Scarcely less hostile was Charles Hawkins, son of the late Sir Caesar, who had vainly championed Gunning in that early contest; Charles's cousin George; and Donald Monro, nursing an old family grievance against the Hunter brothers. In newspapers, in professional periodicals, in lectures, they struck at every aspect of John's career, while Jessé Foot, whom they kept abreast of the conflict, circulated scabrous anti-Hunter tracts. John's philosophy of healing they pronounced unintelligible (as indeed it was to them), his investigations, his museum, the vacuous frittering of a fantast. William Bromfield, a senior surgeon, insisted that John's operation for a popliteal aneurysm was useless. No aneurysm, he said, was operable, since the disease damaged the whole arterial system. "I once saw an attempt of this kind [meaning John's] in which I shall only remark that the patient died; and I do believe that the embarrassments which occurred, as well as the events of the operation, will deter the gentleman who performed it from making a second attempt." The patient, as Bromfield knew, died fifteen months after the operation from totally unrelated causes.

It was bad enough to have to listen to Hunter's grotesque theories; it was intolerable when he encouraged young upstarts—Scots as often as not, the vulgar, pushing breed!—in their maggots. There was the Glasgow doctor, James Moore, for example, with his machine for reducing pain during surgery by compressing the major nerve trunks. An adaptation of the tourniquet, it consisted of two oval iron plates on a screw, covered in leather and adjustable to any part of the body. Moore had repeatedly clamped his own crural nerves between the plates until the blood vessels almost burst, while his father, also a doctor, struck pins deep into his legs. He never felt the pins.

By approaching John Hunter with his compressor Moore made a

shrewd choice, for who was more receptive to innovation? Any device that might lessen a patient's anguish seemed to John worth a try, and he offered Moore a chance to test his machine at the next operation, which was a leg amputation.

"I went to the hospital the day before the operation to try the instrument [ran Moore's account, dated 1784]. The patient had lost all his toes, and had a large ulcer on his foot. . . . Next morning the patient being carried to the operation room, I began the compression at a quarter before eleven o'clock. . . . At a quarter before twelve, I gave him one grain of opium, to diminish the smarting of the wound after the operation, when the compression should be taken off. A few minutes after twelve, the tourniquet was applied, and the amputation performed by Mr. Hunter, at the usual place below the knee. At the circular incision through the skin, the patient did not cry out, change a muscle of his face, or shew any symptom of pain. At the subsequent parts of the operation, particularly during the sawing of the bones, he shewed marks of uneasiness in his countenance, but did not cry out . . . he declared that he had felt hardly any pain except as he himself expressed, at the rasping of the bones, which he added had shaken the whole limb. . . .

"This trial had all the success I expected; there was evidently a most remarkable diminution of pain. . . ."

Moore was too sanguine. Such severe compression carried insurmountable dangers, threatening to injure the nerves themselves, and, by shutting off the blood supply, the tissues to be operated on, thereby increasing the risk of infection. What actually happened to the patient after surgery neither Moore nor Hunter reported, but they never used the machine again. Yet the underlying principle, that of desensitizing the nerves, was sound (as the modern method of injecting nerve-blocking drugs proves).

Sound or not, with Hunter's support Moore could expect nothing but ridicule from the other St. George's surgeons. Whatever proposals John advanced to improve hospital conditions, whatever appointments he supported, the Gunning faction objected to without regard to their merits. When Matthew Baillie presented himself in 1787, with his uncle's backing, as a candidate for staff physician, the plum fell to a Gunning favorite of inferior skill, a Dr. James Ford. Baillie's qualifications, however, could not be ignored forever, and in an election four years later the hospital governors approved him. Home, too, suffered an initial rebuff, not so much for his defects as for his connection with John. The governors had granted a request by Hunter and Gunning that each be assigned an assistant surgeon. Hunter chose Home, Gunning chose Thomas Keate, Surgeon-in-Ordinary to the Prince of Wales. Upon the retirement of a senior surgeon each antagonist exerted himself to secure the vacated office for his assistant. Keate won by a board vote of 134 to 102.

"Your public character and private attachments," Foot gloated in an open letter to John, "would probably not have failed if your candidate had possessed any amiable qualities to recommend him; but a conceited insolence and a pert coxcometry [Foot's coinage], an affectation of manners and an insufferable vanity, marked the nature of the animal so strongly on his canvas that your recommendation failed of its success."

Home was eventually elected senior surgeon, but not while John lived.

The bitterest wrangle centered around the training of the hospital students. In John's view the surgeons skimped their obligations. St. George's, he argued, should organize a medical school, each surgeon to contribute six lectures a term without remuneration. To shame his colleagues, he delivered free lectures at home to his own pupils. But they were not to be shamed into assuming unrewarded duties.

"I do not choose," one of them admitted, "to lose any reputation I may have by giving lectures."

"Which," John observed, "at least is modest."

Another said, "I don't see where the art of surgery can be improved."

By such a lackwit, John reflected, it could not, and he told him, "To see where anything can be improved might be considered as going almost half way towards the improvement itself. Lord Bacon was the cause of all the advances in philosophy since his day by seeing and pointing out where, and how, they might be made."

In their exasperation the surgeons addressed a memorandum to the governors: "On the subject of lectures—to take leave of this point which has been so much insisted on—we must declare our joint opinions, and they are incontrovertible. If they [John's proposals] had been practical and contained principles and rules founded upon judgment and experience, with regard to the authority of others as well as their own, they would have been highly useful; if, on the contrary, they had leaned to physiology and experiment, with a contempt for all other opinions but their own they would have been pernicious. The good therefore arising from lectures, unless under certain conditions, must be at least problematical."

The governors sympathized.

No operation detaining him, John would return to Leicester Square by four o'clock, the conventional dinner hour in upper-class London households. His family rarely saw him at any other time of day. Of the two children only Agnes was still living at home; young Jock was at St. John's College, Cambridge.

There often were guests for dinner, and usually they included one or two former pupils who had made their mark, like Sir William Blizard, the founder of the London Hospital Medical School. Sir William was given to high-flown diction and the ceremonial gesture, and John loved to bait him. One evening, observing him to be unaccustomedly abstemious, he called to him across the table, "Come, fellow, why don't you drink your wine?" Sir William held aloft a finger swollen by a whitlow, explaining that it was painful to lift a glass. All during dinner John chided him for a milksop until Anne put in, "Please to remember, John, you were two days delirious when you had a boil on your finger."

As soon as the meal ended, John withdrew to his study and rested for an hour on the sofa bed. Clift then came to him to take dictation. In the course of a year John received three to four thousand letters from all over the world, and sent nearly as many. The bulk of these concerned elaborate negotiations for procuring museum specimens. To an acquaintance stationed in Africa he wrote:

"I was favoured with your letter, September 30th, informing me of two birds called the Havannah, being shipped on board the *Bull-dog,* but unluckily the birds died on the passage home. I consider myself as equally obliged to you for thinking of me and taking so much trouble. I was sorry at the loss of your insecks, after all the trouble of collecting them, but I hope you will be more successful in future. There is one thing I wish very much to have settled in Natural History, which is, the natural history of swallows; they breed with us in the summer and leave us in the winter, and it is what becomes of them in our winter. Now, if they are with you in the winter and if they should breed with you in that season, it would be a proof that they are birds of passage, and upon the same principle you should have more in the winter than in the summer, as there are four or five different species in this country in the summer. I should like to have specimens of those that are with you in winter, but I cannot say what species they were. It would hardly be possible to get ostrich eggs just going to hatch, and to crush the shell and put them into proof spirits to preserve them till they came to England. If a foall camel was put into a tub of spirits and sent I should be glad. Is it possible to get a young tame lion, or indeed any other Beast or bird? If chameleons were sent it should be in the spring, as then one would feed them on flies through the summer. Are there any cuckews? We have none in the winter. I want everything respecting the bee tribe, such as wasps with their nests, also hornets with theirs. They are a very large tribe. I would have sent you a paper I wrote on the anatomy of bees, which was published in the *Philosophical Transactions*, but upon inquiry I found that it would cost more than it was worth. I am a subscriber to the African Society, but I have not heard of the cachuna things, but as I cannot always attend they may have come without me knowing it. . . ."

In other letters he disclosed his latest findings to the scientific bodies, domestic and foreign, of which he was a member—the Royal College of Surgeons of Ireland, the Chirurgical-Physical Society of Edinburgh, the American Philosophical Society, the Royal Academy of Surgery of Paris, the Royal Society of Science and Belles Lettres of Gothenburg. "Allow me to present to you [Sir Joseph Banks, President of the Royal Society of England] a paper on the natural history of the common bee. It contains the result of experiments and observations made in the course of the last twenty years. . . . I hope next winter to give you the account of the wasp, and probably the hornet. I shall afterwards be able to give the wild or humble bee, and many of those called solitary bees, in which I have made considerable progress; and in time I hope to complete the history of the British bees."

Correspondence done, John emptied his pockets of the stray scraps of envelopes on which he had scribbled notes during the day. Clift transcribed them in the appropriate fascicle, while John made for the dissecting room. Towards midnight, after the rest of the household had retired, Clift would refill the argand lamp. Not until two or three o'clock, when he could no longer keep his hand steady or his eyes open, would John lumber off to bed and a brief, tormented sleep.

Fridays were still busier, the evenings from eight-thirty to eleven being taken up by the deliberations of the Lyceum Medicum Londinense, meeting in the museum. Sunday afternoons, in the Leicester Square building, John presided over informal scientific *conversaziones*. On the first and second Wednesday of the month he joined his fellow members of the Medical Society at Old Slaughter's Coffee-house for a symposium on common diseases. Once a month the Society for the Improvement of Medical and Chirurgical Knowledge gathered at New Slaughter's. In addition, there were frequent conventions of the Royal Society, the Royal Society of Medicine, and the Physical Society.

These gatherings were sometimes stormy, and John took part in them at considerable risk to his blood pressure, as when a former pupil named Andrew Marshal stated that in dissecting the bodies of the insane he had always noted marks of disease on the brain. "I do not challenge your veracity," said John, "only your powers of observation." Marshal demanded an apology. John repeated the slur more forcibly, whereupon Marshal poured a jug of water over his head, and the meeting broke up in pandemonium.

As if John had not enough to occupy him, he was continually embarking upon projects in behalf of private or governmental agencies. Impelled partly by financial necessity, but mostly by his quenchless curiosity, he would grapple with each new problem to the extreme limit of his energies. Under his guidance the Agricultural Society of Odiham was trying to organize the veterinary profession, then in the hands of sow-gelders and quacks, along scientific lines. Funds had been raised to send serious students to the French veterinary schools, the best in Europe. The Revolution obstructed that enterprise. But among the emigrés who reached England was the former principal of the Alfort Veterinary School, Charles Vial de Saint Bel, and at John's instigation the Odiham Society diverted its funds to the establishment of the Veterinary College of London, the first institution of the kind in England, with the Frenchman as director. John subscribed £200 and served as vice-president. From this institution developed the Royal Veterinary College, and later the Royal College of Veterinary Surgeons. Saint Bel liked to recount how England's foremost surgeon once helped him remove "two accessory feet from the fetlocks of the two forelegs" of a horse.

John had also been appointed Deputy Surgeon-General of the Army under Robin Adair in 1785, and upon the death of that beau gallant in 1790 had succeeded him as Surgeon-General and Inspector-General at a stipend of £1,200 a year. He desperately needed the money, so deep into debt had the expense of his museum plunged him. A month earlier, in anticipation of the vacancy, he had written somewhat elliptically to the influential Lord Auckland, Ambassador to the Netherlands:

". . . Our conversation the other day was what naturally arises when there is a perfect confidence in the friendship of the person we are conversing with. I then give your Lordship a short sketch of my intentions, and you have been so kind as to think of them, and has offer'd your assistance. Be assured my Lord, that I then did not throw these thoughts out as a hint, which I do not believe you doo, only was ready to show me how ready you was to serve me, which I have experienced upon every occasion, and be also assured my Lord (that altho' I was not then trying your friendship, yet) you was set down in my mind; and that whenever my intentions were fully digested that I should at once lay open my proposals and ask your assistance because I have not another idea but the good of mankind."

The letter lacked John's customary candor. By "the good of mankind" he was hinting at a bargain—in return for the appointment, the bequest of his museum, to England, which he would otherwise be forced to sell. He would have been grateful for the senior surgeon's post at Chelsea Hospital as well, the usual perquisite of the Surgeon-General's office, but that went to Thomas Keate.

Now England was again at war with France, and it fell to John to reorganize the medical corps for duty abroad, a task to which he brought all his zeal for reform. With his first act in office he created a whole new set of enemies: he broke the monopoly on army medical appointments long enjoyed by the physicians' and surgeons' colleges. Thenceforth, he resolved, those commissions were to be attained only within the forces, after a term of service in the lower ranks. He would tolerate no exceptions, not even to please the Commander-in-Chief, Lord Amherst.

"When I had the Honour of my present Appointment," he replied to an endorsement from Amherst of a friend with no previous military experience, "I wished very much that there should be some System of Promotion, & as those who applied themselves to this Profession stood nearly upon an equal Rank of Life, I conceived it an easy Matter to adopt a System, & such as could be easily adhered to. I proposed it to the Secretary of War, & it was adopted; which was that Gentlemen of that Profession should begin with Mateships of Regiments, that they should be promoted to Hospital Mateships; from Hospital Mate to be Regimental Surgeons; from Regimental Surgeons to the Staff, either as Surgeons, or Apothecaries, and from that Station on the Staff to be Physicians, Purveyors, etc. Now, my Lord, this has never been deviated from since I had the Honour of recommending but once, which was by the Desire of Lord Grenville, & on a particular Occasion. I have never once allowed my Friendship for any one to make one break through that Rule, nor have I allowed the Solicitation of my best Friends, much my Superiors, to make one recede from it. Since the above plan has been adopted, & most religiously executed on my Part, the Physical Gentlemen of the Army have looked up to me as their Protector; and I am certain many have entered as Mates of Regiments upon the Faith of regular promotion that would not otherwise have entered, and I could wish to keep their Confidence with me.

"I hope your Lordship will see the propriety of all this, & I will pledge myself I shall not break through it. . . ."

A good many other bigwigs, who hoped for John's connivance in dispensing patronage, got equally short shrift. Such obduracy was unheard of.

As the theaters of war shifted and the casualties mounted, sharp dispatches flowed daily from Leicester Square. John directed the construction of field hospitals, and expedited supplies. "The Bedsteads found in the Invalid Hospital at the Savoy appear to be in a filthy state. . . . I have therefore desired Messrs. Trotter to send in Twenty Cradles, intended for Hospitals, which remain in their store." He scolded sluggards and malingerers. "When you solicited to be appointed Surgeon to the Royals you could not but be sensible of the Complaint in Your Eyes which You now complain of. . . . You must either repair to Jamaica, or, if you chuse rather to go on Half-pay, propose to me some fit person from that List to be your successor." When a despondent recruit of the 17th Regiment tried to put a bullet through his head, but merely shattered his arm, John demanded that he be court-martialed on the ground that he had damaged army property.

And through it all John managed to keep up his private practice, his attendance at St. George's, his lectures, anatomical lessons, and conferences, his research and his museum.

"Ah, John," exclaimed Maxwell Garthshore, finding him at his dissection early one morning, "always working!"

"Ay," said John, "I am, and when I am gone there will not soon be another John Hunter."

36. DEBACLE

"I had sense enough to know," Clift wrote later, recalling, in a fragmentary autobiography, his second year in Leicester Square, "that things could not get worse and must mend." But they did not mend. Each day brought John closer to bankruptcy. He owed a fortune, most of it for work on his collection, to engravers, printers, animal breeders, taxidermists, and they were dunning him hard. Yet he would neither curtail his museum expenditure by so much as a stuffed gopher nor would he ask Anne to forego her entertainments, though what was to become of her when he died weighed heavily on him. He borrowed more money; he obtained a second mortgage on Earl's Court. Erratically, as the debts mounted, he made petty domestic retrenchments, of which poor Clift, who had received no allowance for months and was running short of clothes, bore the brunt. "Then Mr. Hunter, probably to avoid having a footman in green found writing with him in his study ordered me a coat of twopenny cloth, without a collar, and lined with serge up the fronts to the neck-bands, a pair of corduroy breeches and speckled worsted stockings, unbound shoes with leather strings and full of nails. . . . Haynes several times gave me sixpence . . . so low they [the servants] looked on me. . . . Not trusted with a candle and therefore I must go to bed through the dead bones."

The financial worries, on top of overwork and the harassments of his enemies, strained John's heart to the limit. Pain and the certitude of approaching death were constantly with him. It shook Clift to see him day after day supine on the sofa bed, clutching his chest and gasping for breath.

Gloom pervaded the household. Even the affable Haynes was depressed by it, and vented his humor on Clift. "[He] condescended to call me the West Country Hickey, though what it meant I never exactly understood."

At this time a storm was brewing in yet another quarter. It arose from the submission to the *Philosophical Transactions* of John's fiftieth manuscript, *Observations on the Fossil Bones presented to the Royal*

Society by His Most Serene Highness the Margrave of Anspach. Evidently the editors had sent it to the printer without a careful reading, for when they went over it in proof, they were disturbed by the statement that fossil decay required "many thousands of years."

In religion the average Englishman was fundamentalist. Even the intellectuals paid lip service to the literal interpretation of Biblical history. Still widely accepted was the chronology set forth by the sixteenth-century Archbishop of Ireland, James Ussher, according to which the precise moment of creation occurred on October 3, 4004 B.C., at nine o'clock in the morning. John's "many thousands of years" smacked of heresy.

The phrase was inconspicuous enough, however, for the Royal Society to pass the paper, and it appeared in the eighty-fourth volume of the *Transactions.* What caused profound consternation was a second paper, in which John expounded his theory of terrestrial age, based chiefly on his exploration, thirty-one years earlier, of Portugal's Alentejo plain. Using the term "many thousand centuries," he showed the Mosaic cosmogony to be inconsistent with the observable facts of geology. A single deluge, as described in Genesis, was inadequate to account for the fossil strata that had built up vast land masses: "Forty days' water overflowing the dry land could not have brought such quantities of sea-productions on its surface; nor can we suppose thence, taking all possible circumstances into consideration, that it remained long on the whole surface of the earth; therefore there was no time for their being fossilized; they could only have been left, and exposed on the surface. But it would appear that the sea has more than once made its incursions on the same place; for the mixture of land- and sea-productions now found on the land is a proof of at least two changes having taken place."

Loath to stir up religious controversy, the Royal Society assigned one of its members, Major James Rennell, a geographer, the delicate mission of remonstrating with the testy author. "Now, although I have no quarrel with any opinions relating to the antiquity of the globe," Rennell wrote to John, "yet there are a description of persons very numerous and very respectable in every point but their pardonable superstitions, who will dislike any mention of a specific period that ascends beyond 6000 years: I would, therefore, with submission, qualify the expression by many *years,* instead of *centuries.*"

Of John's own religious convictions neither his writings nor lectures had yielded an inkling. In his boyhood he had been subjected to the rigidly fundamentalist doctrines of the Church of Scotland. In London he had observed the formalities of the only slightly less fundamentalist Church of England. Since his marriage he had been a parishioner in good standing of St. Martin-in-the-Fields, and he numbered many clergymen among his admirers. But he could not bring himself to twist scientific evidence to conform with dogma. "As Moses derives his authority from powers we cannot admit to natural causes and effects," he once declared in words that might serve as a maxim for cosmogonists, "we must leave the first formation of things, and take them as formed."

He ignored Rennell's advice, and the Royal Society rejected the paper. John must then have been cruelly tempted to publish himself this long meditated product of his only venture into geology (and, as it happened, the last paper he ever wrote). But on reflection he, too, hesitated to trouble the faith of the masses, and in the end he consigned the manuscript to his files.

Sixty-eight years were to elapse before it came to light again in John's posthumous *Essays and Observations*, edited by Clift's son-in-law, Richard Owen. By that time John's unorthodoxies seemed mild in comparison to Darwin's. Even so, Owen was constrained to inject an apologetic note: "Some may wish that the world had never known that Hunter thought so differently on some subjects from what they believed, and would have desired him, to think. But he has chosen to leave a record of his thoughts, and, under the circumstances in which that record has come into my hands, I have felt myself bound to add it to the common intellectual property of mankind."

The arena of John's most abrasive conflict continued to be St. George's. There, by his latest maneuver in behalf of the students, he had goaded his antagonists to murderous fury. ". . . I meant to inform you," he had written in July 1792 to Gunning, Keate, and a new member of the surgical staff, William Walker, upon their refusal to reopen discussions of a training program, "of a resolution I have taken respecting the pupils who enter under me, which is, not to account in future with the surgeons of the hospital for the money I receive, but consider it wholly my own."

The chief reason he gave for defying a tradition as old as the hospital, and depriving his colleagues of revenue, was to arouse them to a proper sense of duty. "St. George's Hospital," he went on, heaping outrage upon outrage, "has held its rank among the large Hospitals in London; and nothing could have given it rank but the character of its surgeons. If that is the case, what must be the character of its surgeons at present? I will not say it is a disgrace to be a surgeon to St. George's; but I will say, the surgeons have disgraced the hospital."

He pointed to the drop in students' fees from a peak of £266 in 1789 to less than half that. And what was the explanation? ". . . because I withdrew my attention, finding the surgeons were very ready to receive their share of the profits, but would do nothing to earn it." If they doubted to whom they were indebted for the bulk of the student enrollments, let them inquire of the treasurer. "The surgeons," John concluded, "did not deserve any advantage from my labours. . . . Your obedient servant. . . ."

The ensuing fracas diverted all London. The enraged surgeons turned the letter over to the Board of Governors, with the demand that a Special General Court be convened to rule on it. Was one half-mad old malcontent to be allowed to undermine the time-hallowed prerogatives of his peers? A court hearing was set for March 1 of the following year.

Two days before John sent each governor a copy of his denunciation, vastly expanded. At the same time the surgeons circulated a long counterblast. The decline of the student body, they protested, could be blamed on no failing of theirs. First war, then the rise of other hospitals was responsible. As to the number of students enrolled under John Hunter, "The anatomical lectures of the first reputation were not a great distance from us—they were conducted by the late Dr. Hunter— we had supported them and they supported us. It was fair that he should recommend to the gentleman above-mentioned in preference." In short, John owed his professional popularity to his brother's reputation. The surgeons justified their disinclination to offer the students lectures on the grounds that they considered lecturing inferior to clinical instruction; that if they did lecture, their ideas would be noted down, passed from hand to hand, and so become common property; that the entrance fee would have to be raised.

Tradition prevailed. The court sustained the complainants and ordered John to share his fees as before. But this victory was not enough to appease the injured. The offender must somehow be eliminated altogether. In a further decision of the court the surgeons thought they saw a way.

While overruling John in the matter of fees, the court had conceded that "a Restoration, as far as may be useful, of the antient discipline of the Hospital" was indicated, and had empowered a committee to draft new bylaws. That committee permitted itself to be guided largely by Gunning, who chose a day when John was absent to press his recommendations.

Under the plan, which the committee adopted and the court confirmed without giving John a chance to voice his opinion, the surgeons were to visit their convalescent patients twice a week, a duty formerly shared by their assistant surgeons, to attend personally to dressings, to report every Friday for a staff consultation on pain of disciplinary action. They were to operate only on Mondays, Wednesdays, or Fridays, emergencies excepted, regardless of their personal convenience. Two hours daily, from 11:30 to 1:30 P.M., would be devoted to non-surgical treatment, all dressings to be finished by midday, and any remaining business to be concluded in the afternoon. When a patient died, the surgeon was to perform an autopsy in the presence of all his pupils, followed by an illustrative operation upon the corpse. Once a week a lecture was to be delivered by one of the surgeons in rotation.

What the Gunning cabal intended by all this was to encumber their already overtaxed and ailing opponent with an onus so far beyond his endurance that he would either resign or collapse under it. Until then they had been smugly content with the status quo. Certainly, none of them craved extra work. But they considered the price cheap if it would rid them of John. The bylaws, after all, could be revised again later (as indeed they were). And so, when John next appeared at the hospital and they confronted him with the new rules, they expected him to depart in a rage, never to trouble them again. Great was their dismay when, without a murmur of protest, he accepted the added duties and proceeded to fulfill them as painstakingly as the youngest, halest member of the staff.

There was still another of Gunning's recommendations calculated to rile John. Many of the despised Scottish students who preferred Hunterian teaching came from their homeland with no previous surgical training just as John had come forty-five years before. It was now decreed that to qualify for admission "the pupils shall bring a certificate of their having been bred to the profession."

Four months after this ruling took effect, in October 1793, two young Scots tried to enter St. George's under John Hunter. They had no certificate; they knew of no such requirement. Their plight must have

stirred John, evoking memories of his own gritty beginnings, because
he promised to intercede, though it meant another clash, for which he
had little strength left. He placed the youths' applications on the agenda
of the next board meeting, to be held Wednesday, October 16.

37. ". . . AT THE MERCY OF ANY ROGUE"

On the appointed day John rose at his customary pre-dawn hour in
good spirits. Clift remembered afterwards hearing him whistling a
lively Scottish air. He had five house pupils at the time, and he interrupted a difficult piece of dissection to amuse them with a little disquisi-
tion on children who feigned illness in order to avoid school. He cited
the case of one Master Woodcock, aged twelve, who, following a bout
of rheumatic fever that affected his right knee, was taken to the coast
for a "tepid sea bath." He returned "fat and jolly," but still complaining
of pain. His parents sent for John. When the surgeon arrived, Master
Woodcock was limping pitiably up and down the room. Drawing the
parents aside, John told them to put the boy to bed, place a cluster of
grapes on the other side of the room, and watch through the keyhole.
As soon as Master Woodcock believed himself unobserved, he made a
dash for the grapes without a trace of a limp. The parents duly chastised the malingerer. But John was not consulted by that family again.

The surgeon's merry humor faded when he thought of the ordeal
facing him later in the day at St. George's. Much as he had always
relished a fight, he felt too worn, too ill for this one. To a friend who
dropped in after breakfast he mentioned his fear of a violent dispute.
Yet he could not bring himself to dodge the issue; he must plead for his
two young Scots.

Towards midmorning Goodall drove the black carriage up to the
Leicester Square entrance. John saw neither Anne nor his children, for
they were all in Brighton. In his haste he left behind the list of
patients to be visited that Clift always prepared for him. It was
found by the butler, Robert Adcock, who gave it to Clift. Remembering
that the first call was in St. James's Square, Clift hurried there on foot
and overtook John just as he was climbing back into the carriage. It
was almost noon, the hour of the board meeting. The two short, stocky
men, so alike in looks that they had been taken for father and son, stood

a moment talking. Then John, in a ringing voice, ordered Goodall to drive him to St. George's. Clift recalled later, "I saw him get into the carriage as well as ever I saw him in my life."

The board meeting had been under way for some time when John arrived. The Rev. James Clarke, the hospital chaplain, occupied the chair. The others present included two members of the medical staff, Drs. George Pearson and James Robertson, and two surgeons, William Walker and William Henry Matthew, the latter a governor of the hospital. Until then the first two men had shown no overt hostility to John. Walker and Matthew, however, were vociferous members of the opposition camp.

John plunged straight into his appeal. He did not get far. One of his listeners (the records do not identify him) broke in with an insolent contradiction.

There was no man in the room unaware of John's precarious health, none who did not know how quick he was to anger and how easily anger could kill him. In the comparatively trivial issue at stake a generous foe might perhaps have yielded to the sick, harried old man. They might have found an excuse for his offensive tone in the almost constant pain he endured. They might have weighed his irritability and tactlessness, his impatience and harsh tongue, against the keenness of his mind and the purity of his heart. They might have remembered his services to them as surgeons, the respect he had won for a profession that not long before had been classed with barbering and sow-gelding. ("Hunter," as Sir James Paget observed, "did more than any one to make us gentlemen.") But they did not choose to spare a colleague who had described himself as a giant compared to them.

John stopped speaking and, struggling to control his temper, staggered into the adjoining room. Robertson and one or two others followed him. He groaned and fell senseless into Robertson's arms.

In the board room, the meeting ended with a resolution. "Ordered: that Mr. Hunter's letter to the Board relating to two of the pupils, who were received this day, be preserved for future consideration." The discussion was not reopened.

John died during the afternoon without regaining consciousness. His body was carried down to the courtyard and seated in a sedan chair. In this position, with attendants walking beside the chair and his carriage following, John traveled for the last time the route he had taken so often in the thirty-nine years since he entered St. George's as a pupil—past the graying face of the hospital, through Hyde Park, glowing in its golden autumn colors, along Hyde Park Corner into teeming Piccadilly, skirting Jermyn Street, where he and Anne had shared their first home. . . .

As the procession moved across Piccadilly, Jessé Foot happened to pass it, and he recognized the empty black carriage and baystone horses. He was then finishing his long labor of hate, his biography of John, and when he learned, shortly after, that the sedan chair had borne John's body, he inserted with icy mockery a reference to the funeral of the slain Arcadian Prince Pallas—*Post Bellator Equus, positis insignibus Aethon It lacrymans* (Aethon, the war horse, his trappings removed, follows weeping).

It was five o'clock when Clift saw the chair and the attendants removing the body from it. For weeks after he poured out his grief and anxiety about his future in letters to his sister Elizabeth. "I am at a loss for words to express my ideas. . . . I am afraid our house will be turned quite upside down now the wall and support is gone. I shall know how it is with me in a fortnight or so I suppose when all things are settled a little but I do not care how it is to be. I hope God will provide for us.

"I should like to live in London very much but I don't think I shall ever like any Master as well as Mr. Hunter. Perhaps Mr. Home might take me to serve out my time with him to look after the dissecting rooms but then all my future hopes of learning to draw would be quite put a stop to, and I suppose I should never learn Anatomy under him, for he is quite a different man from Hunter. . . ."

Baillie, meanwhile, had gone to Brighton to fetch Anne and the children, and to Home fell the task John had always insisted every man of science should wish to have performed upon him.

Home's report indicated widespread damage to the arterial system, including arteriosclerosis, undoubtedly the immediate cause of the angina pectoris Jenner had diagnosed years before.

"The aorta immediately beyond the semilunar valves had its cavity larger than usual, putting on the appearance of an incipient aneurism; this unusual dilatation extended for some way along the ascending aorta, but it did not reach so far as the common trunk of the axillary and carotid artery. The increase of the capacity of the artery might be about one-third of its natural area; and the internal membrane of this part had lost entirely the natural polish and was studded over with opaque white spots, raised higher than the general surface"—a picture consistent with the terminal ravages of syphilis.

John went to his grave with scant ceremony and no official honors. At St. George's the hostility towards him persisted; his colleagues there did not even pass a vote of condolence. The minutes of the next board meeting merely recorded the fact of his death, referring to him as "one of the surgeons," and in the next meeting, "a vacancy for a surgeon having been occasioned by the death of John Hunter, Esq., one of the surgeons, a motion was made and seconded that Everard Home, Esq., succeed him in office."

With few exceptions, the press was hardly more effusive, but then there was little space for domestic news of any kind, for across the Channel a revolution was approaching its climax. The *Gentleman's Magazine*, in its Obituary of Considerable Persons for October 1793, noted under the date of the 16th: "Guillotined at Paris, in her 38th year . . . Marie Antoinette, the beautiful widow of the late French king," and following this, with the age wrong by three years: "In his 68th year John Hunter Esq."

A longer obituary that the *Gentleman's Magazine* published later reads like a satire on John's educational shortcomings. "As a man of letters, independently of his profound scientific studies, he had traced the practice of surgery to the earliest ages. He was well acquainted with every practitioner mentioned by Pliny, with all the Greek and Roman authors who had written on the subject, as well as with every modern one who had contributed to the perfection of the art. . . . As a man well versed in ancient history, the Egyptian chronology was familiar to him, as far as related to the antiquity of anatomy: as a scholar, distinguishably classic, he knew that Homer was an anatomist, at least had ideas of anatomy, as well as an epic poet."

The *Star*, a new evening newspaper, wrote of John briefly as "the eminent surgeon and valuable man . . . the first surgeon in the world." The only important newspaper to give him full meed of praise was the *Public Advertiser*, which called him "the greatest philosophical surgeon, and the greatest comparative anatomist which the useful art that he practiced had ever known," and it appealed to the nation to raise a statue to him in the Temple of British Fame of St. Paul's Cathedral beside those of Johnson and Reynolds.

The proposal won no more support than did Anne's efforts to have him buried in Westminster Abbey. He was buried in the crypt of St.

Martin-in-the-Fields, Trafalgar Square, where the Hunters had worshiped for many years.

The funeral took place at quarter past four on the afternoon of October 22. John had left his financial affairs in so shaky a state that expenses had to be kept down. "No candles," the sexton noted in his register. Only three carriages followed the hearse, carrying Anne, young John and Agnes, Matthew Baillie, Everard Home, and a few friends. Heartbroken little Clift nearly missed the funeral. Although Anne had promised he could stay with her until she found him a new position, that as long as she lived he would never want for a friend, in her own grief she forgot his.

"My cloaths was not made soon enough to go to the Burying," he wrote to his sister, "and none of the servants went to the burying but I was acquainted with the under taker and so I went to the Church and he put me in the vault—none of our people saw me there I believe and I did not want them to."

He wrote years later: "From the very beginning I fancied, without being able to account for it, that nobody about Mr. Hunter seemed capable of appreciating him. He seemed to me to have lived long before his time and to have died before he was sufficiently understood. The more I have seen, the more I have known, the more I have learned and the more I have thought, the stronger the conviction grows that I shall never look upon his like again."

Anne composed an epitaph, hoping to have it inscribed on a tablet in the vault. But the rector told her that the regulations forbade it.

Here rests in awful silence, cold and still,
One whom no common spark of genius fired;
Whose reach of thought Nature alone could fill,
Whose deep research the love of truth inspired.

Hunter! if years of toil and watchful care,
If the vast labours of a powerful mind
To soothe the ills humanity must share,
Deserve the grateful plaudits of mankind,—

Then be each human weakness buried here
Envy would raise to dim a name so bright:
Those specks which in the orb of day appear
Take nothing from his warm and welcome light.

VIII. AFTERWARD

38. THE HEIRS

In his will, drawn up three months before his death, John appointed as executors his wife, his nephew, and his brother-in-law. To his son, he left Long Calderwood. The Earl's Court estate and part of the contents of the Leicester Square house were to be sold, his museum to be offered to the government at a price agreeable to the executors, or, if rejected, to any purchaser they might approve. Out of the proceeds they were to pay his debts, and divide the residue equally among Anne and the children.

But so heavy were the debts that no residue seemed likely. A mortgage of £4,000 remained on the Earl's Court estate with interest accumulating at 5 per cent. There were other 5 per cent loans amounting to £7,800, £275 to be refunded to Hunter's house pupils, and a blizzard of bills for sundry services rendered. "Hatchett and Co., coach-builders of Long Acre [Clift noted in his diary], £650; Mr. Sharp, engraver, for the small head of Hunter to the work on the blood, £50; W. Skelton, print-seller, in the Haymarket, £45; Savigny, Pall Mall, surgeons' instruments, £1 10s.; W. Skelton, engraver, Pimlico, £30; George Bailey, Piccadilly, birdman, £2; Antonio Sartini, plaster-caster, £1; Peter Woulfe, Staples Inn, Holborn, fossils, £60; John Hunter, picture-frame maker, Swallow St., Piccadilly, £34; Mr. Jones, Apothecary, Great Russell Street, £31. . . ."

With the total liability amounting to £19,000, Anne's outlook was bleak. Clift wrote incoherently to his sister: "Mr. Hunter's coachman and the footman and the butler are discharged, and Mrs. Hunter's coachman, for the Both carriages and horses are sold, and the Horses at the Country house are sold and since Mr. Hunter's footman has gone and I have had to go to all Mrs. Hunter's acquaintances with cards, and yesterday I was out at Earl's Court with Miss Hunter and the lady's maid to pack up some books and things to bring to town—I think it must seem very strange to Miss Hunter to ride in a Hackney coach, being used to ride in one that was reckoned the handsomest coach that was at Court when Mrs. Hunter had it to go to court in. . . ."

The first portion of the estate to be disposed of, some of it by auction, some by outright sale, consisted of furniture, plate, surgical instruments, a collection of minerals, a vulture, a sheep, and a "Great Dog." It fetched £2,677, 13s, 4d. James Christie, the founder of the gallery that still bears his name, conducted the auction in his "Great Room in Pall Mall." The furniture included three Chippendale pieces from Hunter's study—a desk, a rolltop escritoire, and a sideboard, all crammed with notebooks and manuscripts that the family had neglected to remove. Appraised at £30 to £40, these went for £15 to that watchful man, Everard Home.

Two more auctions followed at Christie's. The Earl's Court property brought £10,300. Also, £1,300 were realized from John's art collection, numbering 120 paintings and engravings, most of them mediocre but with a few fine Reynolds and Hogarths; from the possession he valued least—his library; and from the farrago of bargains he had been unable to resist—Chinese ivory puzzle balls, Chinese josses and mandarins, armor, an acre (according to Clift's measurement) of landscapes and figures painted by Zuccarelli as models for tapestries, an "Electrifying apparatus."

The significance of one Hunterian curio eluded Christie. It was the wooden mask John fashioned to avoid bee stings. "A most curious and interesting article, ladies and gentlemen!" the auctioneer finally ventured. "A covering for the face used by the South Sea Islanders when travelling to preserve their faces from snow storms." He knocked it down to a Mr. Walker for three shillings, sixpence, in a lot comprising "a wooden and another pair of ancient shoes, a leather doublet and various other oddities."

The proceeds fell far short of the sum owed by the estate, and Anne's last hope was the museum. Baillie and Home petitioned Parliament. Pending the outcome, Anne made further retrenchments. She sublet the town property for seven guineas a week—all but the Castle Street Building, since it contained the museum—moved into a small house in suburban Blackheath with John and Agnes, and withdrew completely from the fashionable society she had once graced. Her widowhood was not comforted by the publication of Jessé Foot's biography.

For his private amusement Foot commissioned a cartoonist to extra-illustrate his copy of the biography with sixteen scurrilous drawings. One drawing, captioned "Rascality," showed John gleefully thrusting a lancet down a small boy's throat. In another, "John Hunter in his own Trance," he lies prostrate on the ground—an allusion to his heart attacks. In another, he advances with arms outstretched to embrace a trio of monstrosities. In a fourth, a grinning John dissects the body of Percivall Pott. The caption: "Poor Hunter goes to Pott at last."

Anne received some small financial help from the government thanks to the efforts of Lord Auckland, who at John's death had written to a colleague: "I am not in very good spirits this evening. My old and worthy friend John Hunter died yesterday suddenly." In 1794 and again in 1795 Auckland persuaded the Prime Minister, William Pitt, to carry Anne's name on the Civil Lists for a pension. But for the Hunterian Museum Pitt showed no enthusiasm. England was at war with Napoleon, and being trounced on land and sea. "What! Buy preparations!" said the Premier. "Why, I have not enough money to purchase gunpowder!"

He was reinforced in his stand by the men of science he consulted. One of them, identified in contemporary accounts as "a surgeon of inconsiderable repute," uttered a judgment seldom surpassed in its fatuity. He dismissed the museum as being "just as valuable as a pig's pettitoes." Nor was the Hunters' old friend, Sir Joseph Banks, encouraging, even though he had given John half of his own preparations. While conceding the usefulness of the museum as an aid to the study of anatomy, he belittled its importance for natural history. The petition was tabled.

Anne Hunter did not have the solace of her children's company for long. John was commissioned an ensign in the Second Battalion of the Royal Regiment of Foot, and in 1794 he sailed with it to the Mediterranean, where he took part in an attack on Caprera Island. Agnes married a veteran of the American Revolution, Captain (later Sir

James) Campbell of the nineteenth Light Dragoons, an event that occasioned Anne's first verses since John's death—*To My Daughter, on Being Separated from Her on Her Marriage*.

Clift took a less poetic view of the nuptials. "I think for my part," he told his sister, "they have made too much haste about it so soon after the poor old Mans death—Everything has been getting ready there for some time past, and the Bed and all is ready for them to get into I believe—"

He was living wretchedly in the unwanted museum, trying to feed and clothe himself on seven shillings a week. He had no other regular source of income nor even a clearly defined status in the confused Hunter ménage. Occasionally he earned a few extra shillings as a penman. An actor, Charles Mathews, paid him a guinea to copy out a play by Joanna Baillie. After assisting Home for months in the lecture room, he received what the surgeon termed, with a flourish of magnanimity, a "Christmas box." It contained half a guinea.

Yet nobody could have performed more conscientiously for pay the duties Clift assumed for love. He was endlessly deciphering and transcribing John's tangled notes and papers, endlessly cleaning, arranging and labeling John's preparations. To buy alcohol in which to preserve them, he often went hungry.

"I was down at Blackheath last Sunday to see Mrs. Hunter but she did not say anything to me about a place," he complained to his sister, "nor did she give me anything to put in my pocket, she never gave me as much as sixpence yet, and now I am obliged to pay for my own letters. I shall enquire soon who is to pay for them as they never gave me any money they can't expect that I can pay for them."

The executors presently fixed his salary at £21 a year. Home assured him that if the museum were sold he would get at least £100 to go on taking care of it. At the same time he made it clear that he expected Clift to serve him as faithfully as he had John Hunter. Home's requirements were extensive. They included menial domestic chores in his new house in Sackville Street, secretarial work of all sorts, help in his medical research, and illustrations to accompany his papers. These demands galled the forlorn youth, whose dislike of Home had grown since John's death. "Quite a different man from Hunter," he told his sister. "I never knew such a man as he is, for he hardly ever comes to our house now and when he does, he hardly ever speaks ten words." Yet Clift dared not risk a quarrel. He needed money badly, having fallen in love with a nineteen-year-old beauty named Catherine Anne Pope.

Had Matthew Baillie been less burdened, Clift might have fared better. But John's talented nephew was trying to keep up a practice beyond his strength. Like others of his line, he had a tendency to tuberculosis. He was a husband of three years' standing—he had married Sophia Denman, one of the twin daughters of the obstetrician, Thomas Denman; he had two children and an expensive house in Lower Grosvenor Street; and he was putting the final touches to his *Morbid Anatomy*, a work John Hunter himself would have been proud to sign. It was the first systematic account of how diseased organs look, and the first textbook on pathology as a separate subject. Clift had drawn some of the plates for Baillie, who, more openhanded than Home, paid him a guinea each. One plate showed a pair of lungs in which the air sacs were greatly distended, an abnormality known as emphysema. Those particular lungs had belonged to Samuel Johnson. Baillie obtained them from William Cruikshank, his associate in the Great Windmill School and one of the doctors present during Johnson's last illness. A footnote explained that emphysema accounted for the great cham's "heavy form, rolling and puffing."

Still less could Anne Hunter help Clift. She was so hard-pressed that when Maxwell Garthshore—John's kindly "Tom Fool"—offered her employment as chaperone to his two wards, she thankfully accepted. These wards were Anne and Jane Saunders, the orphaned daughters of Dr. Richard Saunders, who had been a member of the army medical staff with John on Belle Isle. Evidently Anne served them well, for they both won rich and powerful husbands. Anne Saunders married Viscount Melville, an M.P. and later First Lord of the Admiralty; Jane became the second wife of the Earl of Westmorland, the Lord Privy Seal.

It is probable that these peers, grateful for the fond care Anne had devoted to their brides, added their voices to those of Auckland and others who felt the Hunterian Museum should belong to England. When the petition came up again in 1796, a special House committee was formed to reconsider it. This time many of the country's foremost surgeons, physicians and naturalists were asked their opinions, among them John's pupils, Abernethy, Cline, and Cruikshank. Finally, after three years, the committee recommended that a sum "be granted to His Majesty to enable him to purchase the Collection of Natural History

belonging to the late Dr. [sic] John Hunter, for the use of the public."
His Majesty got a bargain. The sum proposed by the committee and
approved by the executors was £15,000—about a fifth of what John
spent on it.

Before the museum changed hands, Home asked Clift to hand over
all the Hunter notes. He needed them, he explained, to catalogue the
museum, a task for which he said nobody else could qualify. Clift,
seized by an indefinable suspicion, was inclined to refuse and hide the
material, but with his marriage in the offing, less than ever could he
afford to forfeit Home's patronage. He managed to put him off for a
year while he frantically went on transcribing the notes; then, with a
heavy heart, he bundled the lot into a cart and drove it to Sackville
Street. With what Home had acquired at Christie's he now possessed
almost the entire body of John's unpublished writings. Of those writings Clift had transcribed less than half.

Clift did recover a fragment—the beginning of the manuscript of the
Treatise on the Venereal Disease. He found it, to his horror, in Home's
water closet. "The conclusion," he wrote in his diary, "has gone towards
Old Father Thames. I offer to supply as much whity-brown in exchange, but [Home] honestly objected to that, and declared that I was
welcome to what remained; as he considered the manuscript of a work
that had gone through the press of no value. I thought differently, on
account of the few MS. finger-marks of John Hunter."

In 1800 the museum passed into the custody of the Royal College
of Surgeons, which took over the lease on the Castle Street building,
insured the collection against fire or loss, and created a five-man Board
of Curators under the chairmanship of Sir William Blizard. Little Clift
was ecstatic. His starved, lonely years of guardianship had not been
in vain. John's unwritten book would not be allowed to fade into
oblivion; the perpetuation and growth of the museum were now
assured.

Nor did the curators ignore Clift's devotion. They named him Conservator at a salary of £80 a year. This was £20 less than Home had
predicted, but he promised to make up the difference by giving Clift
every Christmas £21 worth of 3 per cent securities until the
principal yielded annual dividends of £21. That promise he kept, and
in gratitude Clift named his second-born child William Home Clift.
Any notion Clift may have entertained, however, that Home was sim-

ply compensating him for past services was soon dispelled. He exacted still more arduous services.

Convening in July 1801, the curators laid down Clift's new duties. Every night before retiring he must verify the security of the museum. The building must never be left unlocked. He must never leave it at night without written permission. He must list every article needed for maintenance, purchase nothing without express authority, and keep a record of every penny disbursed.

Home turned up at the meeting and volunteered to prepare a catalogue. The curators urged him to proceed at once. Shortly after, he got himself appointed to the board, from which vantage point he could tighten his control over Clift. Five years later the exhibits were transferred to permanent quarters in the Royal College of Surgeons' new building in Lincoln's Inn Fields. [k]

With her share of the purchase price Anne Hunter, who had turned fifty-eight, bought an annuity enabling her to live, if not luxuriously, at least in decency. She leased a house at No. 63 Lower Grosvenor Street to be near the Baillies, who lived opposite at No. 72.

Her nephew now stood at the summit of his profession. His *Morbid Anatomy* was a standard work throughout Europe. For its emblem the Pathological Society chose his portrait encircled by the epigraph *Nec silet mors*. He carried the Gold-Headed Cane, a distinction enjoyed by only five other men in British medicine. The cane, with its Malacca staff, long steel ferrule, and solid gold handle, belonged originally, some two hundred years before, to Dr. John Radcliffe, who was physician to William III until he remarked, after examining the king's gout-swollen legs: "I would not have your legs for three kingdoms." Radcliffe bequeathed the cane to the doctor he considered worthiest to carry it after him, Richard Mead. Mead left it to Anthony Askew, as discerning a bibliophile as he was a physician. From Askew it passed to a Scotsman, William Pitcairn; from Pitcairn to his nephew, David Pitcairn of St. Bartholomew's; and from David Pitcairn to Matthew Baillie. [1]

Baillie worked at a furious pace, and under the strain grew cantankerous. When a hypochondriac lady of fashion sent for him to ask if she could safely eat oysters before going to the opera, he stamped out of the house, fuming, "Yes, ma'am, shells and all!"

In her retirement Anne Hunter's poetic output increased, a steady trickle of elegies to departed friends, of epitaphs, songs, and sentimental ballads, never memorable but often deft and ingratiating. Her warmest lyrical moods were inspired by her son's birthdays. After seeing action in various theaters of war, John had been promoted to captain and was stationed on Gibraltar. In 1802 Anne published a small book of poems with a dedicatory letter to him:

"My Dear John, From the moment in which I saw you embark from the pier at Ramsgate, for the expedition to Holland in 1799, till that in which I received accounts of your safe return from Egypt in the present year 1802, I have been too seriously anxious to be poetical on your subject. Now, on the return of peace, I present you with this small volume; you are already acquainted with part of its contents; but there are some things in it which you have never seen. I have great pleasure in dedicating this publication to a worthy young man, and a brave soldier; whom I am proud to call my son."

From a second edition of the poems brought out the following year the dedication was omitted. Nor did Anne write any more poetry to her son. Some sense of shame seems to have inhibited her. In a letter to a friend she referred to him cryptically as "my poor unhappy son." She wrote this after he abruptly resigned from the army, having attained the rank of major. Why John abandoned a successful military career at thirty-seven remains an enigma. He spent the rest of his life in France, a long-faced, pallid man with reddish hair, who never married. He kept a Negro slave, a practice shunned by civilized Englishmen, and in English law a felony. He died in his sixty-sixth year, bequeathing the slave to a Frenchman named Chevin.

The fate of Anne's daughter gave her no cause for rejoicing either. Agnes's marriage to Captain Campbell ended at his instance after fifteen years. He was somewhat imprecise about the nature of his wife's derelictions, but whatever they were, the thought of them so infuriated him that he kept adding codicils to his will, canceling more bequests to her. Eventually none were left. "I will not repeat all that has occurred, or all the causes I have had to alter my opinion with respect to her," he wrote in the first of these codicils, "and before this paper will be perused, the footing upon which my wife and I have now separated will likewise be known to the world [it never was]: my own heart and conscience acquit me of any blame in the transaction; the meaning, purport and intent of this Memo. is to cancel all testamentary bequeathments I have made in her favour, except the provision arranged for her when I was last in Scotland in 1806 from my entailed property there. . . ."

And again: "I have had still further cause to be dissatisfied with the conduct of my wife, and do therefor revoke and recall the provision arranged for her out of my Scottish property as I deem her unworthy and undeserving of any such provision or annuity at the expense of my heirs, she being an ungrateful and unprincipled woman."

And finally: "Now be it known to all men that having had just cause to complain of and be aggrieved by the misconduct, ingratitude, and folly of my wife, inasmuch as to have withdrawn and separated myself from her altogether, my intention is that all and every bequeathment in the above depositions . . . be considered null and of no effect, being but a just mark of the alienation of my once well-founded regard for a capricious, misguided woman, who trifled with the affections of a well-intentioned, and towards her, a liberal husband."

But though his conscience may not have troubled him, the captain's behavior was not exemplary. He fathered two children by a mistress.

Agnes bore him no children. Nor did she bear any to the man she married after the captain died, Lieutenant-Colonel Benjamin Charlewood of the Grenadier Guards. This second marriage, which lasted until her death at sixty-two, appears to have been a happy one. Towards the end, however, Agnes's mind and body deteriorated under repeated paralytic seizures of undetermined origin.

So little do we know about John Hunter's children that it is difficult even to speculate about the mystery that enveloped their last years. Yet one question insistently poses itself: did they too suffer from their father's experimental self-pollution?

Anne published a last book of verse in 1804, *The Sports of the Genii*, and she wrote a number of poems never collected. She showed no inclination to emerge from her social limbo. "I am but a shabby person," she wrote to Joanna Baillie, "however, we scramble thro' Weeks, and Months, somehow or other, as well as we can . . . Adieu! Dear Joanna. . . ."

On January 7, 1821, at the age of seventy-nine, this serene, self-effacing woman died.

"I have had two very hard days," Clift wrote to his wife from the seaside town of Hastings, whither he had journeyed to inspect the beached carcass of a shark. "My fingers are so cut and scratched and swelled that I can hardly hold a pen. . . . I wish and have wished a hundred times that you were all here, hard as the weather is, to see the sea. I wanted William [who was then six years old] to help me twenty times since I have been here only that his apron and sleeves are not made. He would have liked to have helped me when I was up to the knees in a shark's belly. I was obliged to go into the sea to wash my legs and arms before I could go into the town. You must kiss William and Caroline for me. . . ."

From that expedition Clift also brought back a catch of sea urchins and some parasitic worms in the stomach of a haddock. Not even John Hunter had been more ardent in his pursuit of anatomical curiosa. By cajolery, entreaty, flattery, and bargaining, the Conservator procured specimen after specimen, augmenting the Hunterian collection to a grand total of 17,000 exhibits. For the skeleton of Caroline Crachiami, the twenty-two-inch high "Sicilian Fairy," whose portrait John had purchased, he paid the father £10. He persuaded Martin Van Butchell's son to part with the embalmed body of the first Mrs. Van Butchell. A Dorsetshire squire sent Clift a fetus purportedly found in the abdomen of a fifteen-year-old boy, with the affidavit, "I accompanied several gentlemen to the mother of the deceased's house, where they each respectively examined the body, and became fully satisfied that he was a perfectly formed male; a circumstance on which some doubts had been expressed."

In rapid succession Clift came by a Peruvian mummy; the bones of a Tahitian named Terah Pool, who had died of consumption in the London Hospital; the impression made on a wax shroud by a face believed to have been that of Thomas Beaufort, son of John of Gaunt, as well as Beaufort's right hand (forty-two years earlier John Hunter had obtained Beaufort's left hand); a rare specimen of shark, the *Squalus alopecias,* or fox shark, of which Clift cooked a slice and reported, "Made very good eating."

Clift would equip ship captains bound for distant ports with crates and jorums of spirits to preserve any interesting fauna they might chance upon. The results were sometimes unsatisfactory. One crate of animal pelts thus received turned out to be harboring colonies of moths, mice and cockroaches, which overran the museum.

An additional duty that the Royal College of Surgeons thrust upon Clift put him in the way of acquiring some choice human specimens. Charged with dissecting the corpses of executed murderers, he anatomized thirty-six in all, retaining such organs as illustrated structural abnormalities.

Under Clift's management the museum gained international renown, attracting visitors, both laymen and scientists, from the furthest reaches of Europe. In one year he personally conducted through the place—a pleasure that never palled—1,842 of them, including Baron Cuvier, the French naturalist; General Wiebel, physician to the King of Prussia, and Sir James Wylie, surgeon to the Emperor of Russia, Archduke Maximilian of Austria, Prince Christian of Denmark, and the Grand Duchess of Oldenburgh.

For a man whom John Hunter once described as all thumbs without "sense to tie down a bottle," Home had gone far. His private practice was among the most lucrative in London. His taxable income one year came to £21,000. He was a frequent attendant surgeon at duels between celebrities. He treated Lord Camelford, a glittering rake, for a head wound after he had been shot by a Mr. Best in a quarrel over a woman. The wound proved mortal. Home had better luck with George Canning, former treasurer of the navy, whom the Secretary at War, Lord Castlereagh, challenged upon uncovering Canning's plot to have him ousted from the cabinet. At the first exchange Canning took a bullet through the thigh, but after Home's ministrations he was able to walk off the field unaided.

Bloodshed in St. James's Palace opened the portals for Home to still loftier connections. On the night of May 31, 1810, George III's third son, the Duke of Cumberland, was found in his apartment with blood gushing from a gash over his eye; in the adjoining bedroom his valet, Sellis, lay dead on the bed, his throat cut—apparently a case of attempted murder and suicide, though no motive was ever established. Home saved the Duke's life, and the King rewarded him with the rank of Sergeant-Surgeon. He also promised him a knighthood (Home had already registered a coat of arms with the motto, *True*), but before he could confer it he lapsed into insanity. The fat, featherbrained Prince Regent made good the promise after Home removed a wen from his pate. Titles dispensed during the regency, however, did not necessarily imply recognition of professional superiority. When the First Lord of the Admiralty, Lord Melville, recommended a doctor named Farquhar for the honors list, the fourth George declared, "Yes, yes, make him a baronet, make him a baronet. I thought you were going to ask me to make him my physician."

Sir Everard, certainly, rose in the Regent's esteem through qualities other than surgical. He had taken to tippling heavily, and George, himself a confirmed tosspot, welcomed him as a companion-in-cups. The painter, Joseph Farington, wrote of a dinner at Sir Joseph Banks's house: "Sir Everard Home, the celebrated Surgeon, filled his glass with Port Wine every time that the bottle came round contrary to the prevailing recommendation of medical men in these days." He became obese, gouty, and, according to the *Lancet*, "a regular sot [who] never went to bed sober." Clift's daughter, Caroline, remembered him looking "as he has for the last thirty years, a big, fair, serious and rather pretty Brobdignag cherub, but is no cherub in sense. . . ."

To gratify his boozy favorite, the Regent consented to be shown around the Hunterian Museum by him. Sir Everard had Clift spread a scarlet cloth before the entrance. But the only exhibits that appeared to fire the royal imagination were the pickled fetuses. He claimed to see in them a resemblance to a courtier of stunted physique, Sir Thomas Tyrwhitt, a fancy that diverted him for days. "Well now for it," he wrote to the Queen Mother. "It is a pun & a new nickname I have given our little dwarf. I call him the TWENTY THIRD OF JUNE, & now I leave you to guess why? Pray do guess first, & do not let impatience of your curiosity tempt you to turn over this page till you have first guessed all round a little.

"This then is the explanation. What is the twenty third of June?

Answer
The shortest night.

"And sure there never yet was so short a diminutive a dwarf of a Knight, as this said little red dwarf of ours, & doubly now red also from the additional ribbon which now decorates the little person of his Kleine Excellence, by which name he has been received, recogniz'd, address'd, treated and travell'd through all the Courts of Germany.

And I am so full of this idea and it has so completely seized hold of
me respecting him, that I do assure you that I was very nearly tempted
to get Sir Everard Home to go and borrow for me, out of Hunter's
Museum repository, one of the large glass jars, of which there are hundreds there, containing one of the little embryos (ou peutetre ce que
l'on peut appeller aussi fausse couche sans se tromper beaucoup de
nom) in order to tie a little bit of red ribbon over its shoulder, and
then to have it sent, as a cadeau to you to have ornamented the mantelpiece of the chimney of your sitting room, as the most exact and perfect
resemblance of our *little hero,* and far more I am sure, a thousand
times over and over again, than any picture that ever can, or that ever
will be made or taken of him."

In expectation of a legacy, Home attended Banks without fee for
years. Receiving none at the naturalist's death, he billed the Banks
estate £4,000—and collected it. When a staff surgeon at Chelsea Hospital died, he went to the King, dropped to his knees and, tearfully
pleading poverty, begged for the appointment. He got it. The hospital
board later protested that he usually came to meetings drunk and tried
to browbeat his associates.

He was nevertheless considered a good practical surgeon, and he
commanded respectful attention as a lecturer on comparative anatomy.
He read more papers before the Royal Society, 143 all together, than
any other member in its history. "Another Hunter," his audiences began to whisper. The comparison was apt, since most of the original
material had been lifted from John's papers. At first Home acknowledged the source, but gradually the lines of authorship grew blurred.
He was elected Vice-President of the Royal Society, a Master of the
Royal College of Surgeons, and a trustee of the Hunterian Museum.
He shone at the monthly meetings of the Medico-Botanical Society.

But Clift was not impressed. Without suspecting outright plagiarism,
he knew how heavily Home relied on John's notes. He vented his
feelings in secret with a pen, using it like a pin to stick into a hated
image. Finding an old notebook of Home's, he scribbled across the
cover, "The Child's 3-letter Book by Sir E. Home. His only genuine
work." In a wicked sketch he drew of Home the surgeon resembles a
blowfish about to pop.

Yet Clift continued in the role of lackey to Home, even after a raise
in salary to £130 a year eliminated the economic necessity and the
Royal Society had elected him a fellow. Home apparently exerted an

inescapable psychological dominance. "My dear Clift," he commanded, "I wish you to attend my lecture at the Hospital on Tuesday at 12. Let me have the coloured prints of the blood and the sections of the aneurysm for Tuesday." Clift meekly obeyed.

With all of Home's distractions, it is not surprising that he could not get on with the catalogue. At frequent intervals the curators of the museum politely inquired about it. They got evasive replies. The task had scarcely been started as late as 1805, when the Royal College of Surgeons chose the site of its new headquarters. Nor had it progressed much further eight years later, when the construction was finished.

But the curators did not press Home, possibly because he stood so high in the King's favor and the ranks of the profession. They urged him to publish his lectures. He declined at first, with an affecting show of modesty, then bowed to a second request, murmuring as he did so that perhaps the College would care to subscribe to a number of copies. The College did, £165 worth.

But still no catalogue. Finally, in 1816, the curators voted to help Home prepare it. They would divide the collection into sections, each curator to catalogue a section. Home took offense. What, relieve *him*, the spiritual heir of John Hunter, of so sacred an obligation! The curators retracted their decision, and good feelings were restored. But Home produced no catalogue. Instead he prepared two more volumes of his lectures for publication, of which the College again agreed to buy copies.

Soon after the installation of the museum in Lincoln's Inn Fields, Home and Baillie had jointly contributed £1,684, 4s, 4d to the College as a fund for an annual Hunterian Oration to be delivered on the anniversary of John's birth. Home was the inaugural orator. "I am better acquainted than any other man with his talents, his endowments and his merits," said he, "but such is the enthusiasm with which he inspired me, and so little has my partiality been diminished by the lapse of 20 years, which have passed since his death, that I dare not trust myself to proceed further in this history."

On an afternoon nine years later Home was riding in his carriage with Clift to the Kew Royal Botanical Gardens for a meeting of the Medico-Botanical Society. Casually, he recounted a mishap that had befallen him the night before. His chimney had caught fire and the whole house might have burned down but for the prompt arrival of the firemen.

"How did it happen?" Clift asked.

"I was burning Hunter's manuscripts in the fireplace," Home replied.

When Clift could speak again, he said: "I hope, Sir Everard, you have not destroyed those ten volumes relating to the gallery?"

"Yes," said Home.

"And Mr. Hunter's lectures?"

"Yes."

Clift enumerated some twenty other volumes. Home said he had destroyed them all.

"Well, Sir Everard," said Clift, "there is only one more thing to do."

"What is that?"

"To burn the collection." And he wept.

In his grief Clift did not immediately grasp the full implications. Only after he read Home's new volumes of lectures did the truth burst upon him. They bristled with plagiarisms; he recognized them from his own early transcriptions. A flagrant example was a lecture on the stomachs and teeth of whales. Here Home had copied verbatim a manuscript of John's, forgetting that it had been published in the *Philosophical Transactions* Society twenty-seven years before. Clift at last knew Home to be a thief, who had burned John's papers to conceal his theft. By so doing, he had also robbed the British Government of assets that were as integral a part of the Hunterian Museum as the whale skeletons or the embryo series.

Clift never understood Home's motive for confessing to him. Was it to test Clift's reaction against the day when the crime might be uncovered? Did he hope to exact a promise of silence? Had his gifts and his gestures of friendship been intended as bribes? If so, Home had miscalculated. Clift went straight to Sir William Blizard.

No doubt he would have gone to Matthew Baillie first, but tuberculosis had forced Baillie to retire to the country. He died there in September 1823, without learning of Home's betrayal.

To move against the King's crony required prudence, and it was not until the following February that the curators formally reviewed Clift's charges. As he repeated them, he broke down. Neither then nor after could he speak of Home's perfidy without tears. Years later, during a parliamentary hearing, he was asked: "What were your feelings at the time of receiving that information?" "I can hardly describe them," Clift replied, "because I felt that all those hopes that I had entertained, were entirely frustrated and destroyed."

The precise amount of the damage Clift was unable to determine, but according to an inventory he had drawn up before giving Home the material, it numbered "nine folio volumes of dissections of animals, viz.: Vol. 1. Ruminants; Vol. 2. Animals, *Sine Caeco* [i.e., without an intestinal appendage]; Vol. 3. Monkey and its Gradations; Vol. 4. Lion and its Gradations; Vol. 5. *Scalpris Dentata* [chisel-toothed rodents like the beaver]; Vol. 6. Anatomy of Birds; Vol. 7. Of the Tricoilia [Hunter's classification for certain amphibious animals such as turtles, frogs, lizards, and snakes]; Vol. 8. Anatomy of Fishes; Vol. 9; Anatomy of Insects . . . One volume on the Natural History of Vegetables . . . a great number of fasciculi, among them, Introduction to Natural History, many Physiological Observations; Comparative Physiology; comparison between Man and the Monkey; on Muscular Motion . . . Effects of Extracting one Ovarian upon the number of Young produced; Experiments on Ewes, with a view to determine impregnation and Uterine Gestation; On Monsters; On the Skeleton; Dissection of the Tapir; Dissection of the Armadillo with nine Bands; Animals from New Holland; Piked Whale; Bottle-nosed Whale; Fin-back Whale, and Porpoise; Worms in Animals of the Whale Tribe; Bell-Barnacle; On the Eel; Anatomy of the Holothuria [sea cucumber]; Anatomy of the Siren [an eel-like amphibian]; Account of a Unicorn Fish, from Hispaniola; The Earth Worm; Progress and Peculiarities of the Chick; Description of Rymsdyk's Drawings of the Incubation of the Egg; General Observations on Insects; The Bee-tribe; Humble-Bee, Wasp and Hornet, and on Beetles; Anatomy of the Silk-worm; Anatomy of the Moth; Red-piped Coral; On Fossil-Bones, two parts; Observations on Surgery; Observations on Scrofula and Cancer; Lectures on the Principles of Surgery. . . ."

That a quantity of the missing material could eventually be reconstructed was owing to Clift's energy as a transcriber. What he had completed before surrendering the originals included one of the most important of John's posthumous publications—the two-volume *Essays and Observations,* covering an immense range of inquiries from the Sociability of Man and of Animals (John concluded that animals were better mixers) to States of Mind.

Clift guessed, moreover, that Home had not destroyed the last of the papers but had retained some for further pillaging, and he so advised the curators. The chairman directed Home to produce whatever was left. Home swore he had no more, and proceeded to justify his deed.

The papers were crude, he argued, unfit for publication; what little value they contained he had extracted. Besides, he dared to testify, John himself, shortly before his death, had instructed his executors to destroy them.

The curators did not swallow this perjury. Had such instructions existed, why had neither Home nor Baillie ever mentioned them? Sir William summoned Home again. The defendant stood his ground. But he was in anguish. "My mind worried," he noted in a diary, "on account of an Attack by the Board of Curators claiming Mr. Hunter's manuscripts. My urine nearly resembled fluid blood."

Clift meanwhile, playing the detective among Home's servants, discovered that several manuscripts had indeed survived. The curators addressed a third appeal to Home. He flatly refused to discuss the matter further. They thereupon referred the case to the museum's trustees, who opened a special hearing in the spring of 1824.

Home was not invited to attend, but as a trustee himself he had that right, and in person he submitted copies of his apologias, demanding that they be entered in the minutes. Only then did he have the grace to leave the room while his fellow trustees deliberated. They reached no decision. They did, however, agree with Clift that more Hunter papers must exist, and they kept hammering at Home. He finally capitulated to the extent of disgorging 86 fascicles and a 322-page manuscript. As Clift wrote hopefully in his diary, it began to look as if "the phoenix might yet arise from the ashes." But arise it did not. Home's final declaration was an attempt to humiliate Clift. "The Conservator," he said, "feels himself so outraged at my destroying these papers that he has not only complained to the Board of Curators but asserts that in my whole life I have never done him one act of kindness. In the face of this declaration I beg to state that through me he is now in possession of £1,370 in the 3 per cents."

No action was taken against the culprit. He kept all his titles and offices, and though most of his colleagues viewed him with contempt, he continued in favor at court.

In August 1832 he went to bed with an attack of gout. On the last day of the month Clift noted: "Reported at the Board of Curators that Sir Everard Home died this morning at half-past three at his house at Chelsea Hospital, 77th year—*Sic transit gloria mundi*." When a member of the Royal Society delivered a eulogy, Clift wrote that the speaker was not the author; the eulogy had been prepared well in advance by Sir Everard himself.

Further evidence of Home's thievery emerged long after the funeral. Home's son, a navy captain, furnished it. He gave the Royal College eleven parcels of Hunteriana, including a study of the natural history of vegetables he had found tucked away in his father's house. Seven years later he came upon still another bundle, consisting of a treatise on fossils.

In the material Home had consigned to the flames was a scrap of paper—Clift remembered it well—bearing that favorite axiom of John's: "There never was a man who wanted to be a great man ever was a great man."

As soon as the dust of controversy had settled, Clift gave thought to the long delayed catalogue. With so many new accessions, the labor was too vast for one man, but he now had an assistant, a young anatomist from Lancaster named Richard Owen. Owen not only helped complete the catalogue, but resurrected from Clift's transcriptions the *Essays and Observations*. In 1835 he married Caroline Clift.

Clift, all the while, relentlessly hunted new specimens, dodging no risk or discomfort. When a dead sperm whale was swept ashore near Greenwich, he hurried to the spot, propped open the jaws with poles, and crept in. He lost his footing and slid backwards toward the gullet. An alert fisherman retrieved the little man with a boathook. The whale wound up stuffed in the museum.

Clift's fondest hope was that his son, William Home, would succeed him as Conservator. In the fall of 1832, barely a month after the death of his namesake, the boy was riding in a hackney coach. It overturned, breaking his neck. Clift never recovered from the loss, and he aged fast. Owen shouldered the bulk of his duties.

At a meeting of the curators in 1842, when Clift was sixty-seven, they left him standing outside the room while they discussed the affairs of the museum with Owen. Not long after, they notified Clift that though he would retain the title of Conservator, together with a yearly salary of £400, as long as he lived, he must turn over his quarters to his son-in-law. Away from the museum, Clift declined still faster. He died in 1849. On his tombstone in Highgate Cemetery, Owen, the new

Conservator, had this epitaph chiseled: "He carried a child-like simplicity and single-mindedness to the close of a long and honoured career."

40. IN MEMORIAM

One morning in January 1859, a young army surgeon named Francis Trevelyan Buckland, attached to Her Majesty's Second Life Guards at Windsor, sat in the barracks messroom reading the London *Times*. Among the official notices, he came upon an Order in Council that disturbed him: the overcrowded vaults of the Church of St. Martin-in-the-Fields were to be cleared.

"Any person or persons [he read] having the remains of relatives or friends deposited in any of the vaults under the church or in any of the catacombs under the churchyard, situate at the north-east corner of Trafalgar Square, are hereby informed that they may, if they so desire, remove the same before the 1st Day of February 1859. . . ."

The announcement struck a chord of memory. Wasn't John Hunter buried in St. Martin's? Buckland had long venerated the Scot. His late father, the Rev. Dr. William Buckland, Dean of Westminster Abbey and an illustrious geologist, had held John up to him since his boyhood as an ideal. It distressed the Dean that there was no monument to Hunter in all England, and to his dying day he tried to have one erected in the Abbey. But the age had not yet caught up with John Hunter. Even among the members of the Royal College of Surgeons comparatively few grasped the full scope and meaning of his lifework.

To Dr. Buckland's joy, his son showed early in life an affinity for natural history, surrounding himself with monkeys, parrots, woodchucks, mice, snakes, and fish spawn. Later he acquired a bear and a jaguar. He was an inveterate taster of exotic meats, boggling at the flesh of neither bison nor kangaroo, zebra nor giraffe. He strove to popularize whale meat "a century before," as a recent article in the *Annals of the Royal College of Surgeons* noted, "necessity compelled a reluctant nation to make use of it."

When, upon graduating from Christ Church, Oxford, he decided to study surgery, his choice of St. George's Hospital was inevitable. He was house surgeon there from 1851 to 1853. At a centenary dinner in 1856, commemorating John Hunter's years of service, he promised himself that one day the hero of his youth would receive honors commensurate with his merits. The Order in Council, three years later, recalled that promise.

The order coincided with Buckland's annual furlough, and after verifying John's burial place, he hurried to London and St. Martin's. The church officials, he was disgusted to learn, had never heard of John Hunter, let alone that his coffin lay under their feet. At Buckland's insistence they produced the old sexton's registry. In it, penned by a semi-literate hand, was the notation: "Leister Squar. Oct. 22, 1793. M John Hunter Esq. ¼ past 4 o'clock. £6. 10. 2. No candles. No. 3 V. Duty 8 pence. C Aperplexy."

The vestry supervisor, a Mr. Burstall, explained the abbreviations to Buckland. M stood for male, V for vault, and C for certificate. He descended with him to the crypt. It was supported by massive pillars, the spaces between bricked up to form the walls of the vaults. By the light of a bull's-eye lantern, Burstall unlocked the thick, oak door of No. 3 Vault. "I beheld a sight I shall never forget," Buckland wrote years after. "The vault was a good-sized room, as full as it could hold with coffins piled one over the other from the very top to the bottom, and placed in all possible directions, reminding one much of books packed in a box to be sent away. Many coffins were piled up [3,260, by actual count]. . . . The faint and sickly effluvia were truly overpowering and poisonous."

But Buckland was not to be put off, and Burstall sportingly offered to help him. They began dragging out the coffins and dusting off the name plates. From many plates the letters had been eroded away.

As they moved the older coffins, antedating the health regulations that required a body to be encased in a leaden shell, the stench grew foul. After a week of it, Buckland collapsed and had to stay in bed for the rest of the month. Burstall fared worse. Though he did not falter until the task was finished, he was then ill for four months.

The church wardens agreed to postpone the date of evacuation, and Buckland returned to the crypt, bringing two workmen with him. By February 22, he or Burstall had examined all but five of the coffins. Two lay side by side on the floor, and the names could be easily read. Neither was John Hunter. Three were stacked in a corner. Buckland could read only the uppermost name. It was not John Hunter. Now, of the 3,260 coffins, only 2 remained unexamined. He ordered the workmen to lift them down. Time stood still for Buckland as the lowest and last coffin hove into view. "The leaden shell had burst and the lid was loosened; but the cloth covering was in good order, the brass nails upon it bore their polish, and the brass plate was as good as the first day it was put on." He distinguished the letter J, then O . . .

Buckland had the coffin locked in an empty vault and repaired to the Royal College of Surgeons.

On March 28, 1859, sixty-six years after John Hunter's death, his bones were transferred to Westminster Abbey, and in the presence of the members of the Royal College of Surgeons, of numerous civic dignitaries, and of a triumphant Francis Buckland, were reinterred in the north nave beside the tomb of Ben Jonson. In 1862 a brass plaque was affixed, with the inscription:

O LORD, HOW MANIFOLD ARE THY WORKS.

Beneath are deposited the remains of
JOHN HUNTER,
BORN AT LONG CALDERWOOD, LANARKSHIRE, N.B.,
ON THE 13TH OF FEBRUARY, 1728.
DIED IN LONDON ON THE 16TH OF OCTOBER, 1793.

His remains were removed from the Church of St. Martin's-in-the-Fields to this Abbey on the 28th March, 1859.

The Royal College of Surgeons of England has placed this tablet on the grave of Hunter to record admiration of his genius,
as a gifted interpreter of the Divine power and wisdom at work in the laws of organic life, and its grateful veneration for his services to mankind as the founder of scientific surgery.

NOTES

(a) The main house still stands with no major alterations, and is maintained as a national monument by the British Development Corporation. The only other local tribute to the Hunters is a plaque portraying the brothers John and William. When I visited East Kilbride in 1952, I could find few inhabitants who knew much about them. The parish minister was unaware that John and Agnes Hunter had been buried in the churchyard.

(b) Yet the possibilities are being reinvestigated today. Anesthesia, antisepsis and improved surgical techniques have eliminated the grosser dangers. At the University of Oregon Dental School both transplantation and reimplantation are under constant study. "The reimplantation of teeth," writes Dr. Horace M. Miller, head of the Department of Exodontia, "is fascinating. Results seem to be both good and bad. No definite procedure has yet enough cases and enough years behind it to justify any startling conclusions. More interest and clinical work will probably bring out startling developments."

A German oral surgeon by the name of Faust reports that of 270 reimplanted teeth 252 were retained for 1 to 10 years. In 1932 at the University of Pittsburgh School of Dentistry, a student was extracting an abscessed tooth from the jaw of a ten-year-old patient, when he inadvertently dislodged a partially formed pre-molar. A professor of oral surgery, Dr. Harry W. Archer, reimplanted it. Nineteen years later it was still there.

Homogenous transplantation (from one mouth to another) is still frowned upon. Dr. Harland Apfel, a Long Beach, California, dentist, insists that it always fails. But he considers autogenous transplantation, especially of tooth buds in the young, feasible. Since 1947 he has replaced more than a hundred missing first molars with third molars. "Tooth structure," he states, "will continue to grow and form its own new bony crypt followed by pulp and root development." A member of the Oregon group, Dr. George C. Collings, successfully transplanted two unerupted molars in the same patient.

At least two dentists, Dr. Ernest M. Pafford of Phoenix, Arizona, and Dr. Samuel W. Leslie of Toronto, do not agree with the consensus about homogenous transplantation. Dr. Pafford reports:

"We have done 187 over a period of five years. Our percentage of success has been better than 80%.

"Teeth extracted from patients requiring full dentures, orthodontia or the removal of impacted wisdom teeth are preserved in a deep-freeze tooth bank, after the blood type and RH factor have been recorded. The teeth are transplanted after a new bone socket has been cut. They are then wedged solidly into place with the aid of bone chips. The blood clot formed at the time of transplantation reorganizes and re-establishes the circulation of the tooth (as John Hunter assumed some such mechanism would). The blood clot also replaces the missing bone around the tooth. Discomfort diminishes after 18 hours. Several weeks later, when the soft tissues have healed, the patient can chew normally."

More recently, Dr. Leslie, in a paper read before an international congress on plastic surgery, described the transplantation of a tooth bud from an eleven-year-old girl to the jaw of her twenty-two-year-old brother. A year after the transplantation, Dr. Leslie reported, the tooth was developing normally.

(c) A far-seeing decision. The value of the Hunter collection increased so enormously that a few years ago, when the University of Glasgow shipped a portion of it to Belgium for a loan exhibition, a single medieval psalter carried an insurance policy of £120,000.

(d) What remains of the original building today forms the stage door and dressing rooms of the Lyric Theatre.

(e) It is not hard to re-create the scenes of Physick's life and work. The two original buildings of the Pennsylvania Hospital, faced with white pillars and fanlight windows in the colonial style, have been little altered structurally since their erection during the last half of the eighteenth century. Still intact under the domed room of the second building rises the Circular Room, America's first operating theater, now used as an internes' lounge. Here Physick performed his iridotomies, cut out bladder stones, extirpated cancers, ligated diseased arteries, while from the gallery high above students and colleagues looked on in awe. Here he successfully removed from the cheek and neck of one James Hayes a tumor weighing seven pounds that had been twenty years a-growing—a prodigious operation for those days.

The hospital case record book contains a before-and-after drawing of Hayes. It shows no gross disfigurement. The tumor itself is preserved in a jar of alcohol, in the hospital library, near Physick's first set of instruments. Not very many years ago a staff pathologist examined microscopic sections of it. He pronounced it a mixed tumor involving both glandular and connective tissue.

In the administrative office there hangs an oil portrait of Physick by Henry Inman. Seated at a writing table, the surgeon holds a notebook in his right hand, in his left a bandage. He wears a dark frock coat over a white waistcoat. His expression is glacially aloof, the mouth thin, the nose long and aquiline, the brow marble-like under flowing, powdered locks. Beneath the painting is the silver tankard given him by John Marshall. In the Mütter Museum of the College of Physicians of Philadelphia can be seen some of the calculi Physick removed from the jurist's bladder.

Four blocks from the hospital, at 321 South Fourth Street, stands the house Physick occupied at the crest of his fame, and where he treated his private patients. A majestic Greco-Georgian structure of three stories and twenty-two rooms, flanked by a walled garden, it retains its original hand-made red bricks, its massive oak beams, marble fireplaces, and ceiling frescoes. In the vast ground-floor ballroom the surgeon received such celebrities as Benjamin Franklin and the Marquis de Lafayette. The house was bequeathed to the Pennsylvania Hospital by a twentieth-century descendant of Physick.

(f) By the late nineteenth century both the museum building and the Castle Street house had tumbled into ruin. The last occupants of No. 12 Leicester Square were Hawkes and Son, the music publishers. That house was demolished in 1897. A bust of John Hunter marks the approximate site.

(g) Although almost half of the original Hunterian collection was destroyed during the Second World War (see Note k), the giant's skeleton survived, and is on permanent exhibition in the restored Royal College of Surgeons Museum.

In 1909, Harvey Cushing established the cause of Byrne's deformity. Receiving permission to open the skull, he discovered the traces of a pituitary tumor that had undoubtedly upset the glandular balance and promoted abnormal growth.

(h) In 1794, a year after John's death, the property was sold at auction by John's heirs for £10,300, 10s. to a Mr. John Bayne. From Bayne it passed to the Duke of Richmond and thence to the Earl of Albemarle. Towards the middle of the nineteenth century it became a private insane asylum. In 1866 it was torn down. Opposite the site there now stands the Earl's Court District Railway Station.

(i) The portrait ended up in the Royal College of Surgeons, where it hangs today in a small gallery behind the entrance hall. The outlines of the first head Reynolds drew can be discerned beneath a patch of dark paint. The colors are faded, the paint cracked. The original prints from the Sharp engravings, however, remain as clear as the day they were inked.

The life mask is also in the Royal College.

The bearded Hunter passed by a circuitous route to the Apothecaries' Society of London. The man to whom Anne Hunter gave it, an upholsterer named James Weatherall, left it to a nephew, Thomas Knight, a licentiate of the apothecaries, and he bequeathed it to them.

The only other contemporary portraits are a half-length of John as a young man, Hamlet-like contemplating a simian skull, which is sometimes attributed to Gainsborough, and a pencil-sketch profile by Nathaniel Dance Holland—both in the Royal College—and the two Home canvases, the first owned by the Royal College, the second by the Royal Society.

(j) Until the Middle Ages there prevailed such abysmal ignorance about the mechanics of procreation as to preclude even the dimmest inkling that woman might conceive without sexual intercourse. Her reproductive system was considered a mere receptacle for semen, contributing no fertilizing powers of its own. As late as the twelfth century, Armand de Villeneuve, physician to Popes and kings, wondering whether the female could not be dispensed with altogether in the generative process, attempted to cultivate sperm inside a pumpkin.

The idea of artificially impregnating women had been broached twenty years before Hunter by an English clergyman named Coventry. In an unsigned work more literary than scientific, entitled *Lucina sine concubitu,* published as an open letter to the Royal Society, he argued the feasibility of conception without carnality.

Whether or not John Hunter ever read the parson's recommendation, he was the first to put it into practice. His account, posthumously published in 1799, furnished the authority for numerous uterine injections performed during the next fifty years, though almost always clandestinely for fear of religious or legal sanctions. Not until the investigations in 1866 of the American gynecologist, James Marion Sims, did artificial insemination begin to emerge as a recognized technique.

(k) The Hunterian Museum was continually added to by later naturalists until it numbered, at the outset of the Second World War, approximately 66,000 specimens. In the air raid of May 10, 1941, the Royal College of Surgeons building in Lincoln's Inn Fields was hit first by a high-explosive shell, then by incendiary bombs. Two thirds of the entire collection, including all but 3,000 of Hunter's original 13,682 specimens, were destroyed.

(l) Matthew Baillie was the last doctor to carry the Gold-Headed Cane. After his death in 1823, Mrs. Baillie gave it to the Royal College of Physicians, where it has been on display ever since.

BIBLIOGRAPHY

BOOKS

ABERNETHY, JOHN. *Surgical and Physiological Works*. London. 1825.

ADAM, JOSEPH. *Memoirs of the Life and Doctrines of the late John Hunter, Esquire*. J. Callow. London. 1817.

AHLERS, CYRIACUS. *Some Observations Concerning the Woman of Godlyman*. London. 1726.

ANON. *Lives of Great and Celebrated Characters*. New York. 1875.

AVELING, J. H. *English Midwives*. London. 1872.

BAILEY, JAMES BLAKE. *The Diary of a Resurrectionist 1811–1812*. London. 1896.

BALDERSTON, KATHERINE [ed.]. *The Collected Letters of Oliver Goldsmith*. Cambridge University Press. 1928.

BALL, JAMES MOORE. *The Sack-'em-Up Men*. Oliver & Boyd. London. 1928.

BARON, J. *The Life of Edward Jenner*. 2 vols. Henry Colburn. London. 1838.

BASHFORD, H. H. *The Harley Street Calendar*. Houghton Mifflin Co. Cambridge. 1920.

BAYLEY, RICHARD. *An Account of the Epidemic Fever which prevailed in New York during part of the Summer and Fall of 1795*. New York. 1796.

BESANT, WALTER. *London in the Eighteenth Century*. Adam & Charles Black. London. 1902.

BEST, CHARLES HERBERT & TAYLOR, NORMAN BURKE. *The Physiological Basis of Medical Practice*. Williams & Wilkins Co. Baltimore. 1943.

BETHANY, G. T. *Eminent Doctors*. 2 vols. John Hogg. London. 1885.

BIRTH, THOMAS [ed.]. *A Collection of the Yearly Bills of Mortality from 1657 to 1758 Inclusive*. London. 1759.

BLACK, W. *Observations Medical and Political on the Small Pox*. London. 1781.

Blakiston's New Gould Medical Dictionary. Philadelphia & Toronto. 1949.

BLEACKLEY, HORACE. *The Hangmen of England*. Chapman & Hall. London. 1929.

BLOMFIELD, J. *St. George's 1733–1933*. The Medici Society. London. 1933.

BOSWELL, JAMES. *The Private Papers from Malahide Castle.* 19 vols. Yale University Press. 1933.

BRAITHEWAITE, THOMAS. *Remarks on a Short Narrative of an Extraordinary Delivery of Rabbits.* London. 1726.

BRODIE, SIR BENJAMIN. *Autobiography.* Longmans, Green & Co. London. 1865.

BUCKLE, HENRY THOMAS. *The History of Civilization in England.* D. Appleton & Co. New York. 1822.

BUCKLAND, FRANCIS T. *Curiosities of Natural History.* 4 vols. Bentley & Sons. London. 1891.

BUCKLAND, FRANCIS T. *Log-Book of a Fisherman and Zoologist.* Chapman & Hall. London. 1875.

BUTLER, FRANCIS HENRY. *John Hunter,* in the Encyclopaedia Britannica, 11th edition. 1910.

CADOGAN, EDWARD. *The Roots of Evil.* London. 1937.

CAMERON, SIR CHARLES. *A History of the Royal College of Surgeons in Ireland.* Dublin. 1886.

CARHART, MARGARET S. *The Life and Work of Joanna Baillie.* Yale University Press. 1923.

CARSON, JOSEPH. *A History of the Medical Department of the University of Pennsylvania.* Philadelphia. 1869.

CARTWRIGHT, GEORGE. *A Journal of Transactions and Events during a Residence of Nearly Sixteen Years on the Coast of Labrador.* 3 vols. Newark. 1792.

CHANCELLOR, E. BERESFORD. *The History of the Squares of London.* Kegan, Paul, Trench, Truber & Co. London. 1868.

CHANCELLOR, E. BERESFORD. *The Romance of Lincoln's Inn Field.* Richards. London. 1927.

CHAPLIN, ARNOLD. *Medicine in England during the Reign of George III.* London. 1919.

CLENDENNING, LOGAN. *Behind the Doctor.* Alfred Knopf. New York. 1933.

CLIFT, WILLIAM. *Testimony before the Select Committee on Medical Education, May 1, 1834.*

COKE, LADY MARY. *The Letters and Journals.* 4 vols. David Douglas. Edinburgh. 1896.

COPE, SIR ZACHARY. *William Cheselden.* E. & S. Livingston, Ltd. London and Edinburgh. 1953.

CORBETT, JULIAN S. *England in the Seven Years' War.* London. 1907.

CORNER, BETSY COPPING. *William Shippen, Jr.* American Philosophical Society. Philadelphia. 1951.

CORNER, GEORGE W. *Anatomist at Large.* Basic Books. New York. 1958.

CUNNINGHAM, GEORGE H. *London, being a Survey of the history, tradition and historical associations of buildings and monuments.* J. M. Dent & Sons. London. 1927.

DARWIN, CHARLES. *The Descent of Man.* 2 vols. John Murray. London. 1871.

DARWIN, CHARLES. *The Variation of Animals and Plants under Domestication.* 2 vols. John Murray. London. 1868.

DE LA TORRE, LILLIAN. *Villainy Detected.* D. Appleton-Century. New York. 1947.

DOBSON, JESSIE. *William Clift.* William Heinemann. London. 1954.

DORSEY, JOHN SYNG. *Elements of Surgery.* Philadelphia. 1813.

DUNCAN, ALEXANDER. *Memorials of the Faculty of Physicians and Surgeons of Glasgow.* James Maclehose & Sons. Glasgow. 1896.

EDGAR, ANDREW. *Old Church Life in Scotland.* Second Series. London. 1886.

EDGAR, JOHN. *The History of Early Scottish Education.* Edinburgh. 1893.

ERSKINE, WILLIAM. *Lines on Dr. Physick.* The Court of Sessions Garden. Edinburgh. 1839.

FARINGTON, JOSEPH. *Diary.* George H. Doran. New York. 1923.

FITZGERALD, PERCY. *A Famous Forgery.* Chapman & Hall. London. 1865.

FLEXNER, JAMES THOMAS. *Doctors on Horseback.* Viking Press. New York. 1937.

FOOT, JESSÉ. *A Defence of the Planters in the West Indies.* London. 1792.

FOOT, JESSÉ. *The Life of John Hunter.* T. Beckett. London. 1794.

FOX, R. HINGSTON. *Dr. John Fothergill and His Friends.* Macmillan & Co. London. 1919.

FOX, R. HINGSTON. *William Hunter.* H. K. Lewis. London. 1901.

GLAISTER, JOHN. *Dr. William Smellie and His Contemporaries.* Glasgow. 1894.

GLOYNE, S. ROODHOUSE. *John Hunter.* William & Wilkins Co. Baltimore. 1950.

GORDON, MAURICE BEAR. *Aesculapius Comes to the Colonies.* Ventnor Publishers, Inc. New Jersey. 1949.

GOSSE, PHILIP. *Dr. Viper.* Cassell. London. 1952.

GOULD, GUY M. & PYLE, WALTER L. *Anomalies and Curiosities of Medicine.* W. B. Saunders. Philadelphia. 1901.

GRAHAM, HARVEY. *A Doctor's London.* Allan Wingate. London. 1953.

GRAHAM, HARVEY. *Eternal Eve.* William Heinemann. London. 1950.

GRAHAM, HARVEY. *The Story of Surgery.* Doubleday, Doran & Co. New York. 1939.

GRAHAM, HENRY GREY. *The Social Life of Scotland in the Eighteenth Century.* Adam & Charles Black. London. 1909.

GRAY, ERNEST A. *Portrait of a Surgeon.* Robert Hale, Ltd. London. 1952.

335

GROSS, S. D. *John Hunter and His Pupils*. Blakiston. Philadelphia. 1881.

GROSS, S. D. *Lives of Eminent American Physicians and Surgeons of the Nineteenth Century*. Philadelphia. 1861.

HADDIN, J. CUTHBERT. *George Thomson*. John C. Nimmo. London. 1898.

HAGGARD, HOWARD W. *Devils, Drugs and Doctors*. Harper & Bros. New York. 1929.

HAGGARD, HOWARD W. *The Doctor in History*. Yale University Press. 1922.

HARRISON, REV. RICHARD. *The Anniversary Sermon of the Royal Humane Society*. London. 1799.

HAWES, W. *An Address to the King and Parliament of Great Britain on the Important Subject of Preserving the Lives of Its Inhabitants*. London. 1782.

HAWES, W. *Transactions of the Royal Humane Society from 1774 to 1784*.

HEBERDEN, WILLIAM. *A Letter to Dr. Heberden concerning the Angina Pectoris; and Dr. Heberden's account of the Dissection of one who had been troubled with the disorder*. Medical Transactions. 1785.

HEBERDEN, WILLIAM. *Some account of a Disorder of the Breast*. Medical Transactions. London. 1772.

HEISTER, DR. LAURENCE. *A General System of Surgery*. London. 1759.

HOGARTH, WILLIAM. *The Works*. 2 vols. London. 1821.

HOLMES, T. *Benjamin Brodie*. Longmans, Green & Co. New York. 1898.

HOLMES, T. *Introductory Address on the Centenary of John Hunter's Death*. Adlard & Son. London. 1893.

HOME, EVERARD. *An Account of the Dissection of an Hermaphrodite Dog*. Philosophical Transactions of the Royal Society. Part II. 1799.

HOME, EVERARD. *A Short Account of the Life of the Author* [extracted from Hunter's Treatise on Blood, Inflammation and Gunshot Wounds]. London. 1794.

HUNTER, ANNE. *Poems*. London. 1802.

HUNTER, JOHN. *Essays and Observations*. Edited by Richard Owen. 2 vols. John Van Voorst. London. 1837.

HUNTER, JOHN. *Hunterian Reminiscenses*. Compiled by James Parkinson. Sherwood, Gilbert and Piper. London. 1883.

HUNTER, JOHN. *Observations on Certain Parts of the Animal Oeconomy*. Longman, Orme, Brown, Green and Longmans. London. 1837.

HUNTER, JOHN. *The Works*. Edited by James F. Palmer. 5 vols. Rees, Orme, Brown, Green and Longmans. London. 1835.

HUNTER, WILLIAM. *The Anatomy of the Gravid Uterus*. Baskerville Press. London. 1774.

HUNTER, WILLIAM. *Medical Commentaries*. Part I. London. 1778.

HUNTER, WILLIAM. *An Obstetric Diary*. Glasgow. 1908.

HUNTER, WILLIAM. *Two Introductory Lectures*. London. 1784.

JACOBS, H. E. *Joseph Haydn*. Rinehart. New York. 1950.

JARDINE, WILLIAM. *Memoirs of John Hunter*. The Naturalists' Library, Vol. X. W. H. Lizard. Edinburgh. 1843.

JEAFFRESON, JOHN CORDY. *The Real Lord Byron*. Hurst & Blackett. London. 1833.

JESSE, JOHN HENEAGE. *George Selwyn and His Contemporaries*. 4 vols. R. Bentley. London. 1843 and 1844.

JOHNSTONE, R. W. *William Smellie*. E. & S. Livingston. Edinburgh and London. 1952.

KAY, JOHN. *A Series of Original Portraits and Caricature Etchings*. 4 vols. Edinburgh. 1877.

KEITH, SIR ARTHUR. *An Autobiography*. Watts & Co. London. 1950.

KEITH, SIR ARTHUR. *The Cradle of the Hunterian School*. Contributions to Medical and Biological Research. Paul B. Hoeber. New York. 1919.

KELLEY, HOWARD A. & BURRAGE, WALTER L. *American Medical Biographies*. Baltimore. 1920.

KER, W. P. *Collected Essays*. Macmillan & Co. London. 1925.

KERR, JOHN. *Scottish Education, School and University, from earliest times to 1908*. Cambridge. 1910.

KNAPP, LEWIS MANSFIELD. *Tobias Smollett*. Princeton University Press. 1949.

KNAPP & BALDWIN. *Newgate Calendar*. 4 vols. London. 1828.

KNIGHT, CHARLES [ed.]. *London*. 3 vols. Knight & Co. London. 1842.

LANE, WILLIAM COOLIDGE. *Dr. Benjamin Waterhouse and Harvard University*. The Cambridge Historical Society. Publications IV. 1909.

LESLIE, CHARLES ROBERT & TAYLOR, TOM. *Life and Times of Sir Joshua Reynolds*. 2 vols. John Murray. London. 1865.

LIBBY, WALTER. *The History of Medicine*. Houghton Mifflin Co. Cambridge. 1922.

LISTER, JOSEPH. *The Collected Papers*. Clarendon Press. Oxford. 1904.

MACILWAIN, GEORGE. *Memoirs of John Abernethy*. Hatchard & Co. London. 1886.

MACMICHAEL, WILLIAM. *The Gold-Headed Cane*. Macmillan & Co. New York. 1930.

MANNINGHAM, SIR RICHARD. *Exact Diary of what was observ'd during a close attendance upon Mary Toft*. London. 1726.

MARCHAND, LESLIE A. *Byron, a Biography*. 3 vols. Knopf. New York. 1957.

MATHER, GEORGE. *Two Great Scotsmen*. James Maclehose & Sons. Glasgow. 1893.

MEIGS, HOE V. & SOMER, H. STURGIS [eds.]. *Progress in Gynecology*. New York. 1950.

MELVILLE, LEWIS. *The Life and Times of Tobias Smollett*. Faber & Guy. London. 1926.

MOORE, JAMES. *A Method of Preventing or Diminishing Pain in Several Operations of Surgery*. London. 1874.

MORGAN, ALEXANDER. *The Rise and Progress of Scottish Education*. Edinburgh and London. 1927.

MORGAN, JOHN. *Journal from Rome to London 1764*. Lippincott. 1907.

MOSSNER, ERNEST CAMPBELL. *The Life of David Hume*. University of Texas Press. 1954.

MUMFORD, JAMES GREGORY. *A Narrative of Medicine in America*. J. B. Lippincott Co. Philadelphia and London. 1903.

NEWMAN, SIR GEORGE. *Interpreters of Nature*. Faber & Guy. London. 1927.

NOYES, EDWARD [ed.]. *The Letters of Tobias Smollett*. Harvard University Press. 1926.

OPPENHEIMER, JANE. *New Aspects of John and William Hunter*. Henry Schuman. New York. 1946.

OTTLEY, DREWRY. *The Life of John Hunter*. Philadelphia. 1897.

PACKARD, FRANCIS R. *Some Account of the Pennsylvania Hospital from 1751 to 1938*. Philadelphia. 1938.

PAGET, SIR JAMES. *Memoirs and Letters*. Longmans, Green & Co. London. 1902.

PAGET, SIR STEPHEN. *John Hunter*. T. Fisher Unwin. London. 1897.

PARRY, CALEB HILLIER. *An Inquiry into the Causes and Symptoms of the Syncope Anginosa*. London. 1799.

PEACHEY, GEORGE C. *The History of St. George's Hospital*. Six Parts. Bemrose & Sons, Ltd. London. 1914.

PEACHEY, GEORGE C. *A Memoir of John & William Hunter*. William Brendan & Son, Ltd. Plymouth. 1924.

PEPPER, WILLIAM. *The Medical Side of Benjamin Franklin*. William J. Campbell. Philadelphia. 1911.

PLANT, MARJORIE. *The Domestic Life of Scotland in the 18th Century*. University Press. Edinburgh. 1952.

POWER, SIR D'ARCY. *A Short History of St. Bartholomew's Hospital*. London. 1913.

PROTHERO, ROWLAND E. [ed.]. *Letters and Journals of Lord Byron*. John Murray. London. 1902.

PUSEY, WILLIAM ALLEN. *The History and Epidemiology of Syphilis*. Charles C. Thomas. 1933.

RANDOLPH, J. *A Memoir on the Life and Character of Philip Syng Physick*. Philadelphia. 1839.

RAPPORT, SAMUEL & WRIGHT, ELLEN [ed.]. *Great Adventures in Medicine*. Dial Press. New York. 1952.

RICHARDSON, SIR BENJAMIN WARD. *Disciples of Aesculapius.* Hutchinson & Co. London. 1900.

ROBINSON, VICTOR. *Pathfinders of Medicine.* Medical Review of Reviews. New York. 1912.

ROGERS, REV. CHARLES. *The Scottish Minstrel.* William P. Nimmo & Co. London. 1882.

ROHLEDER, HERMANN. *Test Tube Babies.* Panurge Press. New York. 1934.

ROUGHEAD, WILLIAM. *The Fatal Countess.* Dutton. New York. 1926.

SHARP, SAMUEL. *A Treatise on the Operations of a Surgery.* London. 1751.

SPENCER, HERBERT R. *The History of British Midwifery from 1650 to 1800.* London. 1927.

STEPHEN, SIR JAMES FITZMAURICE. *A History of the Criminal Law of England.* 3 vols. Macmillan & Co. London. 1883.

STIRLING, WILLIAM. *Some Apostles of Physiology.* London. 1902.

STOCK, JOHN EDMONDS. *Memoirs of the Life of Thomas Beddoes.* John Murray. London. 1811.

STUART, DOROTHY MARGARET. *Regency Roundabout.* Macmillan & Co. London. 1883.

TAYLOR, TOM. *Leicester Square.* Bickers & Son. London. 1874.

TEACHER, JOHN A. *The Anatomical and Pathological Preparations of Dr. William Hunter.* Glasgow. 1900.

THAYER, WILLIAM ROSCOE. *Journal of Benjamin Waterhouse.* The Cambridge Historical Society. Publications IV. 1909.

THOMPSON, C. J. S. *The History and Evolution of Surgical Instruments.* Schuman. New York. 1942.

THOMPSON, C. J. S. *The Mystery and Lore of Monsters.* Macmillan. New York. 1931.

THOMSON, JOHN. *An Account of the Life, Lectures and Writings of William Cullen.* Edinburgh. 1859.

TIMBS, JOHN. *Curiosities of London.* London. 1885.

TIMBS, JOHN. *Doctors and Patients.* 2 vols. Richard Bentley & Son. London. 1883.

TREVELYAN, G. M. *Illustrated Social History of England.* 4 vols. Longmans, Green & Co. London. 1951.

TRUSLER, REV. JOHN. *The London Adviser and Guide.* London. 1786.

TURBERVILLE, A. S. [ed.]. *Johnson's England.* 2 vols. Clarendon Press. Oxford. 1933.

URE, DAVID. *The History of Rutherglen and East Kilbride.* Glasgow. 1793.

VAN DOREN, CARL. *Benjamin Franklin.* Viking Press. 1938.

VINCENT, HOWARD P. *The Trying-Out of Moby Dick.* Houghton Mifflin Co. Boston. 1949.

WADD, WILLIAM. *Mems., Maxims and Memoirs.* London. 1827.

WADD, WILLIAM. *Nugae Chirugicae*. London. 1824.

WALKER, KENNETH M. *The Story of Medicine*. Oxford University Press. New York. 1955.

WALKER, RALPH S. [ed.]. *James Beattie's London Diary 1773*. The University Press. Aberdeen. 1946.

WALL, CECIL. *The History of the Surgeons' Company 1745–1800*. Hutchinson's. London. 1937.

WALPOLE, HORACE. *The Last Journals of Horace Walpole During the Reign of George III from 1771–1783*. [Ed. by A. Francis Steuart.] John Lane. London & New York. 1910.

WALSH, JAMES J. *History of Medicine in New York*. 5 vols. New York. 1919.

WEINBERGER, BERNHARD WOLF. *An Introduction to the History of Dentistry*. 2 vols. C. V. Mosby. St. Louis. 1948.

WOGLOM, WILLIAM H. *Discoverers for Medicine*. Yale University Press. 1949.

WOOD, EDWARD J. *Giants and Dwarfs*. Richard Bentley. London. 1868.

WRAXALL, SIR NATHANIEL WILLIAM. *The History and Posthumous Memoirs*. 5 vols. Scribner & Welford. New York. 1926.

WRIGHT, REV. ALEXANDER. *The History of Education and of the Old Parish Schools of Scotland*. Edinburgh and Musselburgh. 1898.

YOUNG, JOHN. *William Hunter*. Glasgow. 1901.

PERIODICALS AND PAMPHLETS

Abbreviations

BMJ—*British Medical Journal*

ARCS—*Annals of the Royal College of Surgeons*

AMH—*Annals of Medical History*

BNYAM—*Bulletin of the New York Academy of Medicine*

AJS—*American Journal of Surgery*

JHM & AS—*Journal of the History of Medicine and Allied Sciences*

BHM—*Bulletin of the History of Medicine*

BJHH—*Bulletin of Johns Hopkins Hospital*

AMERICAN DENTAL ASSOCIATION. *Package Library on Implantation, Replantation, and Transplantation of Teeth*.

ANON. "The Bicentenary of John Hunter." *The Lancet*. Feb. 18, 1928.

ANON. *The catalogue of an exhibit of William Hunter's collections of art, coins and miscellany, held at Iveagh House*. London. 1952.

BIBLIOGRAPHY

Anon. "John Hunter." BMJ. Feb. 11, 1928.

Anon. "The John Hunter Centenary." *Illustrated London News*. Oct. 14, 1893.

Anon. "John Hunter's Experiments." *The Lancet*. Feb. 28, 1938.

Anon. "The John Hunter Memorial Service." ARCS. April 1952.

Anon. "Mary Toft's, The Rabbit Breeder." BMJ. July 25, 1896.

Anon. "John Hunter's Remains." BMJ. Oct. 24, 1936.

Anon. *The Trial of John Dunellan*. London. 1781.

Apfel, Harland. "Autoplasty of Enucleated Third Molars." *Journal of Oral Surgery*. Oct. 1950.

Archer, Harry W. *Replantation of Mandibular Second Premolar*.

Bashford, H. "The Bicentenary of John Hunter." *The 19th Century*. Vol. CIII, No. 611. 1928.

Bayley, Richard. *Cases of the Angina Trachaelis*. New York. 1881.

Beekman, Fenwick. "The 'Hernia Congenita' and an Account of the Controversy It Provoked Between William Hunter and Percivall Pott." BNYAM. Sept. 1946.

Beekman, Fenwick. "John Hunter in Portugal." AMH. New Series. Vol. 8, No. 4. 1936.

Beekman, Fenwick. "Long Calderwood." BNYAM. Dec. 1943.

Beekman, Fenwick. "Pott and Hunter." AJS. New Series. Vol. XXXV, No. 2. 1937.

Beekman, Fenwick. "The Self-Education of John Hunter." JHM & AS. Vol. 6. Autumn 1951.

Beekman, Fenwick. "William Hunter's Early Medical Education." JHM & AS. Part I Winter, Part II Spring. 1950.

Beekman, Fenwick. "William Hunter's Education at Glasgow." BHM. March 1944.

Bryce, Thomas A. *William Hunter and His Museum*. An Oration. Glasgow. 1922.

Collings, George G. "Dual Transplantation of Third Molar Teeth." *Oral Surgery, Oral Medicine, and Oral Pathology*. 1951.

"The Dark Ages of Dentistry." *Journal of the British Dental Association*. 5:354–57. 1944.

"The Teeth of Londoners of the 17th & 18th Century." *Dental Record*. 42:237–44. 1922.

Corner, Betsy Copping. "Dr. Melchisedeck Broadbrim and the Playwright." JHM & AS. Vol. VIII, No. 2. 1953.

Corner, George W. & Goodwin, Willard E. "Benjamin Franklin's Bladder Stone." JHM & AS. Vol. VIII, No. 4. Oct. 1953.

Dobson, Jessie M. "The Hunter Specimens at Kew Observatory." ARCS. June 1951.

Dobson, Jessie M. *Introduction to the Hunterian Museum.* Dec. 1950.

Dobson, Jessie M. "John Hunter and the Byron Family." JHM & AS. Vol. X. July 1955.

Dobson, Jessie M. "John Hunter and the Unfortunate Doctor Dodd." JHM & AS. Vol. X. October 1955.

Finlayson, James. "Account of a MS. volume by William Clift relating to John Hunter." BMJ. March 29, 1890.

Finlayson, James. "Was John Hunter a Student in the University of Glasgow?" BMJ. July 8, 1893.

Fitzwilliams, Duncan C. L. "The Destruction of John Hunter's Papers." *Proceedings of the Royal Society of Medicine.* Nov. 1939.

Gask, G. E. "John Hunter in the Campaign in Portugal 1762–3." BMJ. Feb. 20, 1937.

Gilcreest, Edgar L. "John Hunter, the Founder of Scientific Surgery." *The Surgical Clinics of North America.* Vol. 8, No. 6. 1928.

Gordon-Taylor, Sir Gordon. "Some Unpublished Letters of William Clift." ARCS. July 1949.

Guillemain, C. "Contribution à l'histoire de la fécondation artificielle." *Histoire de la médicine.* 5:27–29. 1955.

Guttmacher, Manfred S. "John Hunter, His Enemies and Friends." BJHH. July 1929.

Holland, Daniel J. "A Technique of Surgical Orthodontics." *American Journal of Orthodontics.* Jan. 1955.

Home, Everard. "An Account of Mr. Hunter's Method of Performing the Operation for the Popliteal Aneurysm." *London Medical Journal.* 1786.

Horner, W. E. *Necrological Notice of Dr. Philip Syng Physick.* Haswell, Barrington, and Haswell. Philadelphia. 1838.

HUNTERIAN ORATIONS

From 1814 to 1853 the Hunterian Oration was delivered every year (except 1835, 1836 and 1845) on or about Hunter's birthday, February 14, usually in the Royal College of Surgeons. Since 1853 they have been delivered every other year. Nearly all have been published in the *British Medical Journal, The Lancet,* the *Annals of the Royal College of Surgeons,* or separately as pamphlets within two or three weeks of their delivery. Until 1893 they bore no titles.

1814. Home, Sir Everard.   The Hunterian Oration in honour of surgery and in memory of those practitioners by whose labours it has been advanced.

1815. Blizard, Sir William

1816. Cline, Henry

1817. Norris, William

1818. Dundas, Sir David
1819. Abernethy, John
1820. Carlisle, Sir Anthony
1821. Chevalier, Thomas
1822. Home, Sir Everard
1823. Blizard, Sir William
1824. Cline, Henry—Unpublished
1825. Norris, William
1826. Carlisle, Sir Anthony
1827. Thomas, Honoratus Leigh
1828. Blizard, Sir William
1829. Vincent, John P.
1830. Guthrie, George James—Unpublished
1831. White, Anthony—Unpublished
1832. Cooper, Samuel
1833. Howship, John
1834. Lawrence, William
1837. Brodie, Sir Benjamin
1838. Travers, Benjamin
1839. Stanley, Edward
1840. Green, Joseph Henry
1841. Callaway, Thomas
1842. Babington, George C.
1843. Arnott, James Moncrieff
1844. South, John Flint—Unpublished
1846. Lawrence, William
1847. Green, Joseph Henry
1848. Grainger, Richard D.
1849. Hawkins, Caesar
1850. Skey, Frederic Carpenter
1851. Stafford, Richard Anthony.   Undelivered, but printed by the author
        for private distribution.
1852. Luke, James
1853. Cooper, Bransby Blake
1855. Hodgson, Joseph
1857. Wormald, Thomas
1859. Bishop, John
1861. Coulson, William
1863. Gulliver, George
1865. Partridge, Richard
1867. Hilton, John
1869. Quain, Richard

1871. Fergusson, Sir William
1873. Hancock, Henry
1875. Clark, F. Le Gros
1877. Paget, Sir James
1879. Humphry, George Murray
1881. Holden, Luther
1883. Wells, Sir T. Spencer
1885. Marshall, John
1887. Savory, William Scovell
1889. Power, Henry
1891. Hutchinson, Jonathan
1893. Bryant, T.
1895. Hulke, J. W.   John Hunter the Biologist.
1897. Heath, C.   John Hunter as a Surgeon.
1899. MacCormac, Sir W.   Hunter as the Founder of Scientific Surgery.
1901. Macnamara, N. C.
1903. House, H. G.
1905. Tweedy, Sir John
1907. Butlin, H.   On the Objects of Hunter's Life and the Manner In
 Which He Accomplished Them.
1909. Morris, Sir H.   John Hunter as Philosopher.
1911. Owen, Edmund.   John Hunter and his Museum.
1913. Godlee, Sir R. J.   Hunter and Lister and the Museum of the Royal
 College of Surgeons.
1915. Cheyne, Sir W. W.   The Treatment of Wounds in War.
1917. Makins, Sir G. H.   The Influence Exerted by the Military Experience of John Hunter on Himself and on the Military Surgeons
 of Today.
1919. Bowlby, Sir A. A.   British Military Surgery in the Time of Hunter
 and in the Great War.
1921. Symonds, Sir C.   Astley Cooper and Hunterian principles.
1923. Bland-Sutton, Sir J.   John Hunter, His Affairs, Habits and Opinions.
1925. Power, Sir D'Arcy.   John Hunter, a Martyr to Science.
1927. Moynihan, Sir B.   Hunter's Ideals and Lister's Practice.
1929. Waring, Sir H.   The Progress of Surgery from Hunter's Day to Ours.
1931. Groves, E. W.   Hero Worship in Surgery.
1933. Trotter, W.   The Commemoration of Great Men.
1935. Wallace, Sir C.   Medical Education 1760–1934.
1937. Fagge, C. H.   John Hunter to John Hilton.
1939. Handley, W. S.   Makers of John Hunter.
1941. Burgess.   Development of Provincial Medical Education Illustrated
 in the Life and Work of Charles White of Manchester.

1943. Bonney, Victor. The Forces Behind Specialism in Surgery.
1945. Turner, George Grey. The Hunterian Museum—Yesterday and Tomorrow.
1947. Walton, Sir James. The Hunterian Ideals Today.
1949. Souttar, H. S. Hunter the Observer.
1951. Page, Sir Max. The Hunterian Heritage.
1953. Norbury, L. E. C. The Hunterian Era: Its Influence on the Art and Science of Surgery.
1955. Wakeley, Sir Cecil. John Hunter and Experimental Surgery.
1957. Finch, Sir Ernest. The Influence of the Hunters on Medical Education.
1959. Watson-Jones, Sir Reginald. Surgery is Destined to the Practice of Medicine.

JONES, WOOD. "John Hunter and the Medical Student." *St. George's Hospital Gazette.* Oct.–Nov. 1951.
JONES, WOOD. "John Hunter's Unwritten Book." *The Lancet.* Oct. 27, 1951.
KEITH, SIR ARTHUR. "A Discourse on the Portraits and Personality of John Hunter." *The Lancet.* Feb. 18, 1928.
KEITH, SIR ARTHUR. "John Hunter." *The Medical Press and Circular.* June 6, 1934.
KEITH, SIR ARTHUR. "John Hunter as a Psychologist." ARCS. 1949.
KEITH, SIR ARTHUR. "John Hunter's Beard and Mask." *The Lancet.* Oct. 18, 1919.
KEITH, SIR ARTHUR. "The Life and Times of William Clift." BMJ. Dec. 15, 1923.
LE FANU, WILLIAM R. "John Hunter's Buffaloes." BMJ. Sept. 2, 1931.
LE FANU, WILLIAM R. "John Hunter's Letters." *Bulletin of the Medical Library Association.* Oct. 1945.
LINDSAY, LILLIAN. "The London Dentist of the 18th Century." *Dental Surgeon.* 22:179–81. 1927.
MENZIES, J. CAMPBELL. "Chevalier Bartholomew Ruspini." *The Dental Magazine and Oral Topics.* London. Dec. 1953.
MENZIES, J. CAMPBELL. *Dentistry as Practised 1800–1921.* London. N.D.
MERRIMAN, J. J. *John Hunter at Earl's Court, Kensington.* 1881.
MEYER, A. W. "Truth Overtakes 'Dr. Hunter.'" *California and Western Medicine.* June 1932.
MILLER, HORACE M. "Reimplanting Human Teeth." *Dental Survey.* Nov. 1953.
MITCHELL, G. A. G. "Anatomical and Resurrectionist Activities in Northern Scotland." JHM & AS. Vol. 4. Autumn 1949.

OPPENHEIMER, JANE. "Anne Home Hunter and Her Friends." JHM & AS. July 1946.

OPPENHEIMER, JANE. "John and William Hunter and Some Contemporaries in Literature and Art." History of Medicine. Jan.–Feb. 1949.

OPPENHEIMER, JANE. "A Note on William Hunter and Tobias Smollett." JHM & AS. July 1943.

OPPENHEIMER, JANE. "William Blake and John Hunter." JHM & AS. Jan. 1946.

PEACHEY, GEORGE C. "The Homes of the Hunters." The Lancet. Feb. 18, 1928.

PEACHEY, GEORGE C. "William Hunter's Obstetrical Career." AMH. Sept. 1930.

POWER, SIR D'ARCY. "Epoch-Making Books in British Surgery." British Journal of Surgery. Oct. 1929.

ROBERTS, MORLEY. "John Hunter and Evolution." The Medical Press. May 29, 1929.

ROGERS, FRED B. "Philip Syng Physick (1768–1837): Home and Heritage." Philadelphia Medicine. Aug. 1, 1958.

SCHLEUTER, ROBERT E. "John Hunter. The Man and His Spirit." St. Louis Medical Society. Dec. 20, 1932.

SEGALL, HAROLD N. "The First Clinico-Pathological Case History of Angina Pectoris." BHM. Vol. XVIII, No. 1. 1945.

SIGERIST, HENRY E. "The Johns Hopkins Institute of the History of Medicine during the Academic Year 1941–1942." BHM. Dec. 1942.

SPRIGGE, SIR SQUIRE. "Grand Curiosity as Exemplified in the Life of John Hunter." The Lancet. Oct. 13, 1928.

STEVENSON, LLOYD G. "The Elder Spence, William Combe and John Hunter." JHM & AS. Vol. 10. April 1955.

STEVENSON, LLOYD G. "A Note on the Relation of Military Service to Licensing in the History of British Surgery." BHM. Vol. XXXVII, No. 5. Sept.–Oct. 1953.

STEVENSON, LLOYD G. "The Siege of Warwick Lane." JHM & AS. Vol. VII, No. 2. 1952.

STEVENSON, LLOYD G. "William Hewson, the Hunters and Benjamin Franklin." JHM & AS. Vol. VIII, No. 3. 1953.

THOMSON, STEWARD CRAIG. "The Surgeon-Anatomists of Great Windmill Street." School Bulletin of the Society of Medical History. July 1943.

TOWNEND, B. R. "The Debt of the Dental Profession to John Hunter." Proceedings of the Royal Society of Medicine. Section on Odontology. 1–20. 1919–20.

TOWNEND, B. R. "Mr. Patence, Quack." Dental Magazine & Oral Topics. Dec. 1945.

TOWNEND, B. R. "Oral Magic, Folklore and Tradition." *Dental Magazine & Oral Topics*. (6 articles.) Feb.–July 1938.

TRENT, JOSIAH CHARLES. "The London Years of Benjamin Waterhouse." JHM & AS. Vol. I. Jan. 1946.

VAURIE, A. J. C. "John Hunter and His Contribution to Dentistry." *Dental Cosmos*. Nov. 19, 1929.

VIETS, HENRY. "The Destruction of the Hunter Manuscripts. Was It An Act of Piety?" BJHH. Jan. 1930.

VIETS, HENRY. "A Note on John Hunter at Oxford." *Boston Medical and Surgical Journal*. May 27, 1920.

WILBERT, M. I. "John Morgan." *American Journal of Pharmacy*. Jan. 1904.

YOUNG, JOHN. "Dr. Smellie and Dr. Hunter: an autobiographical fragment." BMJ. Aug. 29, 1896.

MANUSCRIPTS

(in the Royal College of Surgeons)

Cases and Observations and Records in Morbid Anatomy. 2 vols.
  Partly in Hunter's handwriting, these were delivered to the Board of Trustees by Home in 1823.
Cases and Observations. 2 vols.
  Transcript of Hunterian MS. in Clift's writing.
Cases in Surgery. 2 vols.
  Transcript of Hunterian MS. in Clift's writing.
Cases in Surgery and Cases in Medicine.
  Copied in 1833 by a Mr. Grimley from vol. in Home's writing.

347

INDEX

349

15